Management in the Fire Service

Second Edition

by
Harry R. Carter
and
Erwin Rausch

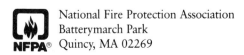

National Fire Protection Association
Batterymarch Park
NFPA® Quincy, MA 02269

Second Edition
J2 2120350
First Printing, April 1989

Managing Editor: Gene A. Moulton
Editor: Deborah A. Shaw
Graphic Artist: Hilary Davis
Interior Design: Frank Lucas
Cover Design: Katerina Kreatsoulas
Composition: Louise Grant
            Cathy Ray
            Publication Services
Production Coordinators: Donald McGonagle
            Debra Rose

NFPA No. MFS–89
ISBN 0–87765–357–7
Library of Congress Catalog Card Number 89–60386
Printed in the United States of America

Contents

About the Authors

This textbook was prepared originally by Didactic Systems, Inc., of Cranford, New Jersey, specialists in the preparation of management development materials. Didactic Systems has served many governmental agencies, as well as some of the largest corporations in the United States, as consultant on management development.

Harry R. Carter is a practicing fire officer in the Newark, New Jersey, Fire Department, where he has served for more than 15 years. His assignments have included the training division, the fire and life safety division, the office of the fire chief, and the fire fighting division. He is currently serving as an aerial ladder company commander for the Newark Fire Department and as assistant chief and training officer for the Howell Township Fire Company #1 in Adelphia, New Jersey, an active suburban volunteer fire department. Carter has extensive teaching experience; he developed the associate degree program in fire science for Ocean County College, where he taught for 5 years. In addition, he has taught at New Jersey fire schools in Somerset, Hunterdon, and Sussex Counties, and is an adjunct faculty member of the National Fire Academy. He holds a Ph.D. in fire service administration and four other degrees in public policy analysis, firesafety administration, social sciences, and business administration. He has published many articles in the news and trade media, including the *New York Times*, *Firehouse*, *Fire Command!*, *Fire Chief*, *Fire Engineering*, and *American Fire Journal*, as well as a book, *Managing Fire Finances*.

Erwin Rausch has held top-level executive positions in manufacturing companies for more than 20 years. He is the author of *Balancing Needs of People and Organizations*, *Management in Institutions of Higher Learning*, *Win-Win Performance Management/Appraisal*, and a large number of business simulations including the best-seller series *Conflict in Management*. He has two engineering degrees and one economics degree, and he has taught evening courses for more than 15 years at Rutgers University and Kean College. Rausch has been President of Didactic Systems, Inc., since 1968 and is credited with developing the comprehensive management concept presented in this text as the Three Cs of Management or the Linking Elements concept.

Acknowledgments

The many persons and organizations who cooperated in the preparation and development of this textbook are acknowledged with gratitude. Special thanks go to the following:

- Charles J. Burkell of the National Fire Academy, Emmitsburg, Maryland, who contributed the segment on leadership, in addition to many contributions in the planning of this edition.
- Arthur Kiamie, Captain of the Cranford, New Jersey, Fire Department, who served as consultant in the preparation of the first edition and contributed valuable suggestions for this edition.
- Stanley J. Kossup, Fire Director of the Newark, New Jersey, Fire Department, for his strong support and personal guidance in the development of the chapter on fire service training.
- Lowell F. Jones, Chief of the Newark, New Jersey, Fire Department, who provided a critical analysis and important suggestions for the chapter on management functions in the fire service.

The cooperation of many publishers and representatives of the fire service who gave permission to use excerpts from their publications and management training materials is deeply appreciated. We are also indebted to the many people and organizations who contributed helpful ideas, suggestions, and materials to the first and second editions, respectively:

First edition:

- Paul A. Battiloro, Westfield, New Jersey, Fire Dept.
- Chief Bell, New Rochelle, New York, Fire Dept.
- N. Bellarosa, Irvington, New Jersey, Fire Dept.
- Matthew Farrell, New York City Fire Dept.
- James Hallinan, New York City Fire Dept.
- John J. Hart, New York City Fire Dept.
- William S. Holleran, Irvington, New Jersey, Fire Dept.
- Robert Horner, Plainfield, New Jersey, Fire Dept.
- John J. Jablonsky, American Insurance Association.
- Louis Luibl, Montclair, New Jersey, Fire Dept.
- Earl J. McCormick, Bloomfield, New Jersey, Fire Dept.
- Roger A. McGary, Merck and Company and East Franklin Township Volunteer Fire Co.
- Malcolm S. McGregor, Acton, Massachusetts, Fire Dept.
- James McKenna, New York City Fire Dept.
- Robert Mellilo, Bloomfield, New Jersey, Fire Dept.
- Frank Miklos, Linden, New Jersey, Fire Dept.

- Maurice Reilley, Plainfield, New Jersey, Fire Dept.
- Charles Swoody, Elizabeth, New Jersey, Fire Dept.
- H. Ray Vliet, Edison, New Jersey, Fire Dept.

Second edition:

- Alan V. Brunacini, Chief, Phoenix, Arizona, Fire Dept.
- Jerry Knight, Fire Chief, St. Petersburg, Florida, Fire Dept.
- Samuel A. Maglione, Director, Orange, New Jersey, Fire Dept.
- Don Sellers, Annapolis, Maryland, artist.
- William Stringfield, Lieutenant, St. Petersburg, Florida, Fire Dept.

A word of thanks is due to Leslie Kendall at Didactic Systems, Inc., who diligently converted dictation and marked up drafts into readable pages, and to Martin Henry of the National Fire Protection Association, for reviewing a draft of the manuscript.

Finally, the editors on the staff on the National Fire Protection Association, Gene Moulton and Deborah Shaw, deserve well-earned recognition for their exceptionally fine efforts in making the published book a far more reader-friendly work than the manuscript submitted by the authors.

Introduction

Like the first edition of *Management in the Fire Service*, this edition explores the skills and techniques used by competent managers in business, government, and voluntary organizations, with particular emphasis on their applications to the fire service. It discusses and recommends approaches that an officer can use to improve the overall performance of a particular fire department unit.

Although management in the fire service might appear to be a single topic, it actually consists of two separate entities: 1) general management concepts, and 2) management functions as they are applied to the various tasks and departments in the fire service. For this reason, this text contains two major segments.

The first segment of *Management in the Fire Service* (Chapters 1 through 5 as well as a significant portion of Chapter 14), primarily deal with fundamental concepts and principles of modern management theory, presenting them as much as possible within the framework of a fire service environment. The second segment of the text (Chapters 6 through 13 and the remainder of Chapter 14) discusses how the concepts and principles apply to specific fire service functions. These chapters are far more detailed in explaining the functions of fire service managers. Chapter 6 provides an overview of these functions and serves as a bridge between the two segments of the book.

The second edition of *Management in the Fire Service* includes many new topics. Chapters on firesafety education and management of financial resources have been added, as well as many smaller sections on such topics as counseling, conflict management, leadership, time management, conducting effective meetings, incident command, and fireground command.

As in the first edition, all chapters in *Management in the Fire Service* end with two sections: 1) references and 2) activities, which are intended to help students integrate the new information obtained from reading into their work in the fire service and to challenge them to explore some of the issues that they might confront as they continue their careers in management.

1

Introduction to Modern Management

This book is a basic management text for present and potential members of the fire service, and for students and members of other fire science-related professions. To those familiar with the fire service, it might seem that management there is totally different from that of other professions. This is partly true because the fire service has many unique management problems, including the need for personnel to be constantly ready for instant changes from tranquil, routine duties to the sudden intensity of fire fighting emergencies.

THE SCOPE OF MANAGEMENT PRINCIPLES

Despite these unique characteristics, the same basic principles that provide guidance for any management activity — from managing one's personal life to managing a grocery store, bank, manufacturing concern, or other profit-oriented business — also apply to management in the fire service. Thus, problems that confront the fire service officer are similar in many ways to those that need to be resolved by the line managers in government, manufacturing, service industries, and retail situations. To help illustrate the similarity, this text provides examples that are drawn both from the fire service and from other areas of management activity.

The uniqueness of fire service management problems is largely the result of the distinctly individualized nature of the fire service, as described in the following excerpt from the National Fire Protection Association's (NFPA) *Fire Protection Handbook*:[1]

> The fire service has many unique management needs. It requires: a
> distinct team spirit; a need for a strong disciplinary influence for concerted

1

and instant reaction on the fireground; a high quality of leadership from its officers; continuous training; an extremely wide range of technical competence; a labor/employer relationship not comparable to that in other occupations; and an ability to deal with the public under both minor and major crisis situations. The fire service is not profit oriented, and it has an obscure productivity pattern. It is a major consumer of tax dollars, uses costly equipment, is heavily dependent upon manpower, and at present has no satisfactory means of measuring effectiveness of its operation relative to cost. Despite the complexity of these needs, the fire service has generally performed well for many years.

Similarity with Other Organizations

Management concepts and principles are essentially universal. For example, every manager is aware of the fundamental principle that management is concerned with the accomplishment of predetermined goals through the efforts of people. This principle, like other basic management principles, is applicable to all organizations that have managerial functions including industry, government, volunteer organizations, and service institutions.

Managers, particularly at higher levels, have always been aware of the management similarities among different organizations. They know that a required body of technical knowledge exists in each organization from which the members can draw.

At lower levels of management, on the other hand, managers must possess some of that technical expertise themselves. Direct supervision of work requires that the manager understand the intricacies of the work at least sufficiently to recognize what is right and what is wrong. Managers who achieve higher levels must supervise more and more different types of functions and, naturally, can no longer be personally present to supervise each one of them. This is why the higher levels of government draw their managers from all walks of life: industry, labor, and other governmental agencies and institutions. A manager who gains experience in an industrial environment can usually do well in a position as a high-level government official. This frequent interchange of managers between different professions and occupations is evidence that, because fundamental management principles exist, it is usually possible for managers to adapt quickly to new environments.

Acceptance of Management Principles

It is commonly believed in the fire service that the application of good management principles must start from the top. This belief is prevalent because lower-level officers frequently feel that it is impossible to practice leadership styles that are different from those used by their superiors. However, this is not always the case. Fire officers who have acquired knowledge about good management techniques and approaches can better convey the necessary information, make informed decisions, and thus achieve superior performance from their units.

In addition, many people believe that good management is merely common sense, steadily applied. However, in reality, much more is involved. For example, decisions that seem obvious and simple from a fire fighter's point of view often are far more complex, and carry more risks and potential problems for the future when seen from the wider perspective of upper management, such as the deputy chief or chief. For the reasons above, among others, the study of management theory can be of great value. More experienced members of the fire service who have never had extensive formal education in management can benefit, as well as those members who are either new in such positions or who aspire to them.

GENERAL APPLICATION OF MANAGEMENT PRINCIPLES

When one embarks on a steady program to learn a new subject or to learn more about a subject, there are often topic areas that might seem to lack direct relevance or that are of little interest. It is easy to dismiss these topics by assuming that one does not really need the information when it appears that there is no immediate application. To do so, however, is to omit some segment that could be of considerable future value.

When some high-level managers and fire service officers think back to how they felt about their initial training in management, they recall that their training often seemed generalized and of little direct value to themselves. Some recall that they felt their training should have been more specifically related to problems with which they were familiar. However, as they progressed to higher-level positions, they often found that many of the topics that had originally seemed to be general and impractical later proved highly pertinent and meaningful.

Thus, what might appear as generalities to an inexperienced person will take on deeper layers of meaning as that person becomes more familiar with a given subject. These deeper layers of meaning are always present, and the student who faces a topic or subject for the first time must exert considerable effort to find them. The results of such effort can be highly rewarding in the future, even though the student does not have the opportunity to apply the newly gained knowledge in class.

There are areas, however, where newly acquired management theory can almost always be readily applied. Few people realize that good management techniques can positively affect their personal lives. For example, careful planning and well thought-out decisions can lead to a better use of family finances. The rewards of this include a higher standard of living and fewer frustrations due to greater insight and enhanced skills in managing the same amount of income. The general application of management theory to one's personal life can also help bring about more meaningful relationships with others, including more effective relationships within families.

As stated previously, many people believe that they will do the "right" thing when faced with a decision or other management responsibility. However, often the stress or emotions involved at the moment prevent rational response unless the manager is well-practiced in the application of management principles. The following are typical examples:

- A supervisor who, when faced with pressure from higher levels of management, is unnecessarily critical of fire fighters, instead of absorbing the pressure and relating to fire fighters as usual.
- A business manager who cuts advertising when business slows down instead of cutting other costs.
- A teacher who chides students for asking "silly" questions instead of realizing that the topic might require additional explanation.

These examples are not only common, but obvious: nonreasoned reactions are often not the best. A few moments of thought between impulse and action can often bring about better actions — and better results.

For good management decisions, managers need a conceptual framework, a theory that provides logical consistency while making it possible to act quickly. To paraphrase the famous English economist John Maynard Keynes (1883–1946): Practical people who believe themselves to be exempt from theoretical influences are usually the slaves of some defunct theorist.

This is not surprising, for although some people scorn theory as being impractical, it is commonly realized that without sound theory there would be no basis for most of our endeavors. Thus, it would seem that there is nothing more practical than good theory.

The Uses of Theory

It is important to clarify the distinction between management theory and application. In this book, theory is discussed first (Chapters 1–5) and then the skills one needs to apply management theory are described next (Chapters 6–14).

Theories exist in every field. Theories are statements that are believed to be true as a result of extensive experimentation or because they are logical conclusions of something that is known to be true. Skills are needed to apply theories. Just as physicists, statisticians, and astronomers apply theories in their respective fields by using mathematical calculation skills, fire officers and fire fighters use skills when applying theories from hydraulics or chemistry (combustion or behavior of gases). The skills needed in the fire service include those required for effective fire investigation, inspection, ventilation, pump operation, and fire stream placement. In other words, scientific theories provide guidelines for the application of fire fighting skills that will help fire fighters and managers make good, quick decisions when needed most—on the fireground.

Similarly, management theories provide guidelines to help managers use skills to make competent decisions about the opportunities, challenges, and problems they face.

There are many requirements that sound management theories must satisfy if they are to be practical, including the following:

1. They must fit real situations. It must be evident, to those affected, that any theory correctly depicts the real world and does not contain significant variations from that reality.
2. They must give equal consideration to both sides.
   a. The organizational unit's need for performance in all the dimensions — productivity, quality, the ability to adapt quickly to changing situations, etc.
   b. The individual employee's or volunteer's need to gain maximum satisfaction from work.
3. They must take into consideration three influences on the effectiveness of a manager.
   a. The manager's personality and leadership style.
   b. The capabilities, maturity, and personalities of the subordinates.
   c. The situation in which all are involved.
4. They must be applicable at all organizational levels. In the fire service a theory must be as useful to a chief as it is to a platoon leader.
5. They must provide a workable guide for an accurate analysis of performance problems so that the specific causes of such problems can be identified and overcome.

MANAGEMENT AND SUPERVISION

The words *management* and *supervision* frequently are used synonymously. Supervisors are sometimes referred to as managers; conversely, managers are referred to as supervisors. There is, however, a significant distinction: It is possible to manage an activity without supervising anyone. Supervision refers to directing the activities of other people, which management does not necessarily require. On the other hand, anyone who supervises the work of another is automatically a manager because supervision of others requires specific planning, setting of goals, and the organization, direction, and evaluations that are essential to the management task.

Generally, the title *manager* is reserved for upper-level management, while the title *supervisor* is used to refer to those managers who directly supervise the line personnel doing the work. It would appear to be more appropriate to speak of first-line supervision, middle-level supervision, and top-level supervision.

The Transition from Fire Fighter to Officer

A difficult period in the life of a new officer occurs when the promotion involves taking charge of a group of former co-workers. It is not a simple task to become fully established as a competent manager. Part of the task includes gaining the respect of the members of the company and, at the same time, exerting strong leadership qualities. Sensitivity to the feelings of others is necessary, and a new officer will become established more quickly if the following guidelines are kept in mind:

1. Do not make changes too quickly. Team members often resent changes in the procedures or policies to which they have been accustomed. A slow approach is sometimes the most effective approach and can often help prevent additional resistance.

2. Move with deliberation in response to challenges from fire fighters or junior officers (except, of course, on the fireground). Rash responses are likely to be costly as well as ineffective. If in doubt as to what course of action to take, consult with another officer, the direct superior, or the personnel officer to avoid mistakes that might be regretted later.

3. Become aware of the distinction between process and content. Although this is a simple distinction, it is sometimes difficult to remember. If an instructor is teaching about pump operation, then the topic — pump operation — is the content, and the acquisition of information by the learners is the process. The inadequate or inexperienced instructor might concentrate solely on explaining the content. Such an instructor is likely to continue a lecture without being aware that attention levels of some learners have decreased appreciably. In contrast, the competent instructor, while being occupied with discussing content, would watch to see if the students were understanding the information. Such an instructor would continually find other means to help students learn more effectively, apply the information so it would be more meaningful to them, and explain portions of the topic that they did not understand. This subject is discussed further in Chapter 14. On the fireground, the content of an activity concerns the fire and how it is to be contained and extinguished. The process concerns the effectiveness with which a team is coordinated, how the team responds, and what major problems occur that need to be rectified in the future. A new officer must be sufficiently self-disciplined to realize the importance of keeping process in mind while performing daily activities. A constant awareness of process helps provide the foundation for future planning because long-term effectiveness is developed through a process that continually improves a team's ability to cooperate and perform successfully.

4. Consider careful planning an important key to success. For example, a fire service officer must always think of tomorrow and beyond. Although the bulk of the work is dealing with current matters, there is much important work to be accomplished at some later date. For example, the chief's most important work concerns long-range planning so that the department will be able to fulfill its needs for many years to come. This

planning is necessary because new stations and equipment take years to obtain. The battalion chief must think in intermediate terms, must devote time to scheduling personnel, and must plan how to develop personnel and techniques that will help make each of the districts more effective. The company officer, concerned only with one team, also must think about the development of personnel skills and capabilities in order to help improve overall performance. Thus, while urgent matters that need to be accomplished during the daily routine are still planned primarily on a day-to-day basis, an important task for the company officer is the on-going, long-range planning necessary for matters that will take place in the future.

5. Regard self-development as a major key to success. An officer who expands his/her knowledge and learns new skills will ultimately be more effective as a manager.

Need for an Environment of Open Communications

New supervisors have a tendency to see their roles and functions from a perspective that does not always lead to maximum performance. A new supervisor, or one who has never received appropriate training, is likely to have developed a mental picture of the job that does not match the way that position is viewed by the supervisor's managers. Upper-level managers must be adequately prepared to clearly communicate the responsibilities they expect lower-level managers to assume. If upper-level managers have insufficient contact with the actual problems and situations in the units they oversee, then frequently there will be a large and disturbing gap between the work that lower-level supervisors perform and the work that would be best suited to their responsibilities. Too often the result is that unreasonable demands are placed on lower-level managers. They are expected to do things for which inadequate time is allotted or that are impossible to handle without additional support. In such a situation, upper-level managers and many subordinates feel that the new supervisor is not capable of performing designated responsibilities in the expected professional manner. These problems are especially prevalent whenever upper-level managers fail to establish an open-communications environment. Resolving and overcoming some of these problems are discussed in later chapters.

Motivation, Communication, Decision Making, and Time Management

Four skill areas are required for effective organizational performance. The following skills link an organization with the people who work for it:

- Motivation.
- Communication.

- Decision making,
- Time management.

Motivation

A major topic throughout this text is how to create a results-oriented work environment that inspires fire fighters and lower-level officers to extend their best efforts. Although many managers speak of motivating and training people, all too often these words have little meaning. In reality, not every employee can be motivated and/or trained by someone else. However, people are more apt to find motivation for their work in a favorable environment. They can also find the desire to learn, and possibly an enhanced ability to learn, in an environment that encourages self-development.

It is the manager's job to see that a favorable environment is developed, if it does not already exist, that allows people to find higher levels of motivation. This requires the continuing development of the manager's skills in the technical sense, as well as in managerial and leadership areas.

Communication

Good communication skills can substantially improve operations by helping to avoid errors and ensuring better cooperation and relationships among people. Communication skills, such as coaching, counseling, and those considered as most essential for giving instructions and commands, are discussed in Chapter 4.

The first skill in communicating efficiently is the ability to put thoughts into words as clearly and concisely as possible. Selection of words and sentences should be appropriate to a specific occasion. The ability to select those thoughts or points that can best convey one's message will help to influence and persuade others. This skill can be improved through practice in speaking before groups and report writing.

The second skill is to send messages effectively. Messages must be geared to the listener. This means that with some listeners you can express complex ideas with few words, while others need lengthy explanations. You must also adjust the speed with which you speak to the ability and experience level of the listener.

Successful communication demands good transmission and receipt of the message. Words carry an emotional impact. This impact can be seen much more clearly when, rather than relying on the tone of the voice alone, the other person's reaction is visible. The ability to understand the emotional reactions of others to certain words and phrases is of great value to people in managerial positions. Also important are using properly worded questions, remaining silent if necessary, and applying the results of feedback or the answers to questions to gradually achieve understanding and agreement. The use of visual aids also can help achieve greater speed and clarity in the transmission of messages.

Secondary messages — those that are not verbally expressed — are transmitted through symbols and nonverbal communication. These include: facial expression; visual, gestural, and aural signs and symbols; stance; clothing; the relationship between the people involved; and the environment in which the communication takes place. Often less than half of the significance of the message is transmitted through words. This is the reason that most people prefer personal contact (rather than impersonal contact, such as by telephone) when discussing complex or lengthy matters. Most people generally feel that the types of subjects that can be discussed in depth through impersonal means are limited, and that important subjects should be handled on a face-to-face basis.

The third skill is the art of listening. Much has been written, and many attempts are being made, to help people listen more attentively. Listening is one of the primary foundations of good communication. Effective listening involves not only the hearing of words but an active search for their meaning and for their relationship to what is already known. It provides the basis on which one can build questions that will help clarify what has been said. It is the key to the discovery of needs and it provides cues for hidden objections that might exist. Listening skills have to be applied not only when listening, but also while speaking. It is essential that the speaker address the listener's reaction in order to respond to a variety of nonverbal cues; this requires listening with eyes, for nonverbal cues, while speaking.

Comprehension levels must also be considered. People who have good comprehension of a topic often understand quickly, while others must listen more attentively and hear more words before they achieve adequate understanding. In some messages, such as listening to the morning news on the radio, the comprehension that is needed might be minimal — possibly not much more than that used in listening to music. However, when listening to instructions, attention to detail is very important. The speaker, therefore, must adapt the message to the listener's ability to comprehend.

Listening not only includes those things that are said but those things which are implied as well. Deeper meanings can be obtained by listening to a speaker's inflections, such as voice pitch or body motion. This can be seen in many social and professional interactions where people often mean something other than what they say. A listener must pay close attention, as well as probe, to understand the intent of the message.

There are two levels of effective listening: passive and active. Passive listening is paying attention to what a speaker is saying. Active listening also includes the responsibility to ensure that, in addition to hearing a speaker's words, the listener also understands the full thought that the speaker wishes to express. The latter is a form of two-way communication. In teaching, as well as in management communication, one-way communication is deficient because it does not allow for feedback. In summary, an effective listener must:

1. **Be empathetic.** Evaluate a speaker's intent through the speaker's perspective.
2. **Concentrate.** This includes making eye contact with the speaker and, if the conversation is face-to-face, getting close enough to observe nonverbal cues.
3. **Organize and evaluate the message.** Ask questions such as:
   - What is the speaker's purpose? What are the main points? How are they organized? Are they being supported by what is being said?
   - Is the speaker consistent? How does what is being said relate to what was said before?
   - Is the message complete? If information has been omitted, what was omitted, and why?
   - Are deeper meanings implied by word choices? Expressive words — embarrassed, cheated, fearful, frustrated, enjoy, glad — might indicate hidden feelings.
4. **Ask relevant questions.**
   - How can this information be used?
   - How does it relate to what you know and/or what you know about the speaker?
   - Is there anything that is not fully understood that should be clarified?
   - Can you paraphrase the speaker's main points so that the speaker knows that you understood the message?
5. **Be a careful observer.** Many visual cues help convey the full meaning of the message. These cues include eye contact, tone of voice, and attention to the presentation or explanations. Are they consistent with the speaker's words or do they appear to contradict them? Nonverbal cues can also send messages; if so, what are those messages?

The following is a self-analysis questionnaire used to check how extensively listening elements can be used in one-to-one situations. Remember that active listening requires two-way communication and feedback. An effective listener should:

1. Look the speaker in the eye when he/she is speaking.
2. Watch for nonverbal communication from the speaker.
3. Integrate interpretations of nonverbal communication with the verbal messages.
4. Concentrate on ideas and feelings.
5. Determine whether agreement or disagreement is needed.
6. Accept responsibility for making certain that the message was received correctly and completely.
7. Summarize what the speaker has said before shaping a response.
8. Determine whether or not there is an influence created by your relationship with the speaker.
9. Watch for nonverbal cues when responding to questions, when asking clarifying questions, or when providing feedback.

Decision Making

Competent decision making is essential to good managerial performance. Many management-training programs teach decision making only in a general way, with a series of steps that are universally applicable to all types of decisions. To do so is almost self-defeating because most people have difficulty applying such a general procedure to specific decisions. Making better decisions must therefore come partially from a better understanding of the general process, as well as from guidance and practice in specific ways to use this process. Methods for making better decisions are discussed throughout this text. Chapter 5 explores the types of decisions that concern planning and setting goals as well as the extent to which other people, including subordinates, should participate in a decision. Applying decisions to fireground strategy is explored in Chapter 10. Chapters 11 and 12 cover important budgetary decisions pertaining to purchasing apparatus, and other finances. Decision trees and decision matrices are covered in Appendix A.

It is necessary to recognize that a decision is rarely a single act. Usually it is a process because making a single decision is not the important thing. Good decision-making skills show themselves in chains of decisions where one small decision is linked to the next one. There are three basic chains for all decisions: 1) for solving problems, 2) for exploiting opportunities, and 3) for managing projects.

Problem-Solving Chains: Decisions in these chains deal with specific deviations from expected results or defined standards. They frequently emerge when a difference is observed between "what is" and "what *should* be." A problem exists, and it must be addressed.

Opportunity-Exploiting Chains: Decisions in these chains are frequently less urgent than in problem-solving chains, but they are still often generated by observing a difference. Here the difference is between "what is" and "what *could* be." In most organizational units, there are many opportunities for improving operations. The officer's role, therefore, becomes one of selecting which opportunities are most desirable and should be given priority now, based on the overall objectives, the current situation, and the mission of the fire department.

Project-Management Chains: Decisions in these chains concern the day-to-day operation of the unit as well as the management of special projects. They are made neither as a result of problems nor in connection with specific opportunities. They are routine decisions, such as what should be included on this month's budget report or which commercial buildings the fire inspection team should visit next week, but also include decisions on projects such as the selection of a new piece of equipment.

The process involved in making the little decisions inherent in each of these chains is composed of four levels: definition decisions, analysis decisions, execution decisions, and follow-up decisions. Each of these, by itself, is also a chain. A *definition decision* might consist of a series of little decisions that answer questions. What is the problem? Has the problem occurred in the past? How does the new problem differ from the previous problem? How does this problem affect the goals? What is the desired result (or outcome) of the decision? Should other people be involved in resolving these questions and, if so, who?

Analysis decisions involve different questions. What data are necessary to make this decision? Where can such data be obtained? Are enough data now available? What alternatives should be considered? What additional data are needed to evaluate the alternatives? How can the data be applied to evaluate the alternatives? Which of the alternatives is best now? Which alternative steps are best after the first (second, third, etc.) have been taken? When and how should other people be involved?

Execution decisions involve other questions. What resources will be needed for this task? In what sequence should the tasks be performed? Which people should be involved? Who should do what? In what way should each of these people be involved in making further decisions?

Follow-up decisions involve still other questions. Where are there deviations from the plan or expected outcome? What should be done about these deviations from the planned or expected results? This last question, then, leads directly back to definition decisions. If there is a deviation from the plan, then this, in effect, becomes a problem, and a problem-solving chain starts from the beginning.

The modern decision-making process usually involves many people whose skills are needed to help the group arrive at a good decision. As a manager you often have to select the people who should be part of the decision-making group. You also have to decide at what point in the decision-making chain the individuals should become involved and what their respective roles should be. This complex topic is discussed further in Chapter 5 in the section entitled "Participation." Competence in decision making brings several benefits:

1. Better, more carefully and thoroughly considered decisions.
2. Development of good decision-making habits that aid in the application of the entire process.
3. Competence and leadership due to successful involvement of others.
4. Better decision making in private life.

It must be recognized that decisions range in complexity. Many decisions that an officer makes are routine, such as ordering monthly supplies. However, the majority of an officer's more important responsibilities are decisions of increasing complexity.

The quality of an officer's decisions depends on an understanding of the process of decision making, and on the continuing development of skills and sound habits—such as the habit of identifying and evaluating choices and alternatives/options. The decision-making process and useful techniques are outlined in greater detail in Appendix A.

Time Management

Time management is essential for efficiency. Time must be managed effectively because the hours in a shift are limited. To get things done, priorities must be set and "time thieves" must be controlled. The "time thieves" are:

1. **Failure to plan the day.** A plan for each day will ensure consideration of all important items and adherence to priorities.
2. **Interruptions.** Time limits must be placed on interruptions depending on their significance.
3. **Failure to delegate responsibilities.** Proper delegation is essential. It allows a manager more time to do important work.
4. **Procrastination.** Unpleasant or difficult jobs are often postponed. Procrastination can be avoided through awareness of the problem as well as the discipline to overcome it. Business consultant Dale Carnegie advises people to first do the things they fear and hate. Once these tasks have been done, the remaining ones seem easier and less unpleasant, and procrastination stops.
5. **Inefficiency.** To avoid unnecessary inefficiency and to increase efficiency: a) Make notes of things to do; b) Keep the importance/urgency diagram in mind (Figure 5.5); c) Handle incoming paper work promptly; d) Avoid any other "time thieves"; and e) Adhere to the list of ways to manage time provided in the following section.
6. **Unnecessary meetings and/or meetings that accomplish little.** Conducting effective meetings is discussed later in this chapter.

Successful time management requires perseverance and self-discipline. The reward, however, is that time can be controlled and that much more can be accomplished. Sustained higher levels of accomplishment, in turn, can bring many rewards, such as salary increases, as well as greater personal satisfaction and the ability to take unpleasant events in stride.

Ways to Manage Time Effectively: Efficient time management should include the following:

1. Prepare lists of things to do in order to identify priorities.
2. Set priorities based on the relative urgency and importance of the task.
3. Establish goals to help accomplish each of the major tasks on the lists and to design specific plans of action.
4. When scheduling, review an entire project to determine what has to be done, estimate the resources needed to do the job, assess the time available and the time needed for its completion, and prepare the actual schedule with specific completion dates.
5. Schedule more difficult tasks to do personally at the most productive time of the day.
6. Whenever possible, reserve some time during the day to deal with unanticipated interruptions and unexpected crises or opportunities.

7. Stay flexible at all times to avoid missing deadlines and to be able to adjust quickly and effectively to new or unexpected priorities.

8. Delegate responsibility to allow time for more important work.

9. To accomplish larger tasks, divide the major project into smaller components that can be scheduled and accomplished easily.

10. Periodically determine whether time is being used in the best possible way at the moment in order to reduce the amount of time wasted.

11. Identify personal time wasters and develop habits to eliminate them.

12. When interrupted, determine whether the interruption is more important and more urgent than what is presently being done and whether it requires immediate attention.

13. When planning a meeting, decide if the meeting is really necessary or if the objectives could be accomplished more effectively in another way.

14. Prepare an agenda for meetings.

15. Make sure that only necessary personnel attend meetings.

16. Make sure meetings are scheduled in such a way that they can run over if necessary to accomplish an objective.

17. Monitor the process used in the meeting to ensure that the meeting moves as smoothly as possible toward its objective(s).

18. Prepare for the meeting by bringing any materials that might be needed.

19. When attending meetings, take notes that better enable proper followup on assignments.

20. Reserve a period of time called "Do Not Disturb" during the day to work without interruption on top-priority tasks.

Conducting Effective Meetings

In the fire service, as in other organizations, there is a continual need for many meetings. A fire officer is involved, either as a leader or as a participant, in many types of meetings, including staff meetings, training meetings, and public meetings. A good understanding of one's role as a leader or participant can enhance one's value and effectiveness in an organization. Enhancement of those skills that make meetings more effective is very important because much work in today's world is accomplished in meetings. Some meetings require strong leaders, while in other situations leaderless team activity brings the best results.

The effectiveness of a meeting depends greatly on the skills of its participants. These skills involve a willingness to sometimes deemphasize personal feelings and needs for the benefit of the group. This willingness does not mean, however, that an individual must accept more of the workload or more unpleasant tasks than anyone else. The skills and abilities for conducting or helping to make meetings effective can be learned but do require extensive practice. There are two types of meeting skills: membership and leadership.

Membership Skills at Meetings

At most meetings, usually one person has a position of greater organizational authority than the other members of the group. This person assumes responsibility for leading the discussion to a successful conclusion. On other occasions, the person who has called the meeting chairs it, irrespective of status. There are also occasions when there is no specific leader, such as discussions among teams in a training class, or when the person who should chair a meeting is absent. In this last situation membership skills at meetings, outlined below, become especially important. Skills for effective participation in meetings include:

1. Ability and willingness to share ideas for the benefit of the team (without regard to personal interests).
2. Ability to understand and be understood by others.
3. Respect for the ideas of others and a willingness to look for advantages in those ideas.
4. Skill in identifying and evaluating alternatives.
5. Skill in giving credit to others.
6. Sensitivity and skill in assuming leadership when the person in authority is absent or when such leadership is needed and no one else assumes it.
7. Competence for contributing effectively to the tasks of the meeting.
8. Competence to accept criticism from others, or to bear rejection of ideas, without negative reaction, and the willingness to resubmit any idea that is believed to be useful at a more appropriate time.
9. Strength to accept a fair share of work assignments being delegated at a meeting.

Participation in and frequency of meetings usually increase as fire personnel move up through the ranks. Fire officers are often in charge of meetings, and it is invaluable that they learn effective membership skills.

Leadership Skills at Meetings

It is the meeting leader's responsibility to guide the meeting to a successful conclusion. This task of the discussion leader is a difficult one, particularly when he/she is not in a position of authority relative to the group. An effective meeting leader must:

1. See to it that the group expeditiously arrives at "good" conclusions, whether that means a single decision or an entire action plan.
2. Ensure that all members are given adequate opportunity to express their points of view.
3. Overcome the common obstacles to group action, including conversation that strays from the topic, the tendency to sometimes avoid or sidestep a difficult decision, conflict that creates deadlocks, and uncooperative participants.

The most demanding and continuous task for a leader is to distinguish clearly between process and content during any group discussion. A competent leader's emphasis should be on what people are doing (process), including adherence to the agenda, participation in and contribution to the discussion, and so on. Except in training meetings or other occasions such as presentations, the leader's content involvement (the subject under discussion) is more limited. The leader of an effective meeting must carefully monitor the process, observe the participants, and contribute views toward the discussion only after all others have had an opportunity to express theirs. The leader must also avoid becoming so absorbed by the discussion topic, even when it concerns an important decision, that the process is lost. Occasional summaries of conclusions reached will ensure that the group has a clear view of where agreements and disagreements exist. To run a successful meeting the leader should do the following:

1. Know what needs to be accomplished. Set objectives for the meeting.
2. Lay the groundwork for the meeting. This includes preparing a tentative agenda and deciding whether the meeting is really necessary. Do not waste everyone's time if the meeting is not necessary and the objectives can be accomplished more effectively in another way.
3. Inform the participants about the objectives of the meeting. They might have suggestions on related matters or on other urgent matters that should be included on the agenda.
4. Provide as much information as possible to participants before the meeting. This saves meeting time because people require different amounts of time to absorb information and/or seek clarification.
5. Do not let the meeting run overtime.
6. Be an effective chairperson.

When starting a meeting, the leader should review the plan of the meeting, then restate the purpose of the meeting, explaining what is to be accomplished. The purpose of a meeting is to sound out the opinions of the group, not to rubber stamp the leader's opinions. It is the leader's responsibility to ensure this. By avoiding directives and premature statement of views, a leader can help encourage free discussion that can lead to good solutions.

Participation is important for a successful meeting. This requires that everyone has sufficient information to participate in the discussion. The leader should invite members to speak, and listen carefully to understand their points. Because some people are reticent, individuals who have not expressed an opinion should be encouraged to contribute or at least agree with the opinions already aired. As the meeting progresses, it is effective to reinforce the involvement of the group. Questions like "Are we moving in the right direction?" or "Have we overlooked something?" will give feedback on whether the group is unified or not.

The time should be watched carefully. The meeting leader should anticipate whether the agenda is being covered adequately in the allotted time and decide with the group on what should be done if it is not. Time management also includes handling any problems that develop with participants. Some people are skilled in finding a flaw in every proposal. The momentum can be maintained by soliciting positive ideas, e.g., "Yes, Ted, you may have a point there, but let's see if there are any offsetting advantages." Over-talkative people are another problem. One solution is to avoid looking at them when they try to speak. If they do break in to speak, a suggestion could be made that the point has already been covered and it would be better to keep the discussion moving forward. Personality clashes between group members must be handled deftly to avoid undermining the atmosphere of the meeting. When hostilities are expected, advance enlistment of the help of another attendee can keep things running smoothly when sparks occur. If a serious conflict seems to develop, the leader should step in quickly to avoid the flare-up by calling on someone else to speak. Again, the meeting momentum is essential and will help cool antagonisms.

If conflicts of interest, as opposed to simple personal frictions, are a serious problem, they must be resolved if the meeting is to accomplish its objectives. If an issue is at stake, the leader should let the discussion run a while to see if a solution is suggested. If agreement cannot be reached, the following techniques can be used.

1. Postpone the issue temporarily.
2. If time permits, set up a subcommittee consisting of the "cooler heads" who represent the conflicting viewpoints. Ask them to record their recommendations and report back at a specified date.
3. If a decision is required of the leader, do not impose a solution in an arbitrary way and, certainly, not before the group has exhausted its own avenues to a solution.
4. If a higher authority must make a decision, it might be appropriate to take the conflict to the boss. This is obviously undesirable if the meeting was set up to solve the problem in the first place, but at times it is unavoidable.

It is a good idea to summarize the content of the meeting regularly to ensure a common understanding of conclusions and agreements reached and to uncover misunderstandings, second thoughts, or additional ideas. The purpose of the meeting cannot be accomplished unless the individuals clearly understand what was decided. At the end of the meeting the leader should take a few moments to check that the group is in basic agreement with the decisions and that everyone is committed to the assignments they have accepted. If any follow-up activities were decided upon, the individuals who volunteered for the task or received the assignment should be reminded of their responsibilities. If the meeting is more than routine, it is a good idea to generate a written summary that clearly states these responsibilities.

In summary, the difference between a meeting that accomplishes its purpose and one that ends in a cloud of uncertainty can be summed up in two words: planning and leadership. Good planning, which organizes a roomful of individuals to recognize their common objective, is discussed in greater detail in later chapters. Leadership helps them work efficiently as a group to reach that objective.

Leadership

Effective leadership is a critical attribute of management in any organization. It is especially important in the fire service, where leadership skills are needed on the fireground as well as in the fire station. Leadership effectiveness involves many complex factors that are both organizational and personal.

Leadership is a process through which an individual influences others toward the accomplishment of common goals. It is dynamic, ever changing, situational, and evolving, and it often involves a melding of values and perceptions. Many management researchers have devoted considerable effort to determine what distinguishes effective leaders from those who are less effective.

Leadership Behaviors

In 1973, Henry Mintzberg focused on the behaviors of managers and what others expected of them. This research led to classifications called "Mintzberg's Ten Managerial Roles" (Table 1.1).[2] Mintzberg determined that these roles accounted for all of the managerial behavior that he observed in his research. Although all of the roles could be applicable for a particular manager, their relative importance could vary from one kind of manager to another.

Leadership Theories

Several theories of leadership have gained recognition. The three most prominent ones are discussed briefly here. More specific aspects of effective leadership are discussed throughout this book but especially in Chapters 3 through 5.

Situational Leadership: Situational leadership theories were developed in the 1960s and 1970s. These theories essentially advocate that, for leadership effectiveness to occur, a leader must be skilled in sensing and reading a situation, and then exercise appropriate skills and behavior for that particular situation. These theories, which are also known as contingency theories, are considered to be contingent on the variables of a situation.[3] The best known of the situational leadership theories is based on Hersey and Blanchard's Life Cycle concept, which is discussed in Chapter 5 (see Figure 5.4).

Transactional Leadership: Recent academic and experimental research on leadership has defined an approach that is based on the role of the leader as an agent of change—the person who rewards those who work effectively to achieve group and organizational goals. Leadership is seen as an exchange process or a

TABLE 1.1 Mintzberg's ten managerial roles. (*Source: Mintzberg, 1973²*)

Figurehead role

Performs symbolic duties, presides at certain meetings and functions, participates in official events even though they are of marginal relevance to the job of managing.

Leader role

Provides leadership, direction, and vision. This role normally pervades all of the manager's other activities.

Liaison role

This is the bridging role, establishing networks, maintaining contacts, "keeping in touch," attending social events, conferences. This role is primarily focused outside of the organization.

Monitor role

The activity of seeking information and data from a variety of sources.

Disseminator role

The activity of passing on factual information that is not available to subordinates or recipients of the information.

Spokesman role

The activity of officially communicating information regarding the organization and its values.

Entrepreneur role

The manager as a change-master, an initiator and designer of controlled change.

Disturbance-handler role

Dealing with unplanned crises, unforeseen events, and people-oriented conflicts (sometimes referred to as "fighting the brush-fires").

Resource-allocator role

When a manager exercises authority in the allocation of physical and human resources.

Negotiator role

The activity whereby the presence of a manager lends resolution to conflict or problem-solving through the negotiation process. This activity is not limited to labor relations and encompasses the full spectrum of promoting consensus.

series of transactions in which the needs of subordinates are met if their performance measures up to their explicit or implicit contracts with their leader.[4] Transactional leadership can be viewed as an equitable exchange process between the leader and subordinate. As perceived by the subordinate, the higher the reward (whether tangible or intangible), the greater the effort he/she will exert to obtain the reward. Therefore, the subordinate's motivation is crucial to the success of the leader. Transactional leaders:

- Recognize what it is that people want from their work and try to reward them appropriately when warranted.
- Utilize and exchange both tangible and psychological rewards for performance.
- Are responsive to subordinates' immediate personal needs and self-interests, especially when they can be met while getting the work done.

Transformational Leadership: The transformational leader is complementary to the transactional leader. Transformational leaders are able to influence and motivate individuals to accomplish more than they ever thought possible. Transformational leaders influence and motivate people through the following attributes:[4]

- **Charisma.** The leader must be able to generate trust and faith through interpersonal dynamics.
- **Competence.** The leader must know what he/she is doing; however it is not necessary to have complete mastery of all the required skills.
- **Honesty.** The leader must be accountable and have the integrity to do what he/she is espousing others to do.
- **Inspiration.** The leader must be able to arouse followers to work harder and better than they thought possible.

It is important to recognize that there are situations in which transactional leadership is more appropriate than transformational leadership. Many times, though, fire departments can rely more heavily on the resources of charismatic leaders who are able to utilize untapped human resources in order to accomplish organizational goals that seem very complex and ambiguous.

It should always be remembered that leadership is a human relations skill because it involves two or more people. The most widely known theories of leadership consistently share the view that the best approach to leadership is appropriate involvement of staff members in each significant decision.

Any activity, conference, or learning that relates to interpersonal communications or group dynamics will help to improve leadership abilities. Similarly, enhancing one's technical skills strengthens the ability to be a competent leader in the fire service.

ACTIVITIES

1. Explain why it is possible for line officers to practice effective managerial and leadership styles that are not necessarily in keeping with those of their superiors.

2. Why is the belief erroneous, that good management in the fire service is merely common sense or doing the "right" thing?

3. Explain why the study of modern management theory can be of value both to experienced fire service officers as well as to those fire service officers who are either new to such positions or who aspire to them.

4. List some of the requirements that a useful management theory must satisfy if it is to be practical.

5. Explain the differences between management and supervision. Include an example of each.

6. What are some of the guidelines that help an officer become established as a competent manager once the transition from fire fighter to officer has been made?

7. Explain the importance of long-range planning.

8. Name the four areas needed for effective performance in linking an organization with its people.

9. Outline briefly some of the basic communication skills that managers should continually strive to improve in order to further increase their competency as managers.

10. How can a manager help an employee find greater motivation?

11. Explain the difference between passive and active listening. Why is active listening essential to good communication, and what must one do to be an active listener?

12. Discuss the three basic types of decision chains?

13. What are the four levels of decisions involved in each decision chain?

14. What are "time thieves"? Name five of them.

15. Discuss some pointers for conducting successful meetings.

16. Define the terms *content* and *process* as they apply to meetings.

17. Give an example of a situation where a fire officer could best use transactional leadership. When might it be appropriate for an officer to use transformational leadership?

REFERENCES

[1]Cote, A. E., ed., *Fire Protection Handbook*, 16th edition, National Fire Protection Association, Quincy, MA, 1986, p. 15-11.

[2]Mintzberg, Henry, *The Nature of Managerial Work*, Harper and Row, New York, 1973.

[3]Yulk, G. A., *Leadership in Organization*, Prentice-Hall, Englewood Cliffs, 1981.

[4]Bass, Bernard, *Leadership and Performance Beyond Expectations*, The True Press, Macmillan Publishing, New York, 1985.

2

Management Theory — Its Roots and Growth

Management theory includes four components: management science, management cycle, behavioral science, and Management by Objectives.

Management science is concerned with the techniques of work methods and time study. The major area of concentration is on the employee; i.e., how can the work best be organized so that the employee can do the job efficiently?

The *management cycle* concerns the manager's task, i.e., how to make the manager's work more effective so that the organizational unit can achieve improved results.

Behavioral science focuses on the way managers and employees behave in the work environment, on motivation, and on the influence of behavior on the amount and quality of work output.

Management by Objectives — or management with goals — is an outgrowth of the management cycle. It is a significant refinement of, and in some major ways supersedes, the management cycle. Many managers, however, still see these two concepts as separate and distinct.

Management science and the management cycle are introduced in this chapter. Behavioral science is discussed in Chapter 3 and Management by Objectives is discussed in Chapter 5. To better understand Management by Objectives, which is a very complex subject and a major foundation of effective management, Chapter 4 provides perspective in the form of a relatively new approach — the Three Cs of Management. This approach attempts to consolidate the four components of management theory into one comprehensive view.

Roots of Management Theory

The Nature of Work

Before the Industrial Revolution in the late 18th century, work was governed by tradition. Sons traditionally followed the work patterns of their fathers; daughters followed the work patterns of their mothers. People generally were born into their lifetime work situations and had little or no choice concerning them. Work followed a pattern, not a plan. For example, the work involved in planting fields, shaping metals, and maintaining households was performed according to work patterns passed down from previous generations.

In Early Times

Even before the Industrial Revolution, competent managers and some type of management theory existed. The pyramids of Egypt, the Great Wall of China, and the magnificent cathedrals of Europe all attest to the competency of skilled managers. The successful construction of the pyramids—the planning efforts, the methods for moving huge blocks of stone, the supervision of thousands of men and women who toiled directly and indirectly in the construction work itself and in the supply of tools, materials, and food—could never have been realized without the efforts of many knowledgable managers. Unfortunately, comprehensive records are not available of the techniques these managers used to guide their work forces.

Despite the tremendous size of some of the projects that required managerial skills, most of the management functions that were performed in the early days of civilization were performed on a small scale. Mass production did not exist. There were no mass production assembly lines, and technology was uncomplicated. Coordinating and bringing together the knowledge of many specialists to accomplish a task was not necessary because there were few specialists and relatively few tasks that required the skills of specialists.

Then, as now, individuals managed their own personal activities. Few people thought of this as management. For example, farming was not considered to be management of an enterprise because most of the product was for personal use. It was a job that through tradition people knew how to do—a job that followed a pattern and was much less complicated than it is now because there were no complex machines to worry about, no chemical fertilizers, no pest-control chemicals, and no bank loans or multipage tax forms.

Although there were some people who might be considered to have functioned as managers, they were few. Noblemen often employed the services of tax collectors (similar in function to today's credit and collection managers) to collect goods, rent, or taxes from tenants, but this can hardly be thought of as management as it is known today. In early times careful management was not as important to profit making from trade with faraway places because such trade was primarily barter.

During the Industrial Revolution

The advent of the Industrial Revolution brought many changes that affected the work patterns of the average person. Hand looms faded from existence and were replaced by textile mills. Potters gave up their wheels and went to work in pottery factories. The small crafts and guilds, the people working at home in their cottages, and the little shops that previously produced cooking utensils, clothing, needles, and other necessities were replaced by something new to civilization — mills, plants, and factories.

This transition brought with it a different kind of existence, as well as entirely new types of work relationships for working people. Workers lost their individuality and no longer functioned independently. They became part of the organizations that made up the work forces of the mills, plants, and factories. Such organizations needed managers.

As in earlier times, not too much was recorded about the management theories of the day. This was primarily because few people could read, fewer could write, and the general public had little or no knowledge of analytic subject areas beyond rudimentary arithmetic.

Adam Smith: Economist and Observer of Management Techniques

One of the first people to write about the way our work patterns affect our lives was the Scottish economist, Adam Smith (1723–1790). In 1776, he wrote *An Inquiry into the Nature and Cause of the Wealth of Nations*, pointing out how the division of labor could help enrich society. Smith believed that greater wealth could be derived from any system or method that helped produce more goods with the same amount of effort as required by previous methods. His famous example was set in a pin factory:[1]

> To take an example, therefore, from a trifling manufacture; but one in which the division of labour has been very often taken notice of, the trade of the pin-maker; a workman not educated to this business (which the division of labour has rendered a distinct trade), nor acquainted with the use of the machinery employed in it (to the invention of which the same division of labour has probably given occasion), could scarce, perhaps, with his utmost industry, make one pin in a day, and certainly could not make twenty. But in the way in which this business is now carried on, not only the whole work is a peculiar trade, but it is divided into a number of branches, of which the greater part are likewise peculiar trades. One man draws out the wire, another straights it, a third cuts it, a fourth points it, a fifth grinds it at the top for receiving the head; to make the head requires two or three distinct operations; to put it on, is a peculiar business, to whiten the pins is another; it is even a trade by itself to put them into the paper; and the important business of making a pin is, in this manner, divided into about eighteen distinct operations, which, in some manufactories, are all performed by distinct hands, though in others the same man will sometimes perform two or three of them. I have seen a small manufactory of this kind

where ten men only were employed, and where some of them consequently performed two or three distinct operations. But though they were very poor, and therefore but indifferently accommodated with the necessary machinery, they could, when they exerted themselves, make among them about twelve pounds of pins in a day. There are in a pound upwards of four thousand pins of a middling size. Those ten persons, therefore, could make among them upwards of forty-eight thousand pins in a day. Each person, therefore, making a tenth part of forty-eight thousand pins, might be considered as making four thousand eight hundred pins in a day. But if they had all wrought separately and independently, and without any of them having been educated to this peculiar business, they certainly could not each of them have made twenty, perhaps not one pin in a day; that is, certainly, not the two hundred and fortieth, perhaps not the four thousand eight hundredth part of what they are at present capable of performing, in consequence of a proper division and combination of their different operations.

It is important to note that the methods of production described by Smith came into being long before he wrote about them, and that they gave evidence of extensive application of management theories. Smith's book helped explain how the changes made during the Industrial Revolution helped bring about greater wealth.

Division of Labor

In the late 1700s, division of labor existed in fire fighting as well as in industry. Undoubtedly, at first, those people who demonstrated exceptional ability to throw water accurately onto a fire, or who could throw it farther, were those who got to disperse the water during a fire. Others carried the water. If there were enough people, water was handed from person to person. This allowed more buckets of water to reach the fire scene because not everyone had to walk to the well to get the water. The fire service, as it existed in those days, benefited from this division of labor.

Fire fighting became more sophisticated when tub pumps came into existence. These large wood tubs on wheels were filled with water and brought to the fire scene. Hand pumps (similar to the hand pumps used on old wells) were located at the tops of the tubs. Water was pumped from the tub pumps into hoses, thus supplying fire fighters with useful but somewhat erratic streams of water (see Figure 2.1). A division of labor was reflected in the operation of these early tub pumps. Runners were needed to pull the pumpers, relay people were needed to supply the tub pumps with buckets of water, pumpers operated the hand pumps on the tub pumps, and hosemen handled the hose. Eventually there were laddermen, and when horses replaced the runners there were out-riders, drivers, and tillermen. When steam-pumping engines came into use in the mid-1800s, there were stokers.

Today, although the scope and complexity of the work of the fire service differs from the early days, division of labor can be seen in the

FIGURE 2.1 An example of the division of labor in the operation of early tub pumps. (Source: Library of Congress)

specialization required by properly staffed fire departments. This specialization of work includes fire fighters, fire officers, secretaries, teachers, ambulance drivers, radio operators, apparatus operators, building engineers, personnel directors, mechanics, accountants, experts in emergency first aid, and emergency medical technicians. Such specialization is continuing as the function of today's fire departments becomes even more complex.

Complex Apparatus Takes Over Many Tasks: In the fire service, much of the division of labor has been reflected in the design of different apparatus. Apparatus have been designed to effectively fulfill many specific functions. Just as industrial machines can perform the operations of many people at once and require only a single operator, many functions of the modern fire fighting apparatus have been combined and automated. Today, one highly trained apparatus operator can perform the specialized functions of many people. For example, with a modern pumper, a skilled operator can:

- Move more than 1000 gallons of water per minute.
- Apply water much more effectively in full or dispersed streams.
- Apply water from the ground or from elevated positions.
- Send messages immediately.
- Climb steep hills that would have required many runners.

- Carry ladders and equipment.
- Perform the work of many horses in getting the fire fighters to the scene more rapidly, so that fewer fire fighters are needed to extinguish the fire.

Complex Skills Required: With the advent of more complex equipment came the need for higher skills and greater knowledge on the part of fire fighters. Today's skilled fire fighter is a specialist who must be knowledgable in many areas, including the following:

- Hydraulics and pump operations.
- Building construction.
- Flammability of materials.
- Rope work.
- Search and rescue.
- Complex respiratory protection equipment.
- Communication equipment.
- Minimizing losses by salvage work.
- Mathematics (for metric conversions, flow rates, etc.).
- Chemistry (for recognizing the nature and components of burning materials, and knowing the most effective means for extinguishing them).
- Emergency medical services.
- Hazardous materials response.

Knowledge in these areas is necessary for fire fighters to function effectively at the fire scene. In addition, the specialized knowledge required of today's fire fighter includes an awareness of such areas as inspection and prefire planning, building construction, fire prevention, codes and standards, public and community relations, and public education.

MANAGEMENT SCIENCE

Management science, which is the first phase of management theory, concentrates on the efficiency of the work processes and on the way the individual worker or employee performs tasks.

The height of the Industrial Revolution in England took place while the United States was involved in the War for Independence and its aftermath. It was not until the late 19th century that a similar economic revolution took place in the United States. The change, like that in England, was a gradual one. Due to the introduction of machines, farming for profit slowly replaced subsistence farming, and factories slowly replaced small trade shops. However, it was not until the United States underwent its economic revolution that a science of management really began. The works of Frederick Taylor, Henry Gantt, Frank and Lillian Gilbreth, and Chester Barnard, each of whom helped establish the groundwork for management science, were important contributions.

The Industrial Revolution increased specialization and gradually resulted in the development of machines that replaced people. Sometimes, several of the more sophisticated machinery could be tended by one little girl and often were. Child labor laws had yet to be enacted.

Behind the little girl, however, was an industry of highly skilled craftspersons who designed and built the machines, and groups of equally skilled mechanics who kept the machines running. Organizing the mechanized work process required far more skill than the more cumbersome hand processes that had existed earlier. Even the small pin factory that Adam Smith described required the planning, the coordinating, and the supervising effort of at least one competent manager. As the complexity of work in all fields increased, more and more managers were required to coordinate the increasingly specialized activities. For example, when one person cuts and sews a complete dress by hand, very little management is required. A single manager could employ hundreds of people if all that has to be done is to provide a place to work and the cloth to use. However, when cutting is done by people with one type of machine and sewing is done by people with several different types of machines—and all the machines must be selected, purchased, and maintained, and the work effort of these people coordinated—then 100 workers would most likely require several managers.

As the need for managers increased, more managerial activity evolved, and management came to be thought of as a science. Gradually, modern management theories emerged, including management science. The focus of management science is on performance with the least amount of effort: How could the maximum amount of output be gained with the least amount of input?

The developers of management science had an interest in making work most effective in terms of output, but not necessarily at the workers' expense. Management scientists, recognizing that workers became fatigued, were concerned about making work as easy as possible so that more could be produced. Much of their concern centered around the following questions: What kind of devices could be used? What kind of methods could be followed? How could wasteful steps—or activity that did not contribute to increased production—be avoided?

Frederick Taylor: The Father of Management Science

Frederick Taylor (1856–1915) was among the first to write about management concepts. In the early 1900s Taylor, a Philadelphia steel mill superintendent who had developed a carefully thought-out system for managing work, saw around him a lack of detailed attention to the way work could best be organized. There were wasted steps and wasted motions. He reasoned that such waste required effort, and if that effort could be used to produce more, everyone would gain. Taylor was not working on a management theory *per se*: he was working to produce more steel at less cost in order to increase profits for his company.

In Taylor's time little attention was given to the way work could best be organized. He observed that few people, if any, worked steadily and energetically all day. He reasoned that if he could somehow scientifically determine what constituted a day's work, he could better tell employees what was expected of them. Taylor felt that, within reasonable expectations, he was bound to obtain a greatly improved output. Therefore, through experimentation, he set out to develop standards for a fair day's work. Following are excerpts from two of his reports.[2,3]

> The first impression is that this minute subdivision of the work into elements, neither of which takes more than five or six seconds to perform, is little short of preposterous; yet if a rapid and thorough time study of the art of shoveling is to be made, this subdivision simplifies the work, and makes the study quicker and more thorough.
>
> The reasons for this are twofold:
>
> First. In the art of shoveling dirt, for instance, the study of 50 or 60 small elements, like those referred to above, will enable one to fix the exact time for many thousands of complete jobs of shoveling, constituting a very considerable proportion of the entire art.
>
> Second. The study of single small elements is simpler, quicker, and more certain to be successful than that of a large number of elements combined. The greater the length of time involved in a single item of time study, the greater will be the likelihood of interruptions or accidents, which will render the results obtained by the observer questionable or even useless. There is a considerable part of the work of most establishments that is not what may be called standard work, namely, that which is repeated many times. Such jobs as this can be divided for time study into groups, each of which contains several rudimentary elements. . .
>
> There is no class of work which cannot be profitably submitted to time study, by dividing it into its time elements, except such operations as take place in the head of the worker; and the writer has even seen a time study made of the speed of an average and first-class boy in solving problems in mathematics. Clerk work can well be submitted to time study, and a daily task assigned in work of this class which at first appears to be very miscellaneous in its character. . .[2]

Further, Taylor states:

> Practically the greatest need felt in an establishment wishing to start a rate-fixing department is the lack of data as to the proper rate of speed at which work should be done. There are hundreds of operations which are common to most large establishments, yet each concern studies the speed problem for itself, and days of labor are wasted in what should be settled once and for all, and recorded in a form which is available to all manufacturers.

What is needed is a handbook on the speed with which work can be done similar to the elementary engineering handbooks. And the writer ventures to predict that such a book will before long be forthcoming. Such a book should describe the best method of making, recording, tabulating and indexing time observations, since much time and effort are wasted by the adoption of inferior methods.[3]

Unlike other managers of his time, Taylor was interested in the well-being of his employees. Well-being, however, had a different meaning in the early 1900s. Although some employers looked upon employees in a paternalistic way and were honestly concerned for the people who worked for them, such concern was less universal than it is today. To a competent manager in Taylor's time, the well-being of employees merely meant increased profits. Business was business, and an employee was an employee. The employer decided what, when, and how something was to be done—and the employee obeyed.

Workers accepted this role of the boss as the decision-maker and regarded the shop or office as a place where one was supposed to work. They accepted, without question, the right of employers to change the nature of the work environment without consulting them. Of little concern was the modern expectation of employees for a say in the way work is or is not done. However, the fact that some employees did expect some say in the nature of their work is evidenced by the rise of trade unions around the turn of the 19th century.

Aside from those who spearheaded the trade unions, most of the people who worked in Taylor's time did not expect any greater reward for their work than to be paid for it. Although workers expected to be treated decently, they did not expect their employers to care whether or not they liked their work, whether or not they were content with their work, or whether or not they were comfortable while doing the work: They worked for money. Later in the 1900s, managers were to become more aware that there were many other incentives that were even stronger than monetary rewards.

Taylor's Method Analysis

What was Taylor really doing? First, he analyzed the work to see what changes could be tried to find methods that would be most productive. Next, he taught these methods to employees. Finally, he timed the people doing the work to see what they would produce if they worked steadily without exerting themselves, and set that as a standard on which their pay was based.

Steps and procedures of time studies stem from Taylor's work. The first step involves analysis to find the best method. Opinion varies as to what should come next. Some believe that standards should be set, and training should follow. Others advocate training first, and then setting standards. In either case, Taylor's work set the stage for the development of increasingly better work methods. In many instances, the precedent was established for machinery to take on an increasing share of the workload. Much of the automation that supports today's high standard of living is based on the work of Frederick Taylor and his followers.

Methods Improvement in the Fire Service

Methods improvement in fire fighting began in the 1700s with the division of labor described earlier (see Figure 2.1).

Hand Pumpers

When tub pumps were first developed, two people were needed to pump — one at each end of the pump handle. However, this method did not pump enough water, nor did it pump water fast enough. The pump handle evolved into a treadle that was worked up and down by a person working at each end, similar to a seesaw.

After these developments, the ultimate hand pumper was designed. This model featured two long wooden bars called brakes, one on each side of the pumper. Fire fighters lined up — as many as 10 on a side — using their combined strength to pump up and down on the brakes. Some pump teams could hit a rate of 140 strokes a minute — a rate that was so exhausting that team members could rarely keep up the pace for more than a minute. Backup teams were needed as alternates when a team of pumpers became exhausted. (It should be noted that in early competitions with steam pumpers, these hand pumpers often out-performed the steam pumpers by shooting a stream of water more than 160 ft into the air.)

Hand pumpers usually were pulled to the fire by 10 to 14 fire fighters or runners, two abreast. However, this number often increased if there were as many available runners as there was room to grab onto the ropes and pull. When the fire gong sounded, volunteer runners in various states of disarray would grab the ropes while other volunteers, often attired in bedclothes during night alarms, joined along the way.

The hand pumper runners were a remarkable lot. They often had to pull a pumper a mile or two at a steady trot, through the heat of summer and the cold and snow of winter. As runners fatigued others would join in along the way. In Boston's 1872 conflagration, a hand-pumper company from the town of Wakefield pulled its pumpers 12 miles to Boston to help fight the fire.

Horse-Pulled Pumpers

Pumper companies started to use horses to pull the pumpers about 1830, creating the next phase in fire fighting efficiency. Many runner companies resisted the change because they considered it "soft" to use horses. They also felt that on short runs people could still outperform horses and get the pumpers to the fires faster. Not until the 1860s — when larger, heavier pumpers came into use, some weighing 8 tons — did horsepower generally replace humans for pulling pumpers (see Figure 2.2). Even then there were some lightweight steam pumpers still being pulled by men.

Gasoline Engines

Early in the 1900s the advent of the gasoline engine, used to pull fire apparatus, marked the next major improvement in fire fighting methods. As originally used by the fire service, the gasoline engine was a tractor-type contraption hooked to the front of a pumper in lieu of horses.

By this time fire fighters had become as attached to the system of using horses to pull pumpers as they had been to the previous system of using human runners. Many fire companies believed that this new gasoline contraption would never measure up to horsepower in speed and efficiency. Oddly, at first, they were right. It actually took a fire company longer to start up the gasoline engine than it took a top-notch horse company to get the horses hitched and out of the fire station. The early engines also broke down frequently.

As a tribute to their work, some horse companies performed their methods and drill so well that they could get the horses from their stalls, harnessed, and out of the fire station in the almost incredible time of 18 seconds. Many pumpers were pulled by horse teams having horses three abreast. The fire horses were as eager and ready to go as the fire fighters. Once out of the fire station, the horse-drawn fire apparatus could go as fast as the gas engines that only had top speeds of 15 miles an hour.

FIGURE 2.2 Horsepower started replacing runners for pulling steam pumpers in the 1830s. (Source: Baltimore Fire Department, Baltimore, Maryland)

However, self-starters eventually were built into the fire apparatus, improving the gas engines. Finally, in the early 1900s, gas engines replaced horses in fire stations all across the country. Thus, the method of moving fire apparatus to a fire has progressed from two or more human runners to two or more horses to, finally, modern pumpers with hundreds of horsepower and very large capacities and complex capabilities.

Examples of Taylor's Influence

Although Frederick Taylor's methods primarily applied to improving production in the steel mills (see earlier in this chapter), they can also be used as a basis for analysis of the fire service. For example, modern fire fighting equipment design reflects the concept of saving time in order to increase efficiency. Conveniently located preconnected hoses and nozzles, instruments and valves in ready-to-use positions, easily accessible ladders, and quick-change couplings are but a few examples of this concept. Breathing apparatus that was previously stored in compartments is now frequently positioned to enable a fire fighter to jump off the truck with the equipment ready for use. Ladders now come in sections so they can be extended to the necessary height. Truck beds have partitions so that two or even three hoses can be laid at one time. Hose-packing procedures are now designed for rapid uncoiling of hoses with less chance that they will become snagged on ground obstructions.

Careful methods study helps bring about further improvements in fire fighting. For example, availability of larger hose diameters, requires new questions. Which is more effective: using two 1½-in. hoses or one 2½-in. hose that can deliver as much water? When determining the answer to this question, one should consider that it often takes more people to reposition one 2½-in. line than it does to move two 1½-in. lines and, as the fire comes under control in one area, the second 1½-in. line can be moved to attack the fire elsewhere. However, a 2½-in. line often can deliver more water at higher pressure than two 1½-in. lines, possibly controlling the fire sooner. Evaluation of the water flow as well as personnel requirements in various probable situations can help answer such questions. Lightweight 1¾-in. hose, which is used most often now, has proved to be more effective than either of these options.

Despite the many benefits resulting from Taylor's work, there were flaws that brought about major problems in the actual practice of management science. One such problem was the fear among employees that they, by working harder and more efficiently, would work themselves out of their jobs, thus causing many of them to be laid off. Employees were also afraid that higher and higher standards would be set, and that this would gradually lead to increased labor for the same amount of pay.

Employee concerns were not the only significant problems brought about by the application of management science. Other problems involved imperfections in the flow of information and of material, which often created wasted time. This waste was considered to be as serious as slow work or poor methods.

Henry Gantt, one of Frederick Taylor's successors as a management scientist, addressed that problem.

The Work of Henry Gantt

Like Taylor, Henry Gantt was also concerned with the problems involved in increasing steel mill production. However, Gantt recognized the answers to some of the problems Taylor had failed to solve. Gantt's research focused on how to avoid problems that occur when a machine breaks down, leaving people all along the production line standing idle. He also studied the problems created when a worker or one operation takes longer than necessary, and everyone's work connected with that operation is necessarily slowed down. In addition, he examined the consequences of a part not being available when needed.

Work Flow

The problem of work flow was as frustrating to employees as it was to managers. For example, an employee on piecework could lose both production time and wages on a given day due to a work interruption caused by any or all of the following: 1) lack of material, 2) absenteeism on the line, 3) slow worker on the line, or 4) a machine breakdown. Such loss, of course, was clearly unfair and resulted in many complaints from employees. Employees who were paid by the day found that, because something had gone wrong, there was no work and they were made to bear the company's loss. The problems that resulted in slowing down the flow of work and production caused a financial drain on business and were constant sources of dissatisfaction to employees. Many of these problems contributed to bitter struggles between management and labor.

Gantt devised a work flow system for solving the problems of slow-ups and losses in production time that resulted in lost revenue for employers and lost wages for employees: the Gantt charts and the Task and Bonus plan, described as follows.

The Gantt Charts: Gantt created detailed schedules in chart form that are still used today. Called "Gantt charts," these schedules indicated which work-related functions were to be done, and when they were to be done. The schedules often showed how the work was to be "routed," or where the semifinished batch of work was to be taken after a specific part was completed.

The Task and Bonus Plan: Gantt devised a task and bonus plan to help solve the loss of production and pay problems. In simple terms, Gantt's plan meant that, when an employee was assigned a task (based on a predetermined amount of piecework that could be used as a standard for a day's work), the employee would be paid for that work even if, due to some uncontrollable circumstance, the standard could not be met. On the other hand, if the employee exceeded the set standard, a bonus — calculated at an even higher rate — would be paid for all work completed above the standard. Gantt's plan thus gave the employee protection against undue loss of pay while maintaining the incentive to work harder. Gantt recognized that there had to be some leeway, some room for revision, and greater flexibility than Taylor had allowed. This included an awareness that sometimes standards could be set that were out of line with what employees could reasonably be expected to do, and that there were many unforeseeable circumstances and situations that could disrupt any schedule.

The Work of Frank and Lillian Gilbreth

Two outstanding contributors to the study of management were Frank (1868–1924) and Lillian (1878–1972) Gilbreth. Frank's family wanted him to go to college, but he decided that he could make more money faster if he went to work; the work he chose was bricklaying. It is of interest to note that many of the innovators in management theory placed heavy emphasis on making a good living for themselves as well as for others.

Gilbreth soon found that bricklaying, as it was done in the 1880s, was a very inefficient business. Bricks were dumped in no specific order into a pile near the bricklayer. The bricklayer would walk to the pile, pick up an arbitrary number of bricks, and return to the wall that was being built. At the wall, the bricks were put down, spread with mortar, picked up again, and finally placed in location. Gilbreth asked several bricklayers for their opinions as to the best ways to go about their jobs. Each one came up with a different answer. From this experience, Gilbreth devoted the rest of his life to the business of finding different ways to make work more efficient.

Early Method, Time, and Motion Studies

Frank Gilbreth initially experimented with a variety of ways to eliminate wasted motion. For example, he found that bricklayers could work much faster when bricks were neatly arranged in right-side-up positions and located as close as possible to the bricklayers.[4] If the bricks were within arm's reach, time was saved in reaching for them. If the mortar was conveniently located, it saved time and motion scooping it up and troweling it. Furthermore, if the bricklayers spread the mortar with two sweeps instead of three, one-third of the time of that function would be saved. Gilbreth designed better scaffolding, better rigging, and better hods to carry the bricks. To eliminate fatigue caused by stooping, he designed scaffolds that moved upward as the work progressed. Because of his success in finding more efficient ways to work by saving time and motion, Gilbreth advanced from apprentice bricklayer to owner of a construction company within 10 years.

Gilbreth called his system speed work (which should not be confused with speed-up). Speed work was not a system based on a faster pace; rather, speed work was based on the principle that performing a task more efficiently would eliminate wasted time and would improve the efficiency of the work. For example, Gilbreth found that, by applying his methods to bricklaying, some 2800 bricks could be put in place each day instead of 900 bricks, without loss of quality. Therefore, this system combined quality with quantity in order to gain the greatest productivity from a task.

Gilbreth started an internationally successful contracting business in 1895. He married Lillian E. Moller in 1904, and they founded a management consulting firm in 1911. Many of the largest corporations in the United States employed the Gilbreths as efficiency experts.

Lillian Gilbreth graduated from the University of California with a master's degree in literature. She already had five children when, in 1915, she earned a Ph.D. degree in industrial psychology at Brown University. Lillian also became interested in methods, time, and motion studies. As the Gilbreths became increasingly involved with their discoveries, they began to look at smaller and smaller motions. They used motion-picture cameras to record exact movements involved in a particular piece of work. These motion pictures even contained special clocks showing the exact amount of time for each motion.

The Gilbreths worked in more detail and in finer measure than Taylor. They labeled and grouped 17 basic elements of job motion with titles such as search, find, select, and grasp; wait-unavoidable and wait-avoidable; and rest and plan. Their work led to the establishment of precise performance standards, published in books of standards where industrial engineers could look up just how long it would take to perform a particular job function. For example, to find out how long it should take an employee to punch two holes in a piece of metal with a certain machine, one could look up the standard time for each of the motions required to accomplish such a function and add them up.

Flow Process Charts

The Gilbreths also developed flow process charts. These charts provide a picture of the sequence of functions involved in a job so that wasted handling or backtracking can be identified and avoided. The chart shows all the steps that need to be performed on a product in order to complete it.

A similar analysis can be made of an individual performing a job function or a series of job functions. Entries under "details of method" in such a flow chart would include: waiting for assignment, receiving orders, walking to storage, retrieving material, performing the operation, and so on.

After her husband's death, Lillian Gilbreth took over their business and became one of the leading engineers of her day. She worked as professor of management at Perdue University from 1935 to 1948. Lillian also specialized in the human engineering side of management, successfully managing a large household in addition to her other work. The Gilbreth's raised 12 children, two of whom wrote the book *Cheaper by the Dozen*, a testament to their parents' managerial expertise. Frank B. Gilbreth, Jr., and Ernestine Gilbreth Corey describe in the book how their mother and father organized and managed a household of 14 members, where each child had an individual job, and each kept a plan and job description that was posted for everyone to see.

Differences Between the Gilbreths and Taylor

Taylor, Gantt, and the Gilbreths differentiated three basic elements in their work: 1) methods study, 2) motion study, and 3) time study. Methods study deals with how work can best be arranged and what portion of the work could be eliminated. Motion study concentrates on the individual motions to see how they can be simplified or shortened. In addition, time study determines how long the improved methods should take, and what, therefore, makes a reasonable performance standard. It also analyzes how much time a particular job function should take when all of the factors involved are considered including fatigue, rest, fumbling, and so on.

A basic difference between Taylor's and the Gilbreths' studies is that Taylor was concerned with large segments of work, e.g., putting five or six pieces of material together, moving materials 10 or more feet, repeated walking back and forth, or the lifting, carrying, and placing of materials to more convenient locations — all operations that took 5 to 10 minutes or more. In contrast, the Gilbreths were concerned with much finer units of work, e.g., reaching 6 inches, grasping, or the turning of a screw with repetitive motions that took only split seconds.

Fire Fighting Drills as an Example of the Gilbreths' Work

Fire fighting drills are an example of how the careful elimination of wasted motion can lead to better job performance. For example, a team of fire fighters practicing a strategy can seemingly perfect it and then, with constant repetition, refine it down to the fastest possible time with the least amount of fumbling and error. While this constant repetition can be monotonous and unpleasant in many ways, it can also be beneficial. Although at times it might seem to an individual that he/she has become a piece of machinery, there is no doubt that a well-drilled fire team will get the hoses laid and the ladders mounted more effectively and faster than a team that has not been drilled thoroughly.

Drill is as precise as a Gilbreth motion-study plan. However, drills have diminished in importance because so much of the routine of fire fighting work is accomplished through good equipment organization on the truck rather than by the individual fire fighters. The fire apparatus operation is organized so well today that fire fighters practically step off the trucks ready to take the hose line into the fire. Despite such organizational perfection, the drill remains an important function in the fire service. The best and fastest fire fighters still are those that are members of well-drilled companies and that understand and utilize method and motion theories.

In addition, drills can provide great satisfaction in being a member of a smoothly operating team. Practicing routine drills need not be demotivating. As any successful athlete knows, there is a great thrill when the team executes a perfect play; generally, the thrill of accomplishment more than offsets the monotony of repetitious practice.

The Work of Chester Barnard

Chester Barnard, former vice president of the New Jersey Bell Telephone Company, theorized that the personal objectives of the people in an organization must be coordinated with the overall objectives of the organization. This recognition of the importance of objectives and of the need to satisfy people was something new and important in management science.

In many organizations the individual objectives (the goals) of the employees and the overall objectives of the organization are not defined clearly or understood. Generally, although methods have been improved, when an organization has not clarified what its objectives are, the application of even the best management methods can fail to bring full benefits.

Barnard concluded that it was most important for a manager to have the ability to weigh all the strategic factors intelligently and thoroughly in order to make proper decisions when selecting objectives. He believed that making proper decisions was the core of effective management, and emphasized the necessity for keeping objectives clearly in mind so the organization would adapt to changing circumstances and progress toward its objectives.

THE MANAGEMENT CYCLE

Henri Fayol's Work

Of all the people who studied how a manager's work should be organized, few showed greater understanding or wrote about it more clearly and intelligently than Henri Fayol, a French mining director. Fayol spent his entire business career of more than 50 years as the industrial manager of a coal mine. He attacked management problems with the same scientific, rational methods as Taylor and Gantt, but in an entirely new area.

In his book *General and Industrial Management*[5] (written in French in 1916; translated into English in 1949), Fayol outlined what managers should do, how they should do it, and how they should relate to each other. Fayol saw the role of management as a cyclical set of specific functions, gradually leading every project or task to a satisfactory completion.

Management Skills

Fayol divided a manager's skills into five main functions: 1) planning, 2) organizing, 3) commanding, 4) coordinating, and 5) controlling. These functions, described as follows, form a cycle of management because they blend in with one another to form a total concept of management (see Figure 2.3).

Planning: Fayol perceived planning in three stages: long-range planning, medium-range planning, and short-range planning. Planning sets the aim and charts the course. Anything that is done haphazardly without a plan is likely to be less than satisfactory, whether it is painting the kitchen, managing a business, or attacking a fire.

Long-range planning involves decisions that will have a major effect on reaching goals far in the future, often up to 5, 10, or even 20 years from the present. Personal long-range plans can set the course of an entire lifetime, e.g., they can involve choosing a career or a marital partner. In business, long-range plans can include the products the business will offer, the geographic areas it will serve, and the markets it will penetrate. Long-range planning in the fire service involves matters such as the number and location of fire stations, the planning of water supplies, and sometimes the purchase of major apparatus.

Because long-range planning generally deals with large-scale major decisions that can have major consequences, this type of planning is done primarily by top management. Long-range planning is one of the most difficult functions of management because there are so many options and so many courses of action a manager can take. There are many different concerns to take into account, and the consequences of management decisions are vitally important.

Medium-range planning requires skillful foresight and forecasting, but the projects generally are not as large or as distant as those involving long-range planning. As a rule of thumb, a medium-range plan is usually for goals that can be accomplished in 1 to 5 years. Buying an automobile is a good example of medium-range personal planning. A yearly inspection schedule or the routine maintenance of a fire engine are examples of medium-range planning in the fire service.

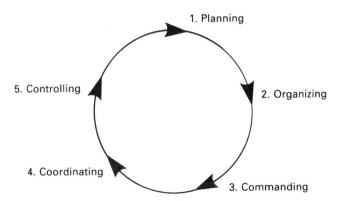

FIGURE 2.3 Pictorial representation of Henri Fayol's management cycle. (Source: Fayol, 1949[5])

Short-range planning covers all of the scheduling that will have an immediate and direct effect, such as planning a party or planning a week's work schedule. For example, if the work schedule for next week is not prepared, people might stand around and waste time. Such consequences of failing to manage properly can help instill a strong incentive for making short-term planning a habit.

As Henri Fayol saw it, planning is like looking into both the near and the distant future and then laying out a course of action that best leads to the accomplishment of the established goals of a person or organization. Planning is often considered difficult and unrewarding because few plans materialize exactly as constructed, and often many adjustments must be made as time progresses. Planning, therefore, is sometimes looked upon as wasted effort and, because there usually are many other seemingly more urgent and important things to do, planning is often badly neglected.

Organizing: Organizing is the assembling of all the pieces necessary to carry out the plan. Organizing and planning are closely related. Planning can be compared to the work of the architect, and organizing can be compared to the work of the builder.

A fire station can be used as an example of the difference between planning and organizing in the fire service. A plan to paint the fire station might have to be started a year in advance because it will have to be budgeted. However, the actual painting of the fire station is an organizing job: The paint, brushes, and rollers have to be purchased and work assignments made. Good organization requires that the paint, rollers, and brushes are made available at the right time, and people are assigned to specific tasks. Important questions also have to be answered. Will four inexperienced persons be able to do the job more quickly and as well as two experienced persons? Would it be best to spend more money and hire professionals? Without good organization, few plans will be followed. Accordingly, not only is much of the planning effort wasted when planning procedures are not organized, but much less will be accomplished.

Fayol believed that of all managerial activities, good organization and good selection are the most difficult. To Fayol, organizing meant "a place for everything, and everything in its place; a place for each person, and each person in his place." Implicit in organizing is order, which to Fayol was more than a matter of neatness. As an example, Fayol presented the case of a yard full of carefully and neatly stacked steel ingots. All of the ingots were evenly stacked, thus giving an impression of orderliness. On closer inspection, Fayol discovered that ingots of six different sizes for several different uses were mixed together. In like manner, a superficially "stacked" fire station might not always be the best organized station for quick response when an alarm sounds.

Commanding: One of Fayol's principles of command was that each person have only one superior giving orders. When two different people are telling one person what to do or how to do it, confusion is created. Fayol alluded to the uneasiness that surfaces when an individual has two leaders. He believed that maintaining a distinct chain of command was of the utmost importance.

This principle of unity of command—one person being in charge—is absolutely essential during emergencies. That is why the concept is so meaningful for the fire service and for military troops. However, when there is no emergency, this same principle also has disadvantages. For this reason the unity-of-command principle has lost popularity as work has become increasingly more complicated. Therefore, specialized experts are often needed to advise an organization in the performance of various aspects of its work. For example, a particular fire officer might be highly knowledgable in fire and arson investigation, while a company officer finds it difficult to direct the fire fighters in such an investigation. Thus, when it is necessary to conduct an investigation that requires the work of several fire fighters, the officer in the department who is the most knowledgable might be called in to provide technical direction even though the company officer is still in charge of the fire fighters. The decision not to adhere to the unity-of-command principle during nonemergency periods can sometimes be a good decision.

Coordinating: Fayol perceived coordinating as the force that pulls together all the people and their work into a common cause. Coordinating is what makes a real team; an organization, business, government, or fire department cannot function effectively if its parts are working at cross purposes.

In any organization there are separate areas, separate specialists, different departments, layers of command, levels of communication—all sorts of groups, policies, ideas, and even orders—that can work against one another and cause confusion or disharmony. When this happens, the unity of purpose is lost.

The need for the segments of the work to proceed in harmony (or in unity of action) was Fayol's hallmark. Fayol found that lack of coordination often is caused by one or a combination of these situations:

- Each segment of an organization not being interested in or knowing little or nothing about the other segments.
- Each unit of an organization working in too much isolation from other units.
- People not having sufficient regard for the general interest.

In the fire service, lack of coordination rarely happens. However, there have been instances—especially where the areas of jurisdiction among several volunteer companies were not clarified—when problems have occurred. Fayol's suggested remedy for lack of coordination was weekly conferences of department heads to keep in touch with the latest developments and to coordinate plans of action. Unity of action is the objective of coordinating, and some managers have found that weekly conferences are not sufficient in helping to achieve harmony and unity; thus, even closer coordination of effort is required on some matters.

Controlling: Fayol defined controlling as a verifying process in which weaknesses and errors are found and rectified, thus preventing them from reoccurring. It involves making certain that procedures are adhered to and orders are carried out, and that the job actually gets done.

In the previous example of organizing the painting of a fire station, suppose the paint begins to peel? This is a control problem. The reason for the peeling must be found, and many things must be considered. Was the peeling the fault of the paint? Was it the fault of the wall surface? Was it the way the paint was applied? After the reason has been established, the problem must be corrected and prevented from reoccurring.

An important application of controlling as it relates to the fire service is in the area of training. Any errors or omissions during previous emergencies must be analyzed and, through training, skills for improved procedures must be developed.

Some management theorists have used various other terms to overcome misunderstandings of Fayol's original definitions. Planning and organizing are commonly described as the first steps in a management cycle; however, some theorists follow with terms such as executing, implementing, staffing, leading, and follow-up—all words that essentially describe the same set of functions as Fayol's final three functions. To a new manager some of these terms and their use might seem confusing and not to have much meaning. However, such terms usually take on more meaning when a manager actually faces job-oriented problems and decisions.

The many terms that are used by different people to describe the management cycle indicate, to some extent, one of the difficulties of working with the cycle concept. The skills a manager needs for each step are not easy to define, thus making it more difficult to train people to become more proficient. Because different theorists have emphasized different terms and approaches, a certain amount of confusion has developed about the specific elements of the cycle. The total concept of the management cycle, however, is an important one that every manager should understand. Fayol's definitions are used in this text because the terms are appropriate for the fire service.

ACTIVITIES

1. Why was Adam Smith's description of workers in a pin factory important form an economic point of view? From a management point of view?

2. For the following jobs, determine whether management functions are needed. Defend your reasoning by listing the managerial functions you believe necessary for each job.
   (a) Owner of a small business.
   (b) Short-order cook in a chain restaurant.
   (c) Truck driver delivering produce to a large city.
   (d) Fire fighter rookie.
   (e) Fire chief in a small town.
   (f) Acting fire chief of a volunteer department.
   (g) Arson investigator.

3. Consider the reasons for the evolution of the division of labor in the fire service.
   (a) Do you feel that the fire service is becoming too specialized in its division of labor? Explain your answer.
   (b) Do you feel that the division of labor has made the job of fire fighting more successful? Explain your answer.
4. Following are five of Frederick Taylor's elements of scientific management. Explain how at least three of these elements can be applied to the fire service.
   (a) Elimination of wasted steps and wasted motions will increase productivity.
   (b) Employees work for money; they do not care about job satisfaction.
   (c) The employer decides what is to be done and the employee obeys.
   (d) Standards can be developed for a fair day's work so employees will not become tired.
   (e) One job takes a specific amount of time.
5. If fire fighters were paid only for the fires they fight and not for the time they spend preparing for fires, how might Gantt's Task and Bonus Plan provide more monetary reward?
6. (a) Explain how the Gilbreth's method, time, and motion studies can be applied to managing work in the fire service.
   (b) Which of these studies do you feel is most beneficial to the fire service? Why?
7. From the following list of duties, determine which category of Henri Fayol's management cycle is described.
   (a) Drawing sketches for a new communications center in a fire station.
   (b) Devising rescue procedures during a high-rise fire.
   (c) Setting up a department meeting to discuss an inspection group's findings on hotels in the municipality.
   (d) Determining the efficiency of existing apparatus and existing station locations.
   (e) Seeking answers to why fire department response time has decreased by two minutes.

REFERENCES

[1]Smith, Adam, *An Inquiry into the Nature and Cause of the Wealth of Nations*, W. Strahan and T. Cadell, London, 1776; reprinted as *The Wealth of Nations* by Modern Library Giants, New York, 1937.

[2]Taylor, F. W., "Time Study," *Management: Analysis, Concepts, Cases,* Prentice Hall, Inc., Englewood Cliffs, NJ, 1964, pp. 248–49.

[3]Taylor, F. W., "*A Piece Rate System,*" Shop Management, Harper & Row, New York, 1947, pp. 176–177.

[4]Gilbreth, Frank B., "Motion Study," *The Writings of the Gilbreths,* Richard D. Irwin, Inc., Homewood, IL, 1953, pp. 55, 63, 65.

[5]Fayol, Henri, *General and Industrial Management,* Pitman Publishing Corp., New York, 1949.

3

The Impact of Behavioral Science on Management Theory

At the start of the 20th century, industry's increasing production capabilities became a serious problem for workers. As more high-speed machines were invented to help produce more goods in less time, workers had to increase their work pace in order to keep up with the machines. Many workers became "slaves" to the machines they operated, and the question of treating humans like machines became a moral issue. For example, although Henri Fayol's principles of management and Frederick Taylor's techniques of efficient work helped bring about advances in technology with resultant gains in productivity and wealth, critics of their ideas felt that the techniques advocated by management science were basically inhuman—even antihuman—in their application.

Management theory had converted many work situations into meaningless, repetitive small tasks and movements, rather than fulfilling career goals for workers or creating more pleasant working conditions. As each new machine was built to handle a particular step in an overall process, the workers tending such machines became mindless automatons. Work, the critics charged, was becoming fragmented, repetitive, oversimplified, mind-deadening, and dead-ended. Workers began losing pride and interest in their work. And, even at the higher wages paid for it, work had grown steadily less responsive to human needs for satisfaction, growth, and recognition.

Working situations were controlled by owners who were impersonal and distant, and the workers began to protest. Such protests marked the beginning of another major step in the development of management theory. While management science concerned itself mainly with material operations and increased output through greater precision of movements, new behavioral theories were concerned with the ways in which workers—the most important element in an organization—could become more effective. These new theories were not simply a matter of seeking ways to increase worker happiness instead of productivity. In the long run, behavioral management theorists argued, peak organizational performance could be attained only by matching the organization's goals with the personal goals of the employees. It was theorized that an organization would be most effective when its employees found satisfaction in the work itself as well as in the overall importance of their particular tasks; productivity would improve as employee satisfaction improved.

IMPROVEMENT OF WORKING CONDITIONS

History often draws too sharp a line between contrasting movements such as scientific management and the behavioral, or human relations, approach to management. Even in the earliest days of the factory system, and long before the first writings on management theory appeared, recognition of human needs and human growth possibilities was evident in the actions of at least a few business owners.

The Work of Robert Owen

In the early 1800s in Scotland, Robert Owen demonstrated that concern for working people and concern for profits were not necessarily a contradiction. Owen began work in the textile business at the age of 10. By the time he was 23 he owned a successful cotton mill in Manchester, England. Six years later he bought other mills in New Lanark, Scotland, which he rebuilt into a model community for his workers. The working conditions and community facilities in Owen's model community were outstanding for their time. In 1813, in his "Address to the Superintendent of Manufactories,"[1] Owen urged his fellow industrialists to follow his lead:

> Since the general introduction of inanimate mechanism into British manufactories, man, with few exceptions, has been treated as a secondary and inferior machine; and far more attention has been given to perfect the raw materials of wood and metals than those of body and mind. . . A well-directed attention to form the character and increase the comforts of those who are so entirely at your mercy will essentially add to your gains, prosperity, and happiness; no reasons except those founded on ignorance of your self-interest can in the future prevent you from bestowing your chief care on the living machines which you employ. . .

Owen believed in the perfection of human beings through the perfection of their environment and the development of a cooperative society. In later years he expended most of his amassed fortune in a largely unsuccessful effort to spread his ideas in Great Britain and the United States (where he attempted to form the utopian community of New Harmony, Indiana, in 1825).

The Work of Frederick Taylor

A century later in Philadelphia, Frederick Taylor (the father of management science), like Owen, was also concerned about benefits for the "living machines" (a term he employed to describe workers) through the simpler and direct consequences of higher pay (see Chapter 2). Taylor maintained that:[2]

> Scientific management was developed entirely with the idea of getting better wages for the workmen... so as to make them all higher-class men — to better educate them — to help them live better lives, and, above all, to be more happy and contented...

Taylor believed that the main outcome of his ideas would be a "mental revolution" in which workers would come to see their personal goals and the goals of their companies intertwined. Like his predecessor Owen, he was doomed to disappointment when he discovered that his ideas had been misapplied or only partially applied, and nowhere fully realized.

Although management science did lead to greater productivity and higher pay scales, it was practiced with almost total emphasis on efficient operations and with little or no regard for the feelings, needs, or general well-being of the workers.

In its precise observations and measurements (aimed at finding what Taylor called the "one best method" of doing each task), management science had a tone of authority that tended to reinforce traditional ideas of control: work, as ever, was simply what had to be done, and done without question. The worker stood at the bottom of a chain of command. In return for wages, the worker was supposed to accept unquestioningly whatever controls and job conditions managers established.

Despite his expressions of higher intentions, Taylor helped reinforce these traditional views with many of his detailed case studies. One of the most famous was his story of Schmidt, a laborer who worked at loading pig iron into railway boxcars. Taylor described Schmidt as "a man of the type of the ox... a man so stupid that he was unfitted to do most kinds of laboring work."[3] Part of Taylor's instructions to Schmidt were as follows:[3]

> Well, if you are a high-priced man, you will do exactly as this man tells you tomorrow, from morning till night. When he tells you to pick up a pig and walk, you pick it up and walk, and when he tells you to sit down and rest, you sit down. You do that right straight through the day. And what's more, no back talk.

Schmidt, according to Taylor's account, almost quadrupled his daily production (from 12½ to 47½ tons), and earned 60 percent higher wages (from $1.15 a day to $1.85 a day). Yet this situation was small consolation to the labor leaders and social reformers who bitterly attacked Taylor's ideas.

EFFECTS OF MANAGEMENT SCIENCE

The basic ideas of management science were effective from an organizational viewpoint. By standardizing materials, machines, and processes, management science aided in creating efficient organizations that were large and complex. The formation of the mechanized assembly line — the symbol of this standardization — gave individual workers much smaller tasks as production became more accelerated. For example, the new automobile industry, having created a major consumer demand, became a primary user of the assembly line. Hundreds of workers, each contributing a small performance, created finished automobiles in record time. The craftspersons of former times, who often made total assemblies or products substantially on their own terms, now found themselves doing smaller segments of work to exact specifications.

Although management science aided industry, the well-being of workers was still not a foremost consideration. Those individuals who were familiar with constructing an entire product, or who used to contribute to a product's formation in a significant way, had to settle for decreasingly smaller responsibilities. If workers protested, e.g., through intentional slow down or failure to meet production quotas or quality standards, management usually responded by imposing further controls on workers and by further subdividing work responsibilities.

The development of management science has continued without interruption. One of the results was automation — the complete abandonment of people as a vital working force in many production operations. Today, robotics (robotlike mechanisms), ergonomics (human engineering), and computer-assisted production processes are commonly used in many workplaces. Sometimes, even dedicated humanitarians applaud when machines are designed to replace human beings at particularly dull, degrading, dehumanizing, and hazardous jobs.

The basic logic of management science, with its objective measurements and increased production gains, seemed unchallengeable at its inception. It is difficult to imagine that a highly technological society, such as that in the United States, could have been established and sustained without precise organization and scheduling of productive resources. However, management science has flaws.

Dissatisfaction with Management Science

Management science created unprecedented change, growth, and prosperity. Yet it also caused great dissatisfaction among whole classes of American workers. Economist Robert Heilbroner reasoned that progress can cause discontent rather than high morale and contentment:[4]

> Development is apt to be characterized by a growing gap between expectations and achievements. . . by an increased awareness of insufficiency and a decreased tolerance of both poverty and privilege. For the underlying masses, development is apt to be a time of awakening hostilities, of newly felt frustrations, of growing impatience, and dissatisfaction.

A significant number of managers were bothered by the clash between the need for large-scale efficiency and their personal beliefs in individual independence, personal dignity, and equal opportunity. In the 1920s and after, many managers attempted to pay their debts of conscience by establishing humanitarian programs for workers. For example, the physical surroundings of many plants were brightened and improved. Some companies hired social workers to help employees with personal or family problems, and others built cafeterias and initiated educational, recreational, and health programs for employees. Often, while such programs helped offset the stresses of work, they did not affect the nature of the work itself. In many cases, such changes were consciously introduced by managers expecting direct payoffs in good will and productivity. Thus, some workers, suspecting that they were supposed to work harder or to stop asking for pay increases in return for welfare advantages, resented such improvements.

Management science had the effect of creating changes that eventually brought about rising and unfulfilled expectations. This inevitably led to the development of the next major step in management theory. This step was not necessarily intended to replace management science, but was formed to augment, moderate, and refine it. This happened in several ways, as explained in the following paragraphs.

Changes and Unmet Expectations

Management generally feared that, once introduced to the possibilities of change, workers were likely to want more change. For example, manual laborers first found their work systematized and then mechanized. This shift from "bull worker" to machine operator often meant that the worker could produce more and earn higher pay, and perhaps feel like the "high-priced man" that Taylor talked about. The sense of change was still greater for the farm people and immigrants who were drawn to American cities by the vast increase in industrial work. (From 1890 to 1920, urban population grew from less than one-third to more than one-half of the total population.) However harsh factory conditions might have been, they were preferable to the generally dismal conditions of life on the typical small farm of the time.

Having experienced such changes, workers were likely to be disappointed to find they were supposed to work at one routine task for a lifetime. As concentrated industries grew larger, it became much more difficult for workers to think of rising to the top or even talking to managers at higher levels. Workers began to voice dissatisfaction among themselves, and soon discovered that there could be power in numbers. Workers, with the aid of social reformers and labor leaders, began to organize to give themselves a collective choice.

However, effective union organization generally was confined to specialized areas, such as the building trades and clothing manufacturers. The successful organization of industrial unions in the largest mass-production companies was to take many years.

Demand for Increased Educational Opportunities

Educational opportunities expanded tremendously to meet both the problems and promises of industrial growth. In turn, education created expectations that industry could not seem to meet. Industrialists, unions, and social reformers joined in the demand for public education, each group for its own reasons. In 1913 William H. Maxwell, New York City superintendent of schools, expressed his concern about:[5]

> . . .the agitation with which the educational world is now seething for the introduction of industrial or trade teaching in the public schools. That agitation, as everyone knows, originated with the manufacturers. They had practically abandoned the apprenticeship system of training workmen. No longer training their own mechanics, they have found it difficult to obtain a sufficient supply of skillful artisans. . . Out of this dilemma the exit was obvious — persuade the State to assume the burden.

Labor leaders also sought opportunities for school training in the skills that industry needed. Even the most menial factory jobs usually demanded at least a minimal skill in reading and arithmetic. Workers had to be educated to run machines, such as typewriters, addressographs, and duplicators, and to keep records for management. Others had to be educated to work with stopwatches, time-and-motion graphs, and production flow charts — all of which were elements of management science. Unions also fought to bring about an end to child labor, which could be abolished by making it compulsory for children to attend school. Social reformers also saw compulsory school attendance as an antidote to the street delinquency of children whose parents were working long hours in the factories.

Such forces combined to bring about a great increase in educational opportunities. From 1896 to 1918, the number of five- to seventeen-year-old children attending school more than doubled. The number of urban evening schools and free public high schools tripled, and enrollment increased sixfold. Many farm families moved to cities to obtain better education. College enrollment also climbed from 3 percent to 8 percent for the eligible age group, and students took part in such new courses as chemical, electrical, and mechanical engineering, corporate law, and business administration.

The increasing number of people attending school found their horizons broadened at the very time that work was becoming more compartmentalized, more monotonous, and more impersonal. Education was increasingly seen as the means to having a better life.

BEGINNINGS OF THE HUMAN RELATIONS THEORY OF MANAGEMENT

Office and factory workers began to feel that all of the miraculous changes provided by mass production helped to prove the axiom that "the rich get richer and the poor get poorer."

Although many doubts and dissatisfactions concerning the theories of management science were evident, they lacked a focus, a vocabulary, and a set of methods and research results. The possibility of a response, however, came from the newly developing behavioral sciences — psychology and sociology. In 1923 Dr. Robert M. Yerkes of the National Research Council suggested:[6]

> The whole of history is a record of human behavior. Man has always been interested in himself, always observant of his acts. But mostly his descriptions are impressionistic, colored by the purpose and bias of the writer, inaccurate and incomplete. The science of psychology has undertaken to supply carefully controlled and accurate descriptions of behavior, based upon objective measurements of what man actually does in certain definite circumstances. . .
>
> With increasingly safe and abundant knowledge of man's mental traits and capacities, we shall intelligently, instead of blindly and by guess, help to fit ourselves and others into the social fabric. . . We stand on the threshold of a new era. . .

Despite such fervent declarations, the behavioral sciences had little impact on management theory of the time. Such impact, when it finally came about, was undeliberate and virtually unexpected: it was mostly an outcome of the Hawthorne Experiments, a series of landmark studies conducted between 1927 and 1932. Researchers from the Harvard Graduate School of Business Administration conducted the experiments at Western Electric's Hawthorne Plant in Chicago. The original intention of the Hawthorne Experiments was to verify the various management science theories that concerned the effects of physical surroundings, rest periods, and wage incentives on increased worker productivity.

The results of the Hawthorne Experiments were considerably different from the participating researchers' original hypotheses. In the most famous of the experiments, six young women were detached from a department where hundreds of workers assembled a simple telephone relay component. Working in a separate room, under extremely careful observation and friendly attention from the researchers, they were given rest periods of differing durations at various times in the working day. As predicted, their work output began to increase. However, when the rest periods were eliminated, the work output continued to increase dramatically and kept rising almost without interruption with every change in working conditions — whether the changes were favorable or unfavorable.

The Work of Elton Mayo

Dr. Elton Mayo of Harvard interpreted the Hawthorne Experiments in a series of papers and books that made him famous as the founder of the human relations theory of management. Mayo believed experiments, such as the one involving the telephone-component assembly workers, demonstrated the importance of informal social groupings that were often more meaningful to workers than the formal organization of a company, changes in physical surroundings, or money incentives. The young women assemblers, he explained, increased production because of the friendship and trust they developed among themselves and because of the special recognition given them as a group when they were singled out for the experiment. They felt special and acted that way.

Mayo also pointed out that some of the other informal groups observed in the experiments operated to limit production and to fight controls, even when better effort would have brought about higher pay. The reasons, Mayo suggested, lay in the suspicion and distrust these groups felt toward management, and the need they felt to build barriers and intra-group rules for their own protection.

Mayo's broadest conclusions were highly controversial. He disturbed many readers with his sweeping view of the informal group as the workers' last refuge in a cold, inhumane society. His prescriptions for management, involving tactics by which managers would identify and control informal workers' groups, angered many liberal observers who interpreted these ideas as anti-union. Whatever the arguments against Dr. Elton Mayo, he managed to publicize a remarkable series of experiments that included more than 20,000 individual interviews with workers and their supervisors, thus emphasizing a psychology and a sociology of work.

Management theory had been extended beyond physical movement and wage-hour questions to a study of noneconomic questions concerning how workers behave and why. The study of management had thus grown in one leap to embrace a large segment of behavioral science inquiry into motivation, communication, the nature of leadership, the social characteristics of organizations, and the best conditions for employee development and career growth.

Management science and industrial engineering had by no means been displaced by the human relations school of management. Unfortunately, extensive follow-up on the findings of the Hawthorne Experiments was delayed many years by the Great Depression, and then World War II. During this time the term *human relations approach* was gradually replaced with the term *behavioral science approach*.

Experiments on Total Work Environment

The end of World War II in 1945 marked the beginning of a period of wide exploration into the individual employee's total environment. Social and psychological needs were observed in carefully designed experiments, some of which were as painstaking as Taylor's observations. The reasons for such research and the expected results of it are summarized, in part, by Saul W. Gellerman:[7]

> Most recent research indicates that we are overmanaging our enterprises
> to the point where initiative and ingenuity are too often driven to seek
> outlets outside. . . . The majority of employed people at all levels continue

to have little leeway for exercising their own judgment at work. . . . Management will move toward greater flexibility and individual responsibility because there are more efficient principles than the traditional chain of command.

During the 1960s, the development of the behavioral science approach to management evolved from a number of key theories and experiments. Several of these theories are described in the remainder of this chapter, and can be categorized as follows:*

- Theories that emphasize the general characteristics of the individual worker.
- Theories that emphasize the matching of leadership style and the characteristics of subordinate workers.
- Theories that emphasize the matching of leadership style, characteristics of subordinates, and various situations.

Theories on Motivation and Potential for Self-Direction

A number of theories presented after World War II cast new light on the nature of the worker by suggesting that the individual's motivation and potential for self-direction and growth might be far beyond that traditionally assumed.

The Work of Abraham Maslow

Psychologist Abraham H. Maslow was concerned with the total range of human mentality and relationships. His "Hierarchy of Needs," from *Motivation and Personality*,[8] published in 1954, has had a major influence in the development of current management theory. Essentially he believed that "people have basic needs for survival and security, but also express other social and personal needs of a much higher level"[8] (see Figure 3.1). Maslow's five levels of needs are organized according to the following priorities:

1. **Basic Physiological Needs:** Needs that are primarily related to personal survival — the need for food and water to maintain life and the need for clothing and shelter to protect the body from harsh environments.

2. **Safety and Security:** Needs that are concerned with personal safety and security of provisions — the need for self-preservation and the need to ensure future security. These needs are closely related to basic physiological needs.

3. **Belonging and Social Activity:** The need to belong to a group, to have some means of group identification, to receive and give affection, and to participate

---

*These categories are somewhat arbitrary, and mainly chosen for exposition. Most of the theories summarized pay due attention to all three elements, but differ in primary emphasis.

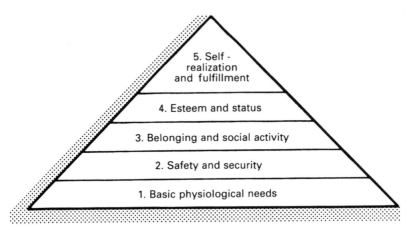

FIGURE 3.1 *Simplified diagram of A. H. Maslow's conceptualization of the five levels of basic human needs.* (Adapted from Maslow, 1954[8])

in some form of social activity. These needs should be met at work as well as away from it.

4. Esteem and Status: The need to have, to receive, and to give esteem and status (all of which are essential to human dignity); self-respect and respect for others are important in a modern industrial society, because the previous three needs are usually satisfied.

5. Self-Realization and Fulfillment: The need to become all that one is capable of becoming. When this need is recognized and at least partially satisfied, work becomes a challenge and provides greater satisfaction.

To some extent, Maslow portrays a pattern of human growth and suggests a human tendency to continually strive for even higher personal objectives. To illustrate this, consider a person who is trapped at the lowest level of physiological needs and thus has to devote all thought and energy to the struggle for food, clothing, and shelter. Once these needs have been satisfied, this person will usually require the assurance that in the future these same needs will continue to be satisfied. Given this assurance, the person will usually want the society of other people, including the pleasures of friendship and group effort. From this stage grows the need for recognition by others and, finally, the need for inner knowledge of personal competence and worth (a quality that Maslow termed self-actualization). This highest level, in particular, raises questions that were largely unexplored by others in management theory during Maslow's time.

A simplistic visualization of Maslow's theory is to imagine a person climbing up the pyramid illustrated in Figure 3.1, one step at a time. However, it is also important to visualize all of the needs represented by the steps of the pyramid as operating to some degree at the same time. For example, a rookie fire fighter, while still seeking a feeling of belonging within a fire department, might simultaneously be looking forward to a time of promotion and to a time when complete self-confidence and personal satisfaction is realized concerning the choice of a career within the fire service.

The Work of Douglas M. McGregor

Professor Douglas M. McGregor of Massachusetts Institute of Technology, a social psychologist, suggested that most organizations operated under certain traditional beliefs. McGregor called these beliefs Theory X and described them as follows:[9]

> Management is a function which demands tight control over every aspect of the productive process. This is necessary because workers are naturally inclined to work as little as possible, to shirk responsibility, to be indifferent to organizational needs, and to resist change. Workers must be regulated by "hard" methods of strict discipline, or seduced by "soft" methods which offer extensive benefits and constant efforts to achieve harmony.

Theory X did not work, McGregor maintained, because it ignored some genuine basics of human nature. He then proposed that managers would be able to see their subordinates more clearly in terms of beliefs that he called Theory Y:[9]

> People do not have an inherent dislike of work. They have motivation to work, a willingness to assume responsibility, and a readiness to help the organization reach its goals. . . .
> . . .the essential task of management is to arrange organizational conditions and methods of operation so that people can achieve their own goals best by directing their own efforts toward organizational objectives.

McGregor pointed out that with Theory X, management takes both a hard and a soft line. He explained that the hard line — tight disciplinary measures when needed — is met by employee antagonism and leads to many forms of resistance. He described the soft line as including such benefits as vacations, pensions, and recreational programs. However, he went on to explain that these benefits are only enjoyable off the job, and each of them tends to encourage passivity on the job.

Theory Y, McGregor argued, would give workers a greater personal stake in their own work. They would be encouraged to use all their knowledge, skills, and ingenuity in accomplishing the organization's objectives. This encouragement would present a difficult challenge but could be implemented, for example, by the process of job enlargement, wherein workers would become responsible for larger and more complex parts of the production process.

The Work of Frederick Herzberg

In the 1950s, Frederick Herzberg led a group of researchers from Case Western Reserve University in an extensive survey process. Engineers and accountants were questioned concerning those aspects of their work that made them feel especially good, and those aspects of their work that made them feel especially bad. Using the answers to these questions as a benchmark, Herzberg developed the "motivation-hygiene theory of job attitudes,"[10] which has since been tested at all levels of work throughout the world.

Herzberg and his associates discovered a number of factors that were frequently listed as dissatisfactions, but rarely as satisfactions. These factors included a surprising number of conditions that had generally been regarded as work incentives (or motivators), such as salary, fringe benefits, and vacation or recreation policies. When these factors were deficient, they caused dissatisfaction. But when they were present, they did not represent important job satisfaction.

Herzberg called these factors the "hygiene elements of work," or "dissatisfaction avoiders."[10] He considered them as a type of preventive medicine that helped keep people from being unhappy. However, they did not do much to make workers happy or to motivate them.

Virtually all the factors listed by workers as satisfactions turned out to be directly connected with the jobs they did. These satisfiers included the nature of the work itself, achievement in a work project, recognition for the work, responsibility for a job, and advancement to greater responsibility.

After repeated studies, Herzberg concluded that most company-wide efforts to improve workers' attitudes and motivation had little effect. These efforts included reductions in working hours, increased wages, improved fringe benefits, friendlier supervision, and company efforts to improve communication about policies. Much of the costs of these expensive programs, Herzberg proposed, should be shifted to job-enrichment programs designed to make jobs more challenging and to give employees greater on-the-job opportunities for initiative, responsibility, recognition, and personal growth.

Herzberg further explained his "hygiene" factors by comparing them to dog biscuits used to attract a puppy's attention. He explained that the food did not motivate the puppy; instead, the puppy's owner was motivated to attract the pet's attention. The dog biscuit offer would have only a temporary effect and would have to be used repeatedly, perhaps with greater frequency. Herzberg suggested that most off-the-job benefits work the same way, and proposed that what is needed to turn on a person's "internal generator is truly important work which makes possible genuine achievement."[10]

Theories on Management Style

The preceding theories dealt largely with the human nature of people as employees. Another important set of theories deals with management style and the ability of managers to affect organizations in many different ways. These theories are closely related and overlap with the leadership theories discussed in Chapter 1.

The Work of Drs. Robert R. Blake and Jane S. Mouton

With the publication of *Managerial Grid®* in 1964, Dr. Robert R. Blake and Dr. Jane S. Mouton offered a model that they felt appropriate to the realities of organizational life."[11] The grid took into account a fact that many behavioral science researchers had noted earlier: High morale among workers did not necessarily equal high productivity. Ideally, they suggested, managers should move the organization to work equally toward maximum concern for people and maximum concern for production (see Figure 3.2, point 9,9).

The *Managerial Grid* acknowledged that some organizations can survive under extreme leadership conditions. For example, at point 1,1 (Figure 3.2), work can continue despite the fact that supervisors shun responsibility or blame, and might be almost totally out of contact with both higher management and subordinate workers. At point 9,1 (Figure 3.2) the sweatshop management approach was considered possible if workers were uneducated and highly submissive to authority. A point 5,5 position (Figure 3.2) could be sustained only with constant compromises between production needs and human needs, with little enduring satisfaction in either direction. Although it accommodated these realities, the *Managerial Grid* also suggested a program for organized leadership to guide toward circumstances considered better for the long-range effectiveness of the organization.

The Work of Chris Argyris

Professor Chris Argyris of Yale University used a parent-child analogy to describe problems between organizations and workers. He observed that, while

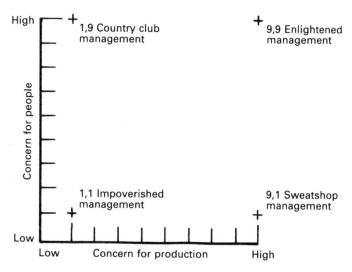

FIGURE 3.2 *The Managerial Grid.* (Source: Blake and Mouton, 1964[11])

most employees come to the job lacking experience, many begin to develop mature characteristics both as people and workers. They are able to develop more self-control, more patience, more appropriate behavior, and the ability to give and take directions, all leading to a higher self-concept. On the other hand, he suggested, most organizations are like unbending parents who refuse to recognize growth and try to keep their "children" childlike and immature; mature workers become frustrated and angry under such management controls.

Argyris contended that these frustrations generally arise because organizations believe they must be committed to one unchanging management style. He felt that managers believe they are obligated to press their authority at all times, even when it might not be required, and that they believe they must direct activity at all times, even if such direction suffocates ideas and suggestions. Argyris also proposed that managers believe that managerial controls, whether in the form of restrictions or incentives, cannot be changed.

For the sake of their own survival, Argyris argued, organizations must learn to adopt a variety of management styles, with workers contributing ideas to the development of such styles. Otherwise, he suggested, the mental health of both the workers and the organization would be threatened by a vicious cycle: Controls designed to make workers "manageable and spiritless" would cause workers to become more dependent. This, in turn, would demand still more controls, thus continuing the cycle.[12]

The Work of Robert Tannenbaum and Warren Schmidt

In 1958, Professors Robert Tannenbaum and Warren Schmidt of UCLA published a simple, but now classic, diagram of leadership behavior called the "Continuum of Leadership Behavior" (see Figure 3.3).[13] The problem they addressed was the difficulty managers find in trying to be democratic while simultaneously maintaining authority and control. The solution they proposed was an ability to operate effectively along the whole continuum from boss-centered to subordinate-centered leadership. This challenge is one that can be met if the leader pays attention to key questions about self, subordinates, and the situation. Some of their questions are summarized as follows:

- **Leader:** What are my own values and convictions? Do I have confidence in my subordinates and a desire to see them grow and advance? Do I feel secure in uncertain situations?
- **Subordinates:** What sort of behavior do they expect from the leader? Do they need independence and want responsibility? Do they feel the problem is important, and do they have the technical knowledge needed to discuss the problem? Do they trust the leader in various styles?
- **The Situation:** What are the demands of organizational policy? What are the time pressures? Is there a need to keep some information confidential?

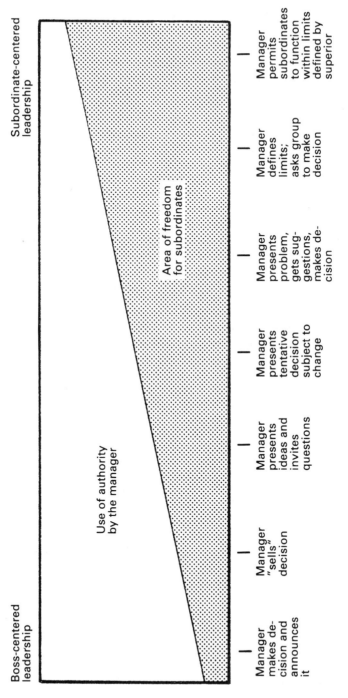

FIGURE 3.3 Continuum of leadership behavior. (Source: Tannenbaum and Schmidt, 1958[13])

Such questions can help to clarify the leader's decisions about how to lead at any given time and might, in fact, confine management/leadership style to a particular segment of the "Continuum of Leadership Behavior" diagram (for example, when *both* leaders and subordinates do not want decision making to be shared). At least two points are considered essential by Tannenbaum and Schmidt:

1. The leader should never shirk responsibility for the decision, no matter how it is made.
2. The leader should always make clear what style of leadership is being used; there should be no attempt, for example, to trick subordinates into thinking that the leader's decision was their own.

The Work of Norman Maier

Norman R. Maier of the University of Michigan designed a grid based on leadership and decision-making considerations (see Figure 3.4). Maier's grid, which is simple in appearance, is rich in complex questions concerning the technical and acceptance quality requirements involved in decisions. These qualities can be summarized as follows:

- **Technical Quality Requirements** are the kinds of specialized knowledge and the amounts of such knowledge needed to reach an effective decision.
- **Acceptance Quality Requirements** are the considerations of the degree of acceptance necessary so that the decision will be effectively implemented by all of those who are, or will be, affected.

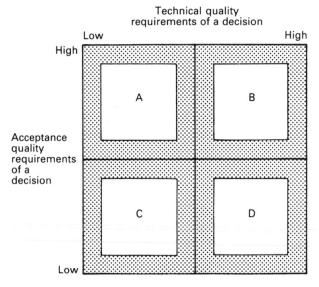

FIGURE 3.4 *Simplified leadership and decision-making grid.* (Based on the work of Norman Maier[14])

According to Maier's grid, a decision with high acceptance quality requirements and low technical quality requirements might involve the reassignment and rescheduling of work shifts (for example, see box A in Figure 3.4). The best decision is one that is acceptable to all people involved. A decision requiring high technical quality and low acceptance quality requirements might involve a choice between two brands of a similar chemical on the basis of elaborate scientific specifications (see box D in Figure 3.4). Only one specialist might have the knowledge to make the choice; he or she should, therefore, make the decision. Most difficult, perhaps, is a decision requiring high technical quality and high acceptance quality (see box B in Figure 3.4). Members of a fire company, for example, might need to choose only one course from a list of ten training courses. In such a case, all or several members of the fire company might have to do their best to become experts about various courses and the qualifications of instructors. The manager then has to draw on this expertise to help the group come to a decision that satisfies its members and, at the same time, uses the knowledge of the "experts" effectively. Maier proposed that participative decisions can be effective because:[14]

> There is more information in a group than in any of its members. Thus, problems that require the utilization of knowledge should give groups an advantage over individuals. Even if one member of the group (e.g., the leader) knows much more than anyone else, the limited unique knowledge of lesser-informed individuals could serve to fill in some gaps in knowledge. For example, a skilled machinist might supply information on how a new machine might be received by workers.

Maier pointed out, however, that a strong leader might be needed to function as the group's central nervous system even when participation levels are high. The leadership skill in this case involves the ability to keep discussion open, balanced, and fair.

ACTIVITIES

1. Explain how Robert Owen and Frederick Taylor attempted to deal with the protests of workers who felt dehumanized by increased mechanization. Why do you think their theories were not widely accepted by the general public and industry?

2. What changes resulted from workers' dissatisfaction with management science? Why do you think workers' attempts at effective union organization were not successful at that time?

3. A major result of automation was the creation of a smaller amount of work for the individual. Increasing automation became a threat to workers who felt they would be replaced by machines.
   (a) Although fire departments have many machines to help prevent and control fires, fire fighters must do a great amount of work

on the job. Discuss and list the fire fighter's work from the moment an alarm is received until the time the fire is extinguished.

(b) If your community's fire department were to become further automated, what types of machines would be needed to perform your duties as a fire fighter? With further automation, how would your duties be different from those listed in part (a) of this activity?

4. Identify the researcher(s) who proposed each of the following theories. Because each theory proposes distinct needs of employees, explain what you think management can do to satisfy these needs.

(a) A climate that provides employees an opportunity to satisfy their self-realization needs is most likely to retain motivated employees.

(b) Because every decision has a technical quality aspect and an acceptance requirement, participative decision making will lead to higher motivation levels only if the manager is skilled in choosing the appropriate type of participation as well as the appropriate level.

(c) Employees tend to respond favorably when given a greater personal stake in their own work.

(d) Employees can find the most motivating job satisfaction in the work itself.

(e) Employees respond most favorably to supervisors who demonstrate highest concern for both production and people.

(f) To achieve the highest level of motivation, managers must be successful in selecting an appropriate level of participation for each decision.

5. (a) Why did the sciences of human behavior and psychology play such an important role in human relations studies?

(b) How did the initial studies of human behavior of workers help form the theories of human behavior in management?

(c) How might the results of psychological studies conducted on members of the fire services be most beneficial?

6. Consider Maslow's five levels of basic human needs (see Figure 3.1). What are a fire fighter's basic human needs on the job? With your class, develop a list of a fire fighter's basic human needs and determine how or if they differ from Maslow's.

7. Your fire company has been informed that the chief has compiled a list of decisions that must be made in the department. Some of these decisions should be made using requirements of high technical quality and high acceptance quality (see Figure 3.4). What types of decisions would involve these requirements?

8. Discuss the philosophies of management science and of the human relations theory of management with a group from your class. The group should then be divided into two sections, with one section in favor of a management science platform and the other in favor of a human relations theory platform. To debate their platforms, the following steps can be used by the sections as a general guide:

   (a) Each section should compile a list of the strongest and most positive aspects of their particular platform, and appoint a spokesperson to use the group's list during the debate.

   (b) Each spokesperson will present the positive aspects of their platform to the entire group in 3 minutes or less. Each spokesperson's goal should be to emphasize and thereby prove that one system of management is better than the other.

   (c) At the end of the two speeches, each member of both groups should write why they believe the positive aspects of one platform were better than the other.

REFERENCES

[1]Owen, Robert, "Address to the Superintendents of Manufactories," *Classics in Management*, American Management Association, New York, 1960, pp. 24–25.

[2]Copley, F. B., *Frederick W. Taylor: Father of Scientific Management*, Vol. 2, Harper & Row, New York, 1923, pp. 237–238.

[3]Taylor, Frederick, *The Principles of Scientific Management*, W. W. Norton & Co., Inc., New York, 1911, p. 47.

[4]Heilbroner, R, L., *Great Ascent*, Harper Torchbooks, New York, 1963, p. 18.

[5]Maxwell, W. H., "On a Certain Arrogance in Educational Theorists," *Educational Review*, Vol. 47, Feb. 1914, pp. 175–176.

[6]Yerkes, Dr. R. M., "Testing the Human Mind," *Atlantic Monthly*, Vol. 131, No. 3, Mar. 1923, p. 366.

[7]Gellerman, S. W., *Motivation and Productivity*, American Management Association, New York, 1963, p. 95.

[8]Maslow, A. H., *Motivation and Personality*, Harper & Row, New York, 1954.

[9]McGregor, Douglas, *Human Side of Enterprise*, McGraw-Hill, New York, 1960.

[10]Herzberg, Frederick, "One More Time: How Do You Motivate Employees?," *Harvard Business Review*, Vol. 46, No. 1, Jan.–Feb. 1968, pp. 53–62.

[11]Blake, R. R., and Mouton, J. S., *Managerial Grid*, Gulf Publishing Co., Houston, 1964, p. 10.

[12]Argyris, Chris, *Personality and Organization*, Harper & Row, New York, 1957.

[13]Tannenbaum, Robert and Schmidt, W. H., "How to Choose a Leadership Pattern," *Harvard Business Review*, Vol. 36, No. 2, Mar.–Apr. 1958, pp. 95–101.

[14]Maier, N. R. F., "Assets and Liabilities in Group Problem Solving: The Need for an Integrative Function," *Psychological Review*, Vol. 74, No. 4, Apr. 1967, pp. 240–241.

4

Modern Management Theory

The foundation of modern management theory was discussed in Chapters 1 through 3. Most of the concepts discussed in this chapter appeared in the literature in the 1970s or before. Although there have been many recent applications of the foundations discussed in Chapters 2 and 3, there have not been any advances in the theory itself. Published research since the 1970s has merely confirmed that the theories discussed in Chapters 2 through 4 apply to all types of different environments and organizations. Specific recent applications include more enlightened and equitable personnel policies and an expansion of the situational leadership approach.[1]

It is apparent that there is more to applying management concepts than just good leadership style. For today's competent managers, most managerial situations require a great deal of hard work and attention to detail to be successful.

An early definition of management still holds true: Management means getting things done with and through people. Not too long ago this was believed to mean that a manager who skillfully delegated work had little involvement in the details of that work. There is more to management today than merely delegating workloads from a position of authority. Today's managerial functions include providing support and helping to direct subordinates, making effective decisions, competence in planning and organizing, being highly perceptive in recognizing the needs of subordinates, and determining solutions to problems that are beyond the capabilities of, or resources available to, subordinates. Thus, even with skillful delegation of authority, there is much that today's competent managers have to do.

Modern management theory sets standards for effective management, but the theory must be adapted to a particular manager's needs. Because each organization wants to achieve different goals, and because each employee has an individual personality, each manager must apply the theory to suit both the organization's needs and the needs of the employees. Within these larger variations there might be smaller variations for particular situations. For example, although a manager might employ democratic decision making most of the time, situations often arise in which an individual decision is the most effective decision. This is particularly true in the fire service. Often, in decision-making situations involving functions such as scheduling inspections, the officer will allow the fire fighters to determine the best solution. However, in other situations, such as operating at the scene of a fire emergency, the employment of democratic decision making is inefficient and inappropriate.

By recognizing that one form of management or one specific type of leadership is not always applicable for all situations, modern management theory allows managers enough flexibility to vary their leadership techniques. Modern management theory also allows flexibility in the decision-making process, depending on the goals of the organization and the employee capabilities. Three *environmental-type factors*, however, influence the way managers apply the theory:

1. **The Situation**: Is there an emergency? What technical knowledge is required for a decision? What information relevant to the decision is available? Who are the people who have to implement the decision or who are otherwise affected by it? How much do these people care about the decision?
2. **The Leader's Style**: What is the natural behavior of the manager or leader? What are the manager's capabilities? What is the reaction of subordinates to the manager's style?
3. **The Competencies of the Subordinates**: What is their knowledge? What is their level of maturity? What are their needs?

When all three factors are considered, it can be seen that a leader needs to use a wide range of leadership techniques ranging from highly participative to highly autocratic. Yet a leader's techniques depend greatly on technical competence and planning and organizing abilities. Leaders must also be able to recognize the technical competence of the individuals they supervise. A fire officer or a training officer would know that, with a group of veterans, less time will have to be spent on training procedures than is necessary with a group of rookies. In this situation, leadership style would vary from one of less visibility for the veterans to one of close guidance for the rookies. This, of course, is a fairly obvious example; but in the day-to-day activities of a fire officer, far more subtle distinctions have to be made. Thus, more accurate guidelines are needed than those that have been offered by older management theories.

Modern management concepts, with behavioral science theories as their basis, help guide managers so that they are better able to utilize available resources. This chapter describes a comprehensive modern management theory that provides some clear management guidelines. It is called either the Linking Elements concept or the Three Cs of Management. Originally synthesized by Erwin Rausch from all relevant management and behavioral theories (such as those discussed in Chapters 2 and 3), the concept has been expanded and refined to become a guide for modern managerial actions.[2] This chapter and Chapter 5 describe this theory and provide some general guidelines for its application. Later chapters apply this theory more specifically to the various functions of management in the fire service and describe how a better understanding of the Linking Elements concept can help fire service managers carry out their duties more effectively.

THE THREE CS OF MANAGEMENT — THE LINKING ELEMENTS CONCEPT

This theory can be called either the Three Cs of Management or the Linking Elements concept, depending on the perspective from which it is viewed or discussed. The *Three Cs of Management* is the descriptive way of viewing this theory. It emphasizes, as will be discussed in greater detail later, that an organization needs *control* and *competence* for effective performance and that it must provide a satisfactory *climate* for the people who make up the organization (see top half of Figure 4.1). At the same time it emphasizes that the individuals in an organization have attitudes about the policies, procedures, and rules that *control* their activities, that they can be effective only if they have the *competence* (knowledge and skills) to perform the tasks required of them, and that they must have a *climate* to meet their needs which is sufficiently satisfying or motivating so that they will not desert the organization or rebel against it (see bottom half of Figure 4.1).

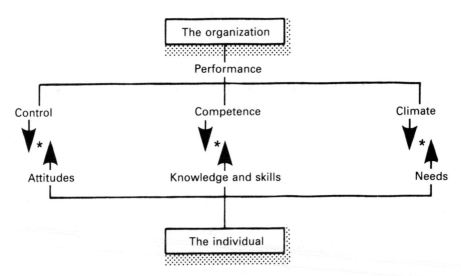

FIGURE 4.1 *Diagram of the Three Cs of Management or the Linking Elements concept. Asterisks (*) indicate the skills (linking elements) a manager must apply to facilitate alignment between the needs and characteristics of the organization and the individuals.*

The *Linking Elements concept* is the functional way of viewing this theory. Rather than emphasizing the Three Cs of Management, this perspective assumes that the need for and conditions of control, competence, and climate are a given. It concentrates on the *linking elements*: those managerial skills that a fire officer or any other supervisor must apply to bring closer alignment between:

1. The *control* needs of the organizational unit and the *attitudes* of its members toward the policies, procedures, and rules with which control is exercised.
2. The *competence* needs of the organizational unit and the *knowledge and skills* that the individuals in the unit currently possess.
3. The *climate* that the organizational unit currently supplies and the climate that satisfies the *needs* and expectations of the individuals in the unit.

In summary, the *Three Cs of Management* are the needs and characteristics of the organization and its members. The *linking elements* are the skills of the organization's management. They are the adhesive that can bind the unit and its members into a powerful, purposeful, and coordinated unit, or can leave them weak and ineffectual in the face of the opportunities, challenges, and problems they confront.

The Three Cs of Management on the top half of Figure 4.1 – control, competence, and climate – define in part the arena where a manager's work is done, and in part they outline the characteristics and needs of an effective organization. The bottom half of Figure 4.1 lists the characteristics that employees bring to the work environment – attitudes, knowledge and skills, and needs. It is important to recognize that there are two needs (control and competence) and one characteristic (climate) for the organization line. An appropriate climate will allow the members of the organization to work effectively and to gain reassurance and satisfaction from their efforts and accomplishments. Similarly, the characteristics and needs with which people come to the organization are shown for the individual at the bottom of Figure 4.1. Their attitudes toward the control requirements of the organization, their personal knowledge and skills, and their needs are characteristics of the individuals in the organization.

The job of a fire service officer, like managers in other fields, is to merge these disparate elements – to bring the needs of the organization in line with those of the employees and to reduce the gaps (see asterisks) between the opposing arrows shown in Figure 4.1. In addition to management and leadership skills, these tasks require personal attributes, sound values (such as integrity, honesty, and empathy), and liking for other people. It is hoped that, as managers acquire greater skill in applying management theory to their organizations, very few individuals who do not share these fundamental values will be selected for managerial/leadership positions.

When a manager aligns the characteristics and needs of the unit and the characteristics and needs of the people in it, the organizational unit will achieve its highest level of performance. A manager must consider the Three Cs of Management as well as the three environmental-type factors (see p. 65) every time a decision has to be made. The competent manager who understands the guidelines provided by the theory can readily assess the three environmental-type factors (the situation, the leader's style, and the competencies of the subordinates). Based on this assessment, the competent manager can apply the guidelines provided by the Three Cs of Management to make the most effective decisions.

Researchers asked managers who were about to make an important decision to choose a preferred course of action. They were then shown how to apply guidelines from the Three Cs of Management to the particular decision. In almost every instance, evaluating the impact of the preferred course of action on each of the Three Cs — control, competence, and climate — produced a better course of action (or decision) than originally contemplated.

The Organization

As illustrated in Figure 4.1, the Linking Elements concept begins by stating the obvious — that an organizational unit, whether it is a fire fighting company, a battalion, an entire fire department, or any other public or private organization, wants to achieve a high level of performance. Business organizations, for instance, might measure performance by quality of products or services, return to stockholders, growth and stability, equality as an employer, and as a member of the community and of society at large. For a fire fighting organization, performance is measured not only in speed and effectiveness of response to emergencies, but also in thoroughness and competence in loss prevention activities and in operational tasks.

In order to achieve a high level of performance, an organizational unit must have control. This means, first of all, that the unit must have direction. It must know where it wants to go and how fast it wants to get there. The unit must have goals that it wants to achieve and standards of performance so that every member knows what to contribute toward the achievement of these goals. Control also means discipline in the sense of a disciplined team, where every individual recognizes the needs of the team and is willing to forego certain personal interests for the sake of achieving the team goals.

Besides direction, an organizational unit needs coordination and cooperation if it is to have control. Coordination means that everybody knows what to do relative to other people; cooperation means that people want to work with each other as required. For example, everyone in a fire company can agree with the goal that hose lines should be laid as quickly as possible when apparatus arrives at the scene; but if coordination or cooperation is lacking, wasted motion will delay the company in achieving this goal. A well-drilled, tightly disciplined team has the coordination to lay hoses and connect them to the water supply much faster than a team that has not attempted to coordinate its actions, or a team that lacks cooperation. In addition, there also must be behavior rules for each individual that establish what the unit can expect from the team members in order to convey expectations to each member of the team.

An organizational unit must also have a high degree of competence if it expects to achieve a high level of performance. Each individual on the team must have the necessary capabilities, knowledge, and skills to perform the assigned tasks well.

And finally, an effective unit must have a favorable climate that satisfies the needs of its members to achieve high-level performance. Climate depends on the satisfaction that people derive from their work. There are two kinds of satisfaction: tangible and psychological. An organizational unit must provide adequately for both kinds. An organizational unit can achieve control, competence, and climate only if the people in the unit have the appropriate characteristics and abilities and are willing to devote them to the organization's goals. The relationship of the individual to the organization is a critical factor in the achievement of performance goals; the manager, the person in the middle, can do much to shape it.

The Individual

Figure 4.1 illustrates the characteristics and needs of the individual that the fire officer manager must balance with the characteristics and needs of the fire department. Individuals come to the fire department with attitudes—personal performance standards and a willingness to work—that might or might not match what is necessary to achieve the fire department's goals. If willingness to work on required tasks and assignments is sufficient to meet the unit's needs, then the manager has very little to do. If it is not, as is frequently the case, then there are a number of skills that the fire officer must apply to gradually bring greater willingness to accept the department's goals. People must work smoothly with each other and with other teams. Good coordination depends on willing cooperation. There are many obstacles to cooperation between individuals and between teams. The officer must be able to recognize serious problems and must have the skills to remove all obstacles to cooperation.

An individual often brings attitudes, a philosophy of life, and/or a morality to an organization that are compatible with the prevailing rules. Sometimes, though, individuals feel that some organizational rules are wrong or that they should not be applied in a certain situation. When this is the case, officers/managers have difficult decisions to make. Sometimes they will have to grant privileges by waiving the rules temporarily. At other times they must demand adherence to the rules, but must also reevaluate to make sure the rules are right for the staff. In many cases they have to work toward obtaining changes in the rules if they consider them no longer appropriate. It is not the officer's task to force people into a mold that will bring some ideal arrangement. Rather, officers must work, wherever possible, to adapt the fire department to the competencies and capabilities of the people, while at the same time helping people adapt themselves to the way the fire department can be most successful.

New fire fighters and newly appointed officers usually come to their fire departments with knowledge and skills deficiencies. They usually lack the knowledge and skills needed for higher-level jobs that they hope will bring them greater work satisfaction. The managing officer must help subordinate fire fighters and officers eliminate these deficiencies so they can develop their abilities in ways that increase their effectiveness in the fire department. The managing officer should also help them prepare for jobs or assignments from which they will gain greater work satisfaction as they progress in their careers.

Finally, every individual expects that the organization will satisfy a complex set of both tangible and psychological needs. On the tangible side, there is the need for adequate income to pay for food, clothing, and shelter as well as for insurance and for a certain level of comfort and luxury. On the psychological side, there is the need to feel secure, the need to belong and to be respected, and the need to find a measure of satisfaction in one's work. There is much that a managing officer can do to create a climate that will raise the satisfaction levels that fire fighters and subordinate officers obtain from their work. In short, it is the officer's responsibility to create an atmosphere in which fire fighters can find the enthusiasm and motivation that will lead to top-level performance, even excellence, in every function, not only during the exciting challenges of fireground action, but at other times as well.

The Linking Elements

The linking elements are the skills and strategies that an officer must apply so that the needs and the climate of the organization will achieve the greatest possible balance with the characteristics and expectations of its employees. Each set of arrows in Figure 4.1 demands competent management in at least one specific managerial skill, which serves as the linking element between the organization and individuals. The primary value of the linking elements (the arrows in Figure 4.1) is twofold:

1. To develop and guide the manager's skills and functions so that the organization will be most effective.

2. To help make better decisions in every managerial function.

Some decisions must be made with split-second timing and do not allow for detailed analysis, i.e., a fireground action. However, most decisions allow enough time to give detailed thought, such as a training procedure, a meeting, granting of a privilege that a fire fighter requests, or holding a counseling session. The Three Cs of Management are useful in checking whether a decision will satisfy:

1. The *control* needs of the organization,
2. The *competence* needs of the organization, and
3. The need to either enhance the *climate* or at least preserve it.

Rechecking of these three issues leads to more comprehensive decision making. Eventually, the triple analysis of how to maintain control, how to build competence, and how to take actions that preserve and possibly enhance the climate will come almost spontaneously, and it will become natural to move through the linking elements analysis quickly.

The linking elements overlap and support each other in many ways. People like to be members of a successful unit; they take pride in the good organization of their unit. They get satisfaction from team work, from their own high competence levels, and from competence of other team members. Good control and competence reinforce a good climate cultivated by officers who know how to satisfy the psychological needs of their staff. A strong positive climate reinforces positive attitudes and a willingness to devote efforts to enhance personal competence, which in turn brings even higher performance levels and still greater personal motivation.

APPLICABILITY OF THE LINKING ELEMENTS CONCEPT

Although linking elements are considered a modern management concept, it is interesting to compare much of the management theory discussed in Chapter 3 with the discussion of uniting the individual with the organization. What the behavioral sciences began, modern management concepts are continuing and improving. The experimentation undertaken by the early behaviorists has now become applied knowledge for the modern manager. For example, Maslow's theories on worker's needs have become the basis of the linking elements concept of satisfying personal tangible and psychological needs. Further, experimental work on motivation and employee reaction to varying levels of disciplined leadership now serve as a basis for improving coordination and cooperation between employees and management.

The evolution from management science (Chapter 2) to the behavioral sciences (Chapter 3) to modern management theory (Chapter 4) to Management by Objectives (Chapter 5) has placed a considerable amount of responsibility on the modern manager. Today's business manager must be concerned about production and profit as well as all facets of a particular field of activity. Today's fire officer must be concerned with extinguishing a raging fire, as well as budgets, prefire plans, and training in hazardous chemicals, among many other things. The skills and strategies needed for each of the linking elements will be explored in detail below (in reverse order).

Climate — Satisfying Tangible and Psychological Needs

Abraham Maslow's hierarchy of human needs, described in Chapter 3, has survived for many years as one of the best explanations of human needs. This model summarizes the elements that contribute to needs satisfaction and highlights the human desire for satisfaction of most if not all needs, in addition to basic protection against physical deprivation. It depicts the need for physiological concerns — *safety* and *security* — and psychological concerns — *social, esteem* and *self-realization* needs.

The managing fire officer should create a climate that will provide the highest possible level of job satisfaction to staff members. To meet that responsibility it is invaluable to listen carefully to what employees and subordinate managers have to say.

Small teams of managers, supervisors, and employees, all of whom participated in a management seminar, were asked the following question about the climate-affecting actions of their superiors:

> If you think back to positions you have held in the past, or if you look at your current position, what actions could your superiors take, or have taken, and especially your direct supervisor, without spending any money, that would bring or have brought additional job satisfaction to you?

The following supervisory practices — the kinds of things the supervisors could do — were compiled from the responses:

- More information about what is happening in the job.
- More freedom to do the job the way I want to do it.
- Being brought into decisions affecting me at an earlier time.
- More guidance.
- More recognition.
- Honest feedback about my work.
- No promises that cannot be kept.
- My boss should know more about what I am doing.
- More interesting assignments.
- Less overseeing.
- More support when needed.
- More confidence in me.

The list is interesting in that none of the items refers to any specific type of work: People are not asking for more technical work, more supervisory duties, or more specialized assignments. Even the general statement "more interesting assignments" is rarely mentioned. To a large extent people are in jobs that appeal to them; nevertheless, one would expect at least a few statements about the specific work that the boss could give them, or has given them.

The picture that emerges from these answers is that people believe that they could obtain much greater satisfaction from their existing jobs if their managers treated them differently. They want to know more about what is happening in the organization, and they want a bigger voice in decisions that affect them. They want to be more free to do the job the way they believe it can best be done, but they do want guidance and training to ensure successful completion. Most important of all, it seems, people want to be recognized for their accomplishments. The fascinating part of these results is that self-realization (the fulfillment of an individual's potential) lies not so much in specific work, but rather comes from the environment. People are, in effect, saying: The work might not be the greatest, but it can come much closer to giving me some self-realization if the boss would provide more safety and security (by being honest, fair, and open), and provide more esteem satisfaction (by providing recognition and participation in decisions). Even though self-realization is a nebulous concept, the supervisor can indeed do a great deal to help subordinates find a larger amount of self-realization in their jobs.

Improving the Motivational Climate

There are many strategies that managers can take to improve the motivational climate in an organization. The strategies require considerable effort, but they can gradually lead to a climate in which there is higher motivation and more satisfaction of psychological needs.

Managers sometimes fail to see their organization and the work involved from the viewpoint of their subordinates. Even though managers share with their subordinates many of the negative and unpleasant apsects that occur at work, e.g., detailed reports, the machinery or gadgets that require repair, lengthy meetings, and mounds of routine paperwork — they often do not realize the responsibilities they possess to eliminate the negative feelings in themselves and others. Managers should also anticipate and prevent friction between members of a group or another group. This provides a more pleasant work environment by increasing the satisfaction of social needs and preventing them from being decreased.

People can tolerate a work environment where there are only a few pleasant events if there is less tension and less frustration. However, the climate is better when a manager accepts the responsibility to balance negative job aspects by providing nontangible job satisfaction. Some of this balance can come from employees, but much comes from the work, from success, from doing things well, and from pride in an accomplishment. To achieve this balance in a fire department as well as in any other type of organization, a manager or officer can apply three strategies to improve the motivational climate: 1) short-term strategy, 2) intermediate strategy, and 3) long-term strategy.

Short-term strategy starts with the recognition that few managers or officers commend their people for as many actions as they should. Short-term strategy involves a manager spending a few minutes, several times a week, to think about and list the actions that subordinates should receive recognition for, and the ways that recognition should be shown. New managers might find only a few items at first. However, as managers acquire greater practice and experience the lists usually become longer.

It is important that recognition be given not only to a few outstanding company members, but also to others who contributed to the best of their abilities. Not all members in a fire company are equal in ability, and commendation for even minor improvements by a less-gifted individual can help to improve the climate for motivation. There are many ways that a manager can acknowledge a job well done to all employees rather than only to the outstanding individuals. For example, a fire officer can commend individual fire fighters or subordinate officers for successful fire fighting operations, yet still give similar commendation to others for different duties, such as fire prevention activities. For every specific job that was done well—i.e., helping others, making worthwhile contributions during a training session or drill, or taking initiative with something that needs to be done—some form of recognition can be given. A manager who takes full advantage of short-term strategy techniques will increase the amount of pleasant experiences for the fire fighters. Newspapers, in-house bulletins, letters, informal notes, and verbal recognition can be used to increase the number of positive, nontangible experiences for fire fighters.

Short-term strategy is based solely on the manager personally providing more recognition and other pleasant work-related events for an employee. The emphasis is on work related because nonwork-related compliments or other positive words are not likely to have the same impact on the motivational climate. They lead more toward the "country club" atmosphere of "1,9" management as depicted in Figure 3.2.

There is a limit, however, to the effect that short-term strategy can have because there are just so many times in the course of a week or month that a fire officer can give direct recognition to a fire fighter. More than just short-term strategies are needed to fulfill a fire fighter's positive work-related experiences. Intermediate and long-term strategies respond to the deficiencies of short-term strategy.

Through *intermediate strategies*, fire officers involve those who command other platoons and other companies, e.g., the chief, or public officials and even the public to provide positive work-related experiences for fire fighters. For example, the chief could be reminded to commend one of the fire fighters for something that occurred recently, people in other companies or on other shifts could be officially commended, or an officer could step aside and let fire fighters accept full thanks from citizens for saving lives, preventing injury, protecting property, or being helpful during an inspection.

Intermediate strategy commendation differs from short-term strategy in that the positive gestures do not come from the immediate superior. This practice shows the fire fighter or lower-level officer that others also recognize work performed well, and increases the number of positive experiences for them.

Long-term strategy employs the types of job improvement programs that were advocated by Frederick Herzberg. Herzberg recommended job enrichment as a major approach to enhance motivation (see Chapter 3). A job that is shifted or revised in such a way that it brings greater personal satisfaction can result in an even higher level of motivation to work on the job and to achievement of job-related goals. The officer, in working to develop a satisfying atmosphere, enriches the job in ways that are important to each individual. Such enrichment takes the form of regular opportunities for the subordinate to:

- Explain solutions for existing or future problems.
- Obtain help with difficulties.
- Report on accomplishments.
- Discuss aspirations for the future, particularly those involving preferences for various work aspects.
- Voice problems and complaints.
- Participate in decisions affecting work or personal needs.

This linking element — improving the motivational climate by providing for the satisfaction of the psychological needs of employees — can help considerably in creating an achievement-oriented climate in which the needs of the employees, as well as those of the organizational unit, are satisfied.

Competence — Increasing and Maintaining Knowledge and Skills

The road to a higher level of technical competence for a department or a company starts with the selection of new personnel or with the promotion of competent individuals to higher positions. Ability to learn and interest in learning should be important criteria in these choices. The selection process itself requires technical competence by the person who does the hiring in order to recognize enthusiasm and ability. If individuals who have insufficient knowledge, abilities, and motivation are hired it will be difficult, if not impossible, to develop high technical competence in them.

Achieving the highest possible technical competence in an organizational unit involves four skills that the competent manager should constantly strive to improve:

1. Good *selection* of new staff members.
2. Careful monitoring of the *positions* so that they are designed and arranged to bring high levels of productivity, quality of service, response flexibility, and satisfaction of employee needs.
3. Appropriate *training*, coaching, and development (see also Chapter 14).
4. Review of *performance problems* to ensure that all obstacles to improved performance are removed, and competent counseling is provided when they persist.

Selection of Members

Careful initial selection of fire fighters and equally careful observation of new recruits during their probationary period enables fire officers to obtain better results from time devoted to basic training. The process of candidate selection and promotion is discussed in detail in Chapter 13. The *Fire Protection Handbook* briefly outlines candidate requirements for fire service personnel.[3]

It is the responsibility of fire department management to notify the personnel agency of existing vacancies in the organization and to request the number of persons needed to fill these vacancies. In connection with recruitment, fire department management has three responsibilities. The first is to recommend appropriate recruitment standards to the personnel agency. The second is to provide the basic training necessary for the new personnel so they can properly perform their assigned duties. The third is to certify, after providing the basic training, that the new members are ready for appointment as permanent fire fighters or, where individuals prove unable to perform satisfactorily, to recommend that their services be terminated before permanent appointment.

Position Management

Once employees have been on a job long enough to exhibit their performance strengths and weaknesses, the manager is then able to explore how to improve strengths and correct weaknesses, thus increasing the organization's effectiveness. In the meanwhile, a manager can rearrange work schedules or delegations of tasks to incorporate a new, unproven member. If the new member is a part of a unit, such as a fire fighting platoon, the workload for the entire platoon might be rearranged to some extent. The changes can simply reflect minor rearrangements to accommodate work preferences of the new person, or they can be more extensive and involve the desires of several team members. Such changes do not have to take place immediately, but can evolve gradually as members discuss with each other the adjustments they would prefer. On the other hand, the leader can also consciously guide changes that take into account the needs of the organizational unit as well as those of its members.

One way to facilitate a more desirable arrangement of positions is by analyzing and breaking into clearly defined tasks the work that has to be done.

These tasks must then be arranged into positions that fit the capabilities and interests of persons who have to perform them. The new arrangement of tasks can then lead to: 1) high productivity; 2) good quality work; 3) ability of the team to quickly and effectively respond to changing demands of the environment, technology, and the community; and 4) the highest possible level of needs satisfaction for the team members.

If the new arrangement does not achieve these four results, tasks must then be rearranged until they are adequately satisfied. Rearrangement of workloads and trial periods for these arrangements is an ongoing process that is especially important whenever a new person joins the organization. A competent manager will usually look at the positions of members in an organization in the same way a football coach looks at the players to decide who should do what during the next play for the best performance. A fire officer will do essentially the same thing at a fire scene by assigning tasks on the basis of the capabilities of the individuals. For example, the engine would most likely be attended by a fire fighter skilled in the operation of the pumper.

In emergency situations, an organizational unit must have backup members capable of handling each task that might come along. As much as possible every fire fighter should be able to perform each one of the tasks that are required. With the thorough training of each fire fighter, fire officers will be better able to choose those that do extremely well in particular areas to take advantage of their strengths. Nonemergency work also needs constant review to see whether the existing arrangement leads to the best possible combination of productivity, response capability, and needs satisfaction of team members.

Appropriate selection of people for tasks and assignments in keeping with their strengths can achieve the highest technical competence of the team, but only for the moment. In the long run, however, it is unwise to use a particular group of fire fighters repeatedly on those tasks that they can do best, because this can make the entire unit heavily dependent upon that group. In the absence of the group the entire unit could become incapable of performing tasks normally delegated to specific individuals. Good technical competence means flexibility and the ability to adapt to many different environments. Thus, for every task, several fire fighters must be available that are capable of performing it. Good technical competence also means continual analysis of deficiencies in knowledge and skills by management in order to take steps to eliminate those deficiencies.

Careful selection of people and assignment of tasks on the basis of strengths and weaknesses, as well as interest, is of similar importance at higher levels. When deciding on selection or promotion to available positions, the chief has a wide range of experience with individual fire fighters' and officers' performance to draw on. Once a new officer has been chosen for a position, the assignments still have to be reviewed in order to assess the skills of the officer in relation to the new position. For example, an officer who has been in charge of fire prevention might not be very interested in such work, or might not be particularly qualified for it. The addition of a new officer who has considerable experience and significant aptitude for fire prevention work might make it advisable to place that officer in charge of fire prevention, and to reassign the officer who was previously responsible for the function, in order to elicit the strongest performances.

Training and Development

Careful employee selection and position management are not enough to ensure high technical competence. Continual training and development are essential even if experienced, competent people are selected and job assignments take full advantage of their strengths:[3]

> At the first level of progression, a Fire Fighter I has demonstrated the knowledge of and the ability to perform the objectives specified for that level, and works under direct supervision. A Fire Fighter II, at the second level of progression, has demonstrated the knowledge of and the ability to perform the objectives specified for that level, and works under minimum direct supervision. A Fire Fighter III, at the third level of progression, has demonstrated knowledge of and ability to perform the objectives specified and works under minimum supervision, but under orders. . .

On-going training, whether in the fire service or in another organizational unit, allows for continual improvement in the staff's competence and knowledge. In the fire service, on-going training is especially necessary for the following reasons:

1. Continual changes in technology create a need for frequent updating of knowledge and skills.
2. Training that includes learning the tasks of others provides for smoother communications.
3. Each fire fighter and officer is more knowledgable and skilled in some areas than in others. Considerable training is needed to eliminate or reduce deficiencies.
4. Career development for those who aspire to higher-level jobs, or more specialized ones, can only occur through broadened knowledge and continuous development of skills.
5. Continual training refreshes knowledge and skills that are not used daily and prepares the fire fighter for the time when specialized knowledge and skills will be essential to dealing well with a situation.

A thorough and continuous training program is the foundation for the level of technical competence needed in a particular organizational unit (see Chapter 14). Yet training, no matter how complete, might not always result in the desired level of technical competence. Performance problems, which are caused by factors other than lack of knowledge or skill, can stand in the way of an organization's achieving real efficiency.

Analyzing Performance Problems: In order to effectively investigate the cause of a performance problem, managers must first recognize that an individual comes into an organization with personal performance standards, which are based on: 1) a willingness to work, and 2) abilities that are reflected by an individual's knowledge and skills. The individual's personal performance standards must coincide and unite with the organization's performance needs in order for an employee's work to be satisfactory. In most cases employees require only training in order to meet organizational performance standards. Sometimes, however, other solutions to a particular performance problem might be needed.

The fire service generally devotes more time to training than do other occupations, due to the inherent danger of the work; however, many personal performance problems exist despite extensive training. Therefore, fire chiefs and officers need to distinguish between those performance problems that can be rectified by training and those that cannot. Fire department managers should first determine if there is a performance problem and whether or not a knowledge/skill deficiency is involved. If the skill has previously been learned, retraining can be arranged to determine whether the problem goes away or whether other causes must be found. Counseling can also provide answers. Before considering retraining or counseling, the fire chief or officer must ask four questions to pinpoint the crux of the performance problem:

Is performance stressful? Tasks might be performed poorly if the fire fighter views them as stressful. Even during an otherwise quiet day a fire fighter might find that an inspection announced at the last minute is stressful. Frantic cleaning and pressing of a uniform before the inspection allows little time for the fire fighter to view the task with enthusiasm. Therefore, the resulting performance problem will most likely not be satisfactory. Training will not help in this situation.

Inadequate knowledge of a task such as an inspection can also make performance stressful. Fire fighters are frequently asked questions they should be able to answer during inspections. Often, inadequate knowledge and insufficient time to prepare for the task might make the fire fighter associate inspections with stress.

The fire chief or fire officer can take steps to eliminate the perceived stress by speaking with the fire fighter and discussing the source of the performance problem exhibited.

Is nonperformance rewarded? Sometimes an officer might require less work when fire fighters object, might call for a rest period when overhaul is being handled haphazardly, or might allow more time for housekeeping because of complaints from fire fighters. Although the officer in charge might feel this is helping the fire fighter, in reality it can be damaging performance standards because it rewards subordinates with less work. Less work for the fire fighter could lead to more requests for a decreased workload. In this example, training can help only *after* appropriate rewards exist for good performance, and where counseling is provided for performance failures.

Does performance matter? A lack of attention on the part of superiors to some aspect of a fire fighter's work gives the impression that performance does not matter. Fire fighters and subordinate officers might come to believe that their superiors do not care whether or not a specific job or task is completed properly. For example, if someone is asked to help prepare a report and no one asks whether that report has been prepared, or if a goal is set to perform a certain number of inspections and no one checks to see that they have been made, then performance motivation could be dampened. Employees interpret the message from management to be that it really does not make any difference whether or not the task is performed well or at all. Here, too, training can improve performance only after there is evidence that good performance does matter.

The lack of attention evidenced in these examples clearly reflects a lack of organization in the fire department. Because the superior officer is responsible for the smooth operation of the organizational unit, steps must be taken on that level to rectify the lack of attention to performance. By solving this problem at the root of the cause, performance standards of the subordinates should increase.

Do obstacles exist? Many obstacles to good performance can exist within a department, in addition to the items already mentioned. For example, a fire fighter might be required to perform a simple task, such as cleaning the fire station's kitchen facilities. However, if the materials to clean the facilities are not available, this constitutes an obstacle to the fire fighter's performance of the task. Other more serious obstacles can exist, such as the lack of a budget for a special project, or the lack of tools necessary to accomplish an assignment. Instructions to carry out a specific task can only be followed effectively after the obstacles have been removed.

These four questions, although representing major sources of performance problems, certainly do not represent all causes of performance problems. Many instances of poor performance result from other needs of the individuals. One such need, for example, is coordination and cooperation with coworkers and with the organization, which is discussed on the next page.

Control — Aligning Control Requirements with Attitudes

Managerial control involves several functions and skills, including 1) achieving a high level of coordination and cooperation, 2) utilizing coaching and counseling, 3) promoting an environment of positive discipline, 4) resolving conflict, 5) creating open communication, 6) establishing sound rules and behavior codes, and 7) instituting a Management by Objectives (or managing with goals) program. The first six of these functions and skills are discussed below. Chapter 5 is devoted entirely to Management by Objectives.

Coordination and Cooperation

Coordination and cooperation are more likely to exist if good policies, such as fair and complete evaluations, are established that will ensure that efforts are guided in the proper direction. The manager or fire officer has two primary responsibilities for achieving the desired results: 1) setting up coordination procedures, and 2) developing the cooperation of subordinates with these procedures and with each other. For example, a coordination procedure for the fire chief or fire officer would be delegating duties when responding to an alarm. After properly delegating the work, the officer then must obtain cooperation in order for the fire fighters or units to work efficiently and to eliminate interference with the work of other units. Coordination might require that members of one company relieve those of another company at the nozzles. Inefficient coordination between the two units might result in time-consuming confusion that could mean the loss of a life in a fire.

Coordination and cooperation between shifts in a department is extremely important. An efficient shift change demands cooperation between the company officer going off duty and the officer taking over. This ensures that everyone understands the continuation of procedures, both significant and minor. After the coordination procedures have been clarified, the on-duty company officer has the responsibility to ensure the cooperation of the fire fighters. At the higher levels the need to coordinate and achieve cooperation is even greater because several companies or different bureaus might be involved.

Achieving effective coordination requires many skills from a competent officer. Not only is it necessary to schedule carefully, to communicate the schedules clearly, and to revise procedures as needed, but the officer must also be sensitive to any indications of unhealthy friction between members of the subunit or others in the department. Competent coaching and counseling of fire fighters and lower-level officers is essential to maintaining good coordination.

Coaching and Counseling

It is important to ensure that fire fighters can do what is expected of them and are willing to do it. An officer can improve cooperation by 1) coaching to help team members acquire competence, and 2) counseling to assist in changing ineffective behaviors. A prearranged counseling interview might be initiated by the employee or the officer; in most cases the discussion will relate to job performance and/or situations where employees are not aware of the obstacles they are creating or the opportunities they are missing.

A distinction must be made between counseling and coaching, terms that are often used synonymously. Coaching, which is as much a part of an officer's job as counseling, concerns assisting fire fighters and lower-level officers to gain greater job-related competence. The primary purposes of coaching are to: 1) help team members identify what learning or practice experiences will best assist them in achieving the desired level of competence, and 2) help develop and implement a plan to achieve these identified competence levels.

Counseling involves helping employees change behavior that detracts from effective job performance, or helping them solve performance problems or personal problems that affect their work. Counseling can extend beyond these purposes to career guidance or to situations when one coworker helps another with handling a personal challenge. Counseling that is not related to work, such as solving family problems or coping with illness, is not a supervisory responsibility. Counseling on those issues should be performed by appropriate outside professionals.

There are three reasons why a fire fighter or officer fails to do what is appropriate in a situation that requires some action.

- **Unawareness**: Not being aware that a certain behavior is required or desirable at a given moment.
- **Inability**: Not having the knowledge and/or the skill to perform the task at the expected level of competence.
- **Unwillingness**: Personal reservations about performing the task at a given moment or not wanting to do it.

In the first two instances, the fire fighter or officer fails to act because he/she is not aware that it is required/desired or because he/she does not have the competence to perform the task as expected. The third reason is different. The individual has the skill to perform the task as expected and knows what is expected, but still will not do it. Different managerial actions are appropriate for these three situations. In the first two, the behavior can usually be remedied through coaching: helping the person become aware that certain behavior is appropriate and/or helping the person to achieve the desired competence level.

In the third situation, the fire fighter or officer must be counseled. The higher-level officer must clarify (as was undoubtedly done during prior coaching) that the behavior is required and why it is required, and then obtain agreement that, in the future, the desired action will be taken. In the event such agreement is not attainable voluntarily, the fire fighter or officer must be convinced that the desired behavior is necessary even though he/she disagrees.

An essential early step in coaching is determining whether a fire fighter or officer has the competence to do something, cannot do something, or is not performing as expected because of unwillingness. The sequence of steps that an officer or manager must take to fully discharge their coaching and counseling responsibilities is outlined in Figure 4.2. Coaching is discussed in detail in Chapter 14.

Performance Counseling

The objective of counseling is to enhance the willingness of fire fighters and/or lower-level officers to face a situation and do something constructive

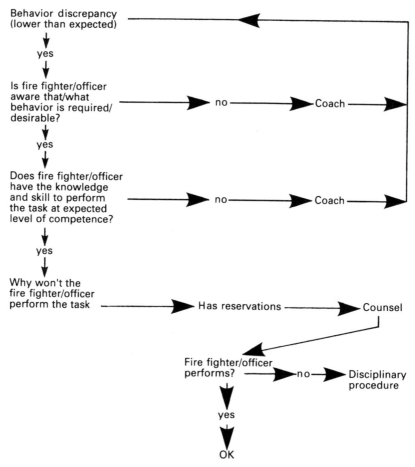

FIGURE 4.2 Coaching and counseling flow chart.

about it. Counseling should define appropriate behavior and assess whether the individual has the necessary skills to perform it.

Counseling involves guiding others toward accepting and possibly even becoming pro-active in changing their behavior. A leader, someone with authority, can often counsel someone best by listening well. In other situations, counseling can involve providing support or explanations to clarify views. There are also situations when it is necessary to use authority and to insist that something be done in a specified way. When counseling fails, disciplinary action, which is discussed later, might be necessary.

Performance counseling is the most common counseling situation. It addresses situations such as: 1) lack of cooperation with other fire fighters and with officers, 2) inappropriate behavior during contacts with the public, 3) unwillingness to adhere to procedures and rules, 4) lack of effort, and/or 5) unwillingness to improve. An officer should proceed gradually from counseling to various disciplinary procedure steps, with the initial aim being to avoid the disciplinary procedures. Performance counseling includes four steps: 1) before the counseling interview, 2) during the counseling interview, 3) preparing an action plan, and 4) follow-up after the counseling interview.

Before the Counseling Interview: To ensure the most successful outcome from the counseling interview and to encounter as few surprises as possible, the officer must be thoroughly prepared. Very few competent managers will start a counseling interview without careful prior preparation. When a counseling situation is initiated by a fire fighter because of a complaint, it usually is best to postpone the actual interview, whenever possible, to have time to think about the issue that has been raised. This preparation should include:

1. Selecting an appropriate place and time for the interview. An effective interview demands a location where the participants can speak in privacy, without being disturbed, and that adequate time be allocated for the discussion.
2. Reviewing any information, performance problems, or issues that are available to refresh your memory on the main issue and any other related issues that might be connected with the planned discussion.
3. Reviewing the options and possible outcomes to ensure that several possibilities have been considered and what their effect/impact might be on the counseling participants or other fire fighters, officers, workers, members of the public, etc.

During the Counseling Interview: There are six components that are essential for a successful counseling interview:

1. Explain the purpose of the session.
2. Explain the challenge or problem.
3. Outline the objectives.
4. Discuss potential disciplinary steps.
5. Allow the subordinate to explain.
6. Conflict resolution.

Explain the purpose of the session. The subordinate involved is aware that a serious topic will be discussed. The subordinate is likely to be fairly apprehensive about the topic, or at least emotionally involved in other ways.

The purpose of the interview should be explained in a positive framework as much as possible. Emphasize the positive outcomes that you hope to be achieved. For example, at the start of a meeting to correct inappropriate behavior, you might say that the purpose of the discussion is to identify obstacles that prevent effective performance by the subordinate and that ways will be sought to help him/her overcome these obstacles. You should stress the benefits to the subordinate in very brief and general terms because the challenge or problem has not yet been discussed. For example, if appropriate, you could point to the fact that there is a good atmosphere in the company, and that everyone benefits from that.

Explain the challenge or problem. Be as specific as possible and do not speak in general terms, i.e., avoid talking about attitude or about general impressions that have been gained from observations. Rather, speak about very specific instances that you have observed, or of which you have knowledge.

On some occasions it might be necessary to be somewhat more general to avoid compromising information sources. Most of the time, however, it is acceptable to tell a fire fighter the sources of the specific complaint. Similarly, when speaking about disruption of training sessions or inappropriate behavior during inspections, it is much more beneficial to cite specific instances than to speak of the problem in general terms.

When explaining the challenge or problem you should, very early on, point out that you are explaining it from your viewpoint. It is important that the fire fighter or lower-level officer clearly understands, at the outset, what you perceive to be the problem or challenge. During the explanation and at its conclusion you should confirm, with probing or with moments of silence, whether the message has been understood correctly and completely. Neither at this time nor, for that matter at any later time, is it essential that the subordinate agree with you. In fact, often they will attempt to defend themselves. For a more successful session it is best to say to a subordinate who reacts defensively: "Please allow me to finish unless I am saying something that is factually incorrect. I have a number of things I want to tell you in addition to the problem (or challenge) that I see and, when I have finished, I will give you all the time you need to tell me your point of view." Explanations should be brief; if well-prepared, you should be able to finish in 3 to 5 minutes.

Outline the objectives. After explaining the purpose of the session and challenge/problem, you also must state, very briefly, a specific objective or objectives. The objective of the counseling session must be outlined to stress the benefits to the fire fighter or officer of achieving the objectives. The objective can best be stated by saying: "As a result of our discussion, I hope that. . . , which will benefit you because. . . "

Discuss potential disciplinary steps. This element should be part of the explanation only if the counseling interview involves a topic previously discussed, and if you are reasonably certain that disciplinary steps might be needed if the individual's behavior does not change. In this case you should explain the consequences that might result if the objective is not achieved.

Allow the subordinate to explain. After you have explained your point of view it is essential that the fire fighter or lower-level officer be given an opportunity to thoroughly explain his/her point of view. The subordinate should be free to refute any statements that have been made. During this explanation you should remain silent except for clarifying probes that indicate your interest and ensure that the person's position is understood thoroughly. Besides providing information about the subordinate's views, the opportunity to speak will reduce the anxiety level or anger that might have existed at the beginning of the discussion or that developed while you were speaking.

Conflict resolution. Frequently, agreement is achieved with a simple exchange of views. The next step in the counseling process is the preparation of the action plan if one is needed. If any disagreements remain, the conflict resolution steps that are discussed later in this chapter should be applied.

Preparing the Action Plan: Setting a goal and preparing an action plan jointly with the subordinate are the final steps of the counseling interview. The plan can be expressed in terms of one or several specific action steps, each one with a completion date. Setting these specific completion dates will help you track progress toward achieving the goal. Among the action steps should, of course, be any support functions that you will be providing. These steps should also be confirmed in any written follow-up. However, writing out a formal goal is not essential for this process. If you and the subordinate agree on one or more action steps, these action steps are adequate. In effect, any series of action steps defines a goal. If a goal is difficult to define in any other way, successful completion of the last action step will elicit the necessary behavior.

After the Counseling Interview: Written follow-up, as mentioned, is not always necessary. If the challenge/problem was a simple one, requiring a minor behavior change, and if there is no conflict, written follow-up is superfluous. It might even be resented unless you always send follow-up memos after meetings and discussions.

There are, however, various reasons why a follow-up memo, or at least a written action plan, might be desirable or necessary as follow-up to some counseling interviews. For example:

1. If the counseling interview was a step in the disciplinary procedure, documentation is necessary.
2. If the issues that were discussed were complex and involved many considerations, a follow-up memo is necessary as a reminder. Written follow-up helps to ensure that the session's participants have achieved full understanding of the conclusions.
3. If the action steps extend over a long period of time, a follow-up letter or memo will help ensure that an accurate picture of the action steps is retained over that period of time.

When writing a follow-up memo that is not part of the disciplinary procedure, but is for one of the reasons listed above, the memo should be very carefully worded to ensure that it is not perceived as a disciplinary step. It should be seen clearly as a confirmation of mutual agreement. It should therefore include some statement that expresses confidence that the agreed-upon steps will be taken. You must refrain from mentioning any negative consequences that might result from failure to complete the steps. Most important, the tone should be highly positive. If possible, repeat the specific benefits or major benefit to the individual from completing the action steps as outlined.

On the other hand, if the counseling interview was part of a disciplinary procedure, then the consequences of a failure to complete the action steps should be defined in the memo.

As the last step in the counseling procedure, it is your responsibility to monitor the action steps by regularly checking on progress. These progress checks should include a review of what difficulties the subordinate might have encountered, and how you could be of help. If the subordinate makes a serious effort to adhere to the action plan, encouragement and possibly commendation are in order, even if the plan steps are not achieved fully. If the action steps are completed as planned, or if the results are better than planned, some form of recognition is essential to ensure fairness and to enhance the image of the entire counseling procedure.

On the other hand, if the action steps are not achieved, then it is important for you to determine if there were valid reasons for failure to complete the action steps. Another counseling session might be needed if the subordinate's reasons are not satisfactory. This counseling interview should follow the same procedure except that, at this point, the disciplinary procedure might become involved. In that case, the consequences of failing to adhere to the action steps should be explained during the counseling interview and a clear understanding of these consequences confirmed. A summary of the counseling process is on page 91.

Disciplinary Procedures

In some situations counseling can lead to disciplinary procedure steps; this is the case whenever a fire fighter or officer fails repeatedly to comply with company or departmental rules or procedures. Reliance on the disciplinary procedure is less likely, however, if a strong climate of positive discipline has been established by the superior officers in the company, battalion, or department.

Positive Discipline—Preventing Disciplinary Action: Many officers and their staff are uncomfortable when they hear the word discipline. To many of them the word is almost interchangeable with the word punishment. To many people, discipline means very tight authoritarian controls, harsh criticisms, or penalties for individuals who do not meet standards or adhere to rules and accepted practices.

Yet, discipline has another, more positive meaning. Positive discipline, which is sometimes referred to as constructive discipline, is similar to the discipline that unites a successful football team as it works in a well-coordinated fashion. It is largely self-generated: All players are aware of the team's objectives, strategies, and tactics so they voluntarily and enthusiastically adhere to their roles within the overall plan. Positive discipline for every organization includes: 1) a common understanding of the rules and of the standards of performance, 2) an awareness of the personal and team benefits of the rules and standards, and 3) a willingness on the part of individuals to make personal sacrifices, if necessary, to help the organization achieve its goals. Positive discipline, therefore, has no negative implications. It is closely related to coaching and to counseling. It is through coaching that members of a team come to understand what has to be done and how it is to be done. Counseling helps them see why it is necessary and to their benefit, so they will achieve the highest level of performance of which they are capable. Effective positive discipline demands the following of the leader:

1. Set fair standards and review them regularly to ensure that they continue to be equitable.
2. Communicate the standards clearly during performance evaluations, coaching sessions, and counseling sessions.
3. Apply the standards equitably.
4. Demonstrate a willingness to discuss company rules and standards when they are considered unfair.
5. Provide appropriate recognition and psychological awards equitably.
6. Criticize constructively and ensure that your suggestions to improve attitude and/or performance are given in such a way that they will bring a positive reaction and will not be interpreted as criticism.
7. Administer the disciplinary procedure in a consistent, equitable way if the steps above do not achieve positive discipline and full cooperation.

Positive discipline requires that fire fighters and officers who deserve commendation and privileges will receive them; and those who violate accepted rules or fail to adhere to reasonable standards will receive gradually more stringent warnings until their behavior conforms with those rules and standards so that the same standards and rules apply to everyone.

A leader who is skillful in establishing an atmosphere of positive discipline has little need to apply disciplinary procedures. However, situations will still arise from time to time when a subordinate will not accept your suggestions and/or instructions to change inappropriate behavior. Under those conditions, after initial counseling sessions have failed, you will have to apply the department's procedure for disciplinary action.

It is of utmost importance that you be thoroughly familiar with the department's disciplinary procedure. It is equally important to the positive climate in your organizational unit that the procedure be applied with compassion for the individual involved. This means reasonable concern for any personal hardship that a disciplinary step might impose on an individual. At the same time, it should be kept in mind that avoiding the disciplinary procedure at all costs is unwise. Ignoring rule infractions by one person or by a few is unfair to all other members of the team.

Conflict Resolution

Counseling and discipline, even positive discipline, often involve some form of conflict. Nonconstructive conflict must be resolved to reduce its negative impact on the organization. Conflict can originate from one or from several of many possible sources. Undesirable conflict can best be avoided by competent management as outlined by the Three Cs of Management theory.

It is important to recognize that it is not always easy to determine when conflict is potentially troublesome and when it is not. Competition for best performance is a form of conflict, yet one would not consider it undesirable until the competition became so intense that one team obstructed the work of another team rather than concentrating solely on perfecting its own activities. In addition, it is not easy for an officer to determine when subordinates' statements are gripes or true dissatisfactions. Every organization, at one time or another, has dissatisfied an employee in some way. Gripes are then aired, and work continues as before. It is important to distinguish this from the more serious indications of conflict with other people or units that can lead to detrimental actions, such as open or hidden refusals to cooperate.

Undesirable conflict *between members of a team*, or between individual members of one team with people in another team, should be avoided. The officer can do this by watching for any indication of serious friction within the team and by using effective counseling as soon as it occurs.

Conflict *between units* is sometimes more difficult to avoid. Good communication between the officers of the units and some measure of goodwill and willingness to talk things out provide the greatest chance for avoiding any serious conflict. When such conflict cannot be avoided, it should be resolved using the conflict-resolution steps described below. The officer's objective in any conflict is to prevent lose-lose situations and, as much as possible, turn these and win-lose situations into win-win outcomes.

Steps for Conflict Resolution

Most behavioral scientists believe that conflict situations are best reconciled when a climate of open communications is established. The following step-by-step procedures help to bring about such open communications and thus lead toward a satisfactory outcome of a conflict situation:

1. Reduce the emotional level. Listen and probe with empathy for the other person's views.
2. Seek to clarify where the core of the conflict lies. In many instances, this identifies misunderstandings or misconceptions that can be clarified through discussion. Conflict is often completely resolved at this early stage.
3. Identify alternatives/strategies that can be considered for resolving the conflict. These range from severe win-lose situations, in which one party wins significantly while the other takes extensive losses, to the far more desirable win-win situation, in which both parties gain something from the resolution of the conflict.
4. Choose the best strategy. Given the information available, choose the strategy that appears to be the best.

5. Implement the chosen strategy. Put the strategy into action and monitor it to see whether the desired results are achieved. Try another approach if the results are not satisfactory.

Five alternatives/strategies that should be considered when in a conflict situation are shown in Table 4.1, and are discussed in greater detail below. A summary of the entire counseling process is shown in Table 4.2, including the conflict resolution steps.

Postpone the conflict: Postponement can be an excellent strategy when the possibility exists that unfolding events will either remove the source of the conflict, or change conditions so that the conflict will be in a different environment where it might be easier to resolve. Postponement sometimes leads to a win-win situation. If agreement appears difficult to achieve because the differences of opinion seem too great, you should suggest that the fire fighter or subordinate officer think about or look at some additional data, while at the same time offering to think about or to investigate some aspect of the situation. An assignment to look over some information in an appropriate book or article can almost always bridge gaps in understanding. The fire fighter or officer will undoubtedly obtain better perspective from it. It is also possible that your own review of the available information or just "sleeping on the issue" might uncover new relevant information that throws a different light on the situation.

Use authority: This generally is a win-lose situation, except in the rare instances when a subordinate wants you to make the decision or when it is clear that the person will soon see the benefits of the demanded course of action. The managing officer is not the sole possessor of authority, however. In any counseling situation, the subordinate can refuse to agree to a course of action, or just refuse to cooperate with some or all of the decision. This, too, is using authority and the subordinate "wins," at least for the moment.

Concede to the other party: This is also a win-lose situation. However, there are useful applications for this option when the conflict involves matters of relatively low importance. Concessions to the other side might have long-term benefits that outweigh the disadvantages of the concession. In this case, what is a win-lose situation in the short run turns into a win-win situation ultimately.

Compromise: A compromise generally produces a lose-lose situation. Each party, however, loses less than it might if it conceded or if authority was used.

TABLE 4.1 The five strategies for conflict resolution.

1. **Postponement**	"Time heals all wounds," and "Leave well enough alone"
2. **Use of authority**	"Might makes right"
3. **Concession**	"Kill them with kindness"
4. **Compromise**	"Split the difference"
5. **Creative solution**	"Two heads are better than one," and "Where there is a will, there is a way"

In compromises, the parties attain something that improves their positions when compared to what they might lose if the conflict continued.

Creative solutions: Creative win-win solutions can allow each party gains over the preconflict situation so that each side wins something from the conflict. Solutions of this type are the most desirable ones. As you improve your skill in conflict resolution, you should always attempt to continue discussions until a solution has been found, or until it becomes clear that no such solution exists. A creative solution satisfies the needs of all parties by giving each party more than they had before the conflict started.

TABLE 4.2 Summary of the counseling process.

Before the counseling interview	Officer reviews the situation, options, and impact of the options on the fire fighter and on others who might be affected.

During the counseling interview	Officer explains:
	• The purpose of the session.
	• The challenge or problem.
	• The objective(s).
	• The benefits to the fire fighter if the objectives are achieved.
	• Disciplinary steps (if necessary) that might be necessary and the consequences of failing to achieve the objectives.
	
	Officer allows the fire fighter to explain the way he/she sees the situation.
	
	Officer uses conflict resolution steps to achieve the greatest chance for a win-win solution and to:
	• Ensure a calm environment and a low level of emotion.
	• Clarify the core of the conflict.
	• Identify alternatives/strategies and lead toward agreement on a win-win solution, if possible; if not, decide on best practical alternative(s) and lead to agreement on it/them:
	  • Postpone if necessary.
	  • Use authority if necessary.
	  • Accommodate/concede.
	  • Compromise.

Action plan	Goals and/or action steps are prepared.
After the counseling interview	Officer might send follow-up memo summarizing the problem, the agreed-upon solution and, if disciplinary action is likely, the consequences of failing to adhere to the agreement. Action steps are implemented. Officer monitors the situation, commends any improvement, takes disciplinary steps, and/or repeats the counseling steps if necessary.

Creating an Open Communication Environment

Many officers have not had training in counseling and therefore might be reluctant to start a private discussion with a fire fighter or a subordinate officer when trying to change attitudes on a conflict or some other matter that might be important to that person. Other officers might step in too abruptly or bluntly and create more harm than good. A good counselor, for the purpose of achieving coordination, need not be a trained psychologist. Rather, an officer can easily become a good counselor by learning the techniques discussed earlier in this chapter and by sharpening a few basic skills. These same skills, incidentally, are also useful when reviewing goals (see Chapter 5), handling grievances, or dealing with other matters that relate to employee achievement and motivation. They include:

- Creating an open climate where communications can proceed smoothly.
- Providing feedback.
- Therapeutic listening.
- Empathetic listening.
- Asking questions.

Johari Window

A diagram for achieving more open communications between two people is the Johari window, which was developed by Joseph Luft and Harry Ingham (Johari is an ancronym combining the first names of the inventors). Each square of the window results from two overall considerations: 1) there are some things that one knows, and some things that one does not know, and 2) there are things that other people know, and there are things that other people do not know (see Figure 4.3). For every discussion, there are two Johari windows — one for each person; the one described here is the window as it applies to the officer.

Area 1, as shown in Figure 4.3, is an area of free activity that represents subjects, topics, and characteristics that are known to the officer and to others. If a fire officer has trained a fire fighter in pump operations, the officer and the fire fighter know that this job is understood and is an area they can discuss freely. They can talk about how the fire fighter has learned the subject and how the officer can help in solving any problems with this operation.

Area 2 is an area that is not known to the officer, but is known to others. This definition could be described as a "blind spot," but it does not contain only unpleasant things. For example, a fire fighter might know that some of the assignments that have been delegated by an officer are not popular with team members. Yet the fire fighter might have difficulty discussing this displeasure with the officer; therefore, the officer has a blind spot about the matter. Area 2 includes all topics that are not easy to discuss in the existing environment, including matters that a fire fighter knows about other members of the team, but are considered confidential. Even if a fire fighter knows that an officer is not

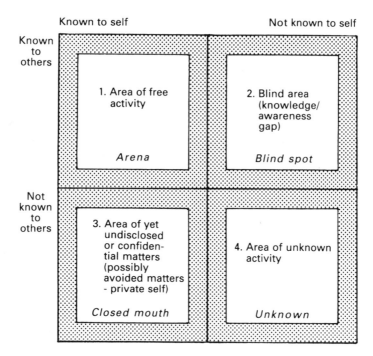

FIGURE 4.3 The Johari window. (Source: Luft, 1963, 1970[4])

aware of these matters, but should be, difficulties in communication with superiors or adherence to personal morality might inhibit open discussion.

Area 3 is an area of closed activity that represents items that are known to the officer, but not known to others. These are things (pleasant, neutral, or unpleasant) that an officer does not want to tell a fire fighter, or does not think about telling. This includes negative information, such as that others do not have a high regard for him/her, as well as positive information, such as words of appreciation that were neglected or sincere compliments that can be given. It also includes information not yet provided.

Area 4 represents those matters that are neither known to the person nor to others. It is a totally hidden area that becomes apparent only if new events bring forth a new awareness. This area could indicate a hidden ability in a fire fighter. A chance happening or a series of events could aid in revealing this ability to the individual and to the department. For example, if the department's official photographer is absent from a particularly spectacular fire because of an illness, a fire fighter might volunteer to photograph the fire operations. Both the fire fighter and the other members of the department might learn that the individual has a hidden talent for on-the-scene photography. On the other hand, a fire fighter might be subconsciously dissatisfied with the job, but would not know this and would not be able to let the department know. In either instance, the hidden area is the most difficult area for good communication because, to both the fire fighter and the officer, there is nothing tangible that can be communicated.

The Johari window has been presented, in the past, as an intensely personal method for achieving self-awareness. It has, however, the much broader application discussed here when used to create a climate of open communications in a work situation. This concept can be used by an officer to open Area 1 and lead to more meaningful discussions.

Although the Johari window applies to both officers and subordinates, it is assumed that the officer will take the initiative to ensure that the discussion will bring the most useful conclusions. The purpose of this communication process, as in any other one, is to increase Area 1 — the area of free activity (see Figure 4.4). This goal can be achieved by:

1. Making sure that you know as much about the topic as possible. In doing this, your "blind spot" (Area 2) is reduced.

2. Identifying what the other person does not know and helping that person obtain the necessary information or knowledge. By seeking information from the other person, asking appropriate questions, listening carefully, and seeking feedback (see Figure 4.4, part A), you can increase knowledge and further reduce your "blind spot" (Area 2).

3. Providing the other person with information and making sure that he/she has the necessary information. Providing information, feedback, and self-disclosure (see Figure 4.4, part B) can help further increase the things your subordinate knows, thereby decreasing Area 3.

4. By accepting responsibility for the communication, you can bring about the largest possible area of free activity (see Figure 4.4, part C). As the arena opens up, an open climate is more likely to develop where communication can proceed smoothly.

There are two methods of providing a climate of open communication. The first is self-disclosure, which means that an individual is willing to disclose what he/she knows and his/her feelings about the work assigned, job problems, or about another person. The second is feedback, which occurs when one person provides a reaction to something that another person has said, by either confirming understanding, expressing agreement or disagreement, or by sharing feelings about what had been said. Feedback helps provide opportunities for free discussion of topics.

Feedback

Feedback can sometimes lead to self-disclosure. For example, if an officer points out that a fire fighter seems unhappy about some of the assignments that have been delegated, the fire fighter might respond by admitting dissatisfaction

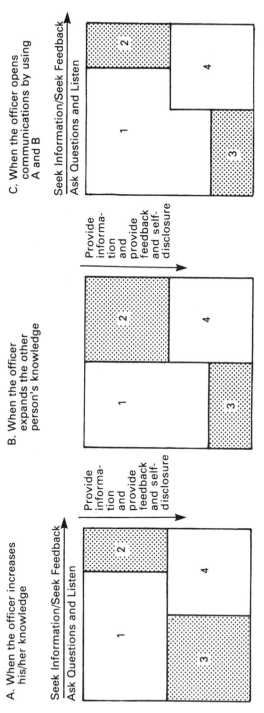

A. When the officer increases his/her knowledge

B. When the officer expands the other person's knowledge

C. When the officer opens communications by using A and B

FIGURE 4.4 *The Johari window under various conditions. (Source: Luft, 1963, 1970[4])*

and revealing why he/she feels that way. If both parties in a discussion are aware of the Johari window and wish to achieve a better understanding of the subject, then both can provide information, practice reasonable self-disclosure, and provide useful feedback. The discussion then can be carried to a successful conclusion for both sides. But even if only one person understands the Johari window well, more open communication can result than if neither is aware of it. Although many officers are apprehensive about even limited self-disclosure to a subordinate because of a fear of losing a leadership role, some amount of self-disclosure about one's feelings, opinions, and experiences can help relax the subordinate so that open communication can start or continue. Once communication proceeds smoothly, feedback then can be given in an open climate.

Providing feedback is not easy. What is intended as constructive suggestions can be delivered too abruptly or bluntly, and can therefore result in intimidation of the person receiving the feedback. On the other hand, feedback can be delivered too subtly or unclearly and can result in misunderstanding. Following are four recommendations that are useful to follow in delivering effective and successful feedback.

1. Feedback should be as factual as possible. This means that it should be based on specific occurrences that can be referred to as examples.

2. Feedback should be timely. To say "Three months ago you did so and so and that was not the best way to go about this" accomplishes very little. Rather, feedback that is given immediately has more impact and more meaning to the person receiving it, and will serve in eliminating future errors.

3. Feedback should be only about things that are under the control of the other person. If a fire officer tells a fire fighter "You really have a lot to learn about water specifications," this feedback offers little in the way of a recommended improvement for the fire fighter. However, if the fire officer says "You really need to learn more about water specifications. Here are two books that will help you. When you're done, we can discuss any questions you have," this offers a definite method of improvement for the fire fighter.

4. Feedback should be given calmly. Feedback that is given in an excited manner is often perceived as a reprimand or criticism. During a discussion when one person attempts to begin communicating, criticism can cause the other person to become defensive and less willing to share thoughts or feelings. Feedback that is delivered in a calm, steady pace allows time for discussion and signals to the individual that the problem that needs to be solved can be dealt with in a calm, steady manner.

Therapeutic Listening: Therapeutic listening helps another person "get things off their chest," and thereby relieves burdensome feelings so that the discussion about a problem can proceed with fewer emotional interferences. During effective counseling sessions the counselor does more therapeutic listening than speaking because persons being counseled must have an opportunity to open up feelings to someone who can, and is willing to, listen without judgment.

A good counselor must not form conclusions until the other person has finished verbalizing feelings. After the opening-up process, questioning by the counselor interspersed with a few direct statements usually will be far more effective than telling the other person what to do. Good counseling requires that the person who is being counseled sees the advantages of looking at a situation from an entirely different perspective with the aid of the counselor, thus enabling him/her to make positive decisions.

Empathetic Listening: Empathetic listening shows the other person that there is a genuine desire to understand that person's point of view, and therefore encourages open explanation and participation by the speaker. Empathy can be combined with a sympathetic attitude for the other person's point of view. It is important to note that one can be empathetic and wish to fully understand the other person without necessarily agreeing.

Use of Questions: Questions, when they are used properly and in moderation can be excellent tools in helping to achieve agreement on an issue. Three types of questions can be used to obtain information about an issue: 1) open questions, 2) reflective questions and statements, and 3) directive questions. All three questions serve to open areas for discussion because they cannot be answered with a simple yes or no.

Open questions are intended to start the other person talking, and generally begin with phrases like: "How do you feel about . . . ?" or "What do you think of . . . ?"

Reflective questions and statements, on the other hand, merely repeat the last point that the other person has made without adding anything significant. They reflect, in different words, what has been said in order to encourage further explanation and lead to new information. For example, the listener may ask: "What you think, then, is that Officer Jones has not been fair in assignments given to you?"

Directive questions are questions that help expand the area of agreement by leading to further explanation of a particular point. Directive questions could start with phrases like: "May I ask why you like. . . ?" or "Am I correct if I say that you agree. . . ?"

Some of the many benefits that good questioning and listening skills can bring include:

- More accurate knowledge about the other person's needs.
- More information about the problem.
- Greater opportunity to recognize potential areas of agreement.
- Greater confidence that the counselor is handling the situation correctly.

It is important to recognize the differences between a meaningful interview and an interrogation. An uninterrupted series of questions (including reflective statements, which often are viewed as questions) can form an interrogation. The best way to prevent an interrogation or an impression of one is to allow enough time between questions for the other person to answer at length and to restate or summarize, from time to time, to show that his/her position has been understood. This establishes more meaningful two-way communication.

Establishing Sound Rules and Behavior Codes

Besides achieving coordination and cooperation, the control linking element (see Figure 4.1) involves aligning the organization's behavior rules with the employee's personal behavior code, philosophy, and morality. A simple example of the alignment of an organization's rules with employee behavior codes is the working hours of a business. When an employee joins an organization, it is the employee's responsibility to work during the designated business hours. Although an employee might be accustomed to waking at 10 a.m., if their job begins at 9 a.m., the employee will have to meet organizational rules by conforming to the starting time. However, alignment of organizational rules with employee behavior is not solely an employee responsibility. Management is also responsible for rule alignment in four ways:

1. **Clarity**: ensuring that all employees clearly understand the rules.
2. **Conciseness**: ensuring that all necessary rules are in writing, but that the set of regulations does not grow to unwieldy proportions.
3. **Enforcement**: carrying out rules with compassion for the needs of individuals, while keeping in mind that every privilege granted can become a precedent, which other people might demand as a matter of right.
4. **Reviewing**: judging the appropriateness of the rules for the organizational unit, changing those inappropriate rules that can be changed directly, and working toward changing those inappropriate rules that require authorization by higher levels of management.

Communicating Rules: Rules exist so that every person in an organization is aware of the correct and incorrect forms of behavior that are required for the organization to be effective. In order to ascertain that all organizational members conform to a set of rules, managers or officers must ensure that all rules are explained and understood, either orally or in writing. Unless members are aware of rules, they cannot abide by them; therefore, it is important that everyone clearly understands the rules.

Concise Written Rules: Many small organizations communicate their rules orally to their staff. Larger organizations commonly issue a written set of rules and regulations, e.g., a guidebook or a handbook. A guidebook, however, can create more problems than it solves. Individuals sometimes associate a written set of rules as a complete set of requirements for an organization. Therefore, any rule that is not clearly spelled out could be open to individual interpretation. Employees might feel that they can do what they believe is right in an unwritten situation because if there had been a rule for that particular situation it would have been in the guidebook. Therefore, attempting to obtain control by compiling a strict, written set of rules requires considerable insight into all avenues of possible interpretation, and also requires considerable effort.

Yet, a small number of written rules can be highly desirable for the most important policies applicable to a particular organization because they set the tone and provide the background for everyone to visualize the rules of reasonable behavior. Beyond that, the best policy is maintaining an open climate in which problems can be discussed and decisions can be made in fairness to all concerned. The manager can set the overall motivational climate by either adhering strictly to a minimum set of rules or by allowing appropriate privileges with the rules that exist.

Enforcing Rules: Every manager or officer knows that once privileges are granted, they are difficult to take away. As soon as others learn that one person has been granted a privilege, they expect the same benefit. Granting of privileges to one person and not to others can give a leader the reputation of playing favoritism or of discriminating against some people. If employees are unionized this situation becomes even more important. If one person is granted certain privileges, the union can use this as a reason to demand that the same privileges be extended to all employees either informally or through a change in the contract.

Officers and managers can avoid problems of special privileges and their consequences by employing wise decision making and positive discipline, as discussed previously. Many officers or managers do not realize how wide the range of choices is for resolving rule problems or problems related to requests for privileges. Decision making in such situations might seem to be a matter of saying either yes or no; however, the manner in which decisions are made allows for a few steps in between yes and no. For example, an officer could approve a request in such a way that it clearly makes it very difficult, or impossible, for the person making the request to ask for another privilege in the future: "I will make an exception in this instance, but only in this instance." Or an officer can deny a request in such a way that the person requesting the privilege feels that the officer has been very fair and has given the request the most favorable consideration: "After much thought, I've come to the conclusion that I cannot allow you to do such and such. I'm sorry that this could not be possible." Wise decision making means that, before making a final decision on a request, an officer can carefully analyze the choices that are available to make a decision, while keeping in mind that privileges already granted are difficult to take away.

A manager can also use positive discipline in a situation where an expected privilege is requested. An approval of the request could be given in exchange for some sacrifice. This would allow the organization to offer the same privilege to

others who request it, provided they are willing to accept the same consequences. For example, John, a fire fighter, requested that he not be assigned to
clean up the living quarters because he was allergic to dust; sweeping and
similar removal of dust caused a form of hayfever. To ensure that other fire
fighters would not feel that excusing John was an act of favoritism, the officer
who excused John from clean-up duties assigned him an equivalent amount of
time on duties disliked by other fire fighters. This resolution employed
constructive discipline: compassion for the fire fighter, respect for rules, and
granting of a major privilege in such a way that it would not set a precedent for
others. (For additional information on rule enforcement, see Chapter 10.)

Review of Rules: A manager who wishes to create the positive motivational
climate that linking elements represent must keep in mind that rules that are
considered unreasonable or arbitrary will not receive unquestionable employee
support. Because of this, the manager should review existing rules for their
applicability and relevance to organizational needs and goals. Innumerable
instances exist where unreasonable or obsolete rules are either being maintained
or ignored at a considerable sacrifice in employee motivation and enthusiasm.
A regular review of rules allows the manager to amend those rules that are
unfair or outdated, or that are detrimental to employees or to the organization.
(For additional information on reviewing rules, see Chapter 10.)

In summary, control depends greatly on a sound approach to planning,
organizing, and implementing the work of the organizational unit. Management by Objectives, which is addressed in the next chapter, provides a technique
for ensuring that the work is planned and that the plan is implemented. The
more skill a manager has in implementing the techniques discussed in this
chapter—with respect to control, competence, and climate—the more likely
that he/she can achieve the best possible alignment between the characteristics
and needs of the organization and those of its members.

ACTIVITIES

1. Describe three environmental-type factors that influence the way a fire
    officer applies management theories.
2. The Three Cs of Management define the work of any manager, including
    fire officers. List them.
3. What are the Linking Elements? Give some examples for a fire officer.
4. An organizational unit must have control. What is a fire officer's role in
    achieving organizational control?
5. An individual comes to an organization with personal characteristics and
    needs which must be balanced with those of the organizational unit. What
    is a fire officer's role in facilitating this balance?

6. An effective unit must have a favorable climate that satisfies the needs of its members. List five things a fire officer can do to improve the organizational climate?

7. The following methods can be used to improve the motivational climate of fire departments. Identify whether each method is short-term strategy, an intermediate strategy, or a long-term strategy, and explain why.
   (a) Special recognition by the municipality's mayor for a subunit's inspection work.
   (b) Preparation of a certificate of commendation to a fire fighter by the immediate superior for outstanding work in fire prevention.
   (c) Formation of a softball league for the fire department members.
   (d) Revision of work assignments related to departmental goals.
   (e) A local newspaper article describing the steps taken by the fire department in a recent house fire.
   (f) Individual sessions with fire fighters to discuss their career aspirations.

8. An organizational unit must have high technical competence if it is to achieve high-level performance. A fire officer is responsible for ensuring competence in four areas of responsibility. Describe how these responsibilities (or skills) can help achieve the best performance.

9. Why is on-going training of personnel necessary in the fire service?

10. How can a fire officer best facilitate coordination and cooperation among staff members? For each of the following situations, describe the steps a fire service officer could take to ensure good coordination and cooperation?
    (a) Assigned departmental tasks.
    (b) Laying hose at the fire scene.
    (c) Bickering among members of a subunit.
    (d) Competition between two subunits.

11. Explain the differences between coaching and counseling. When should a fire officer coach and when should he/she counsel a fire fighter?

12. What are the four steps required for effective performance counseling?

13. What are an officer's major tasks or responsibilities in achieving an atmosphere of positive discipline?

14. List the five steps that often lead to satisfactory conflict resolution.

15. What are five alternatives/strategies that should be considered in any conflict situation?

16. How can the Johari window be used to create a climate of open communications

17. (a) Outline the positive and negative aspects of: 1) a written set of organization rules, and 2) an oral set of organizational rules.
    (b) Explain how you think a fire department's rules can best be communicated to: 1) a new recruit, and 2) a newly appointed officer.

18. Identify the linking element(s) that would be most applicable for a fire officer who must help solve each of the following problems:
    (a) Animosity between two fire fighters in the same subunit.
    (b) A previously capable apparatus operator who is no longer performing satisfactorily.
    (c) A new fire fighter who returns from inspecting industrial occupancies with insufficient data on the inspection forms.
    (d) Over a three-month period, required fire apparatus maintenance work by assigned fire fighters is consistently three days late.
    (e) After fighting a particularly tragic fire, an experienced fire fighter's motivation seems to decrease.

REFERENCES

[1]See also Blanchard Training and Development, Inc., materials, Escondido, CA; Peters, T., and Waterman, R., *In Search of Excellence*, Harper & Row, New York, NY, 1982; and Peters, T., and Austin, N., *A Passion for Excellence*, Random House, New York, NY, 1985.

[2]Rausch, Erwin, *Balancing Needs of People and Organizations*, Bureau of National Affairs, Washington, D.C., 1978, Didactic Systems, Inc., Cranford, NJ, 1984.

[3]Cote, A. E., ed., *Fire Protection Handbook*, 16th edition, National Fire Protection Association, Quincy, MA, 1986, p. 15-12.

[4]Luft, Joseph, *Group Processes: An Introduction to Group Dynamics*, Mayfield Publishing Company, 1963, 1970.

5

Management by Objectives

The concept of managing with goals, whether it is called Management by Objectives (MBO), management by results, or some other name, can be a central strategy in achieving the desired balance between needs of organizations and their staffs. The most important elements that help a manager achieve effective *control* (from the Three Cs of Management discussed in Chapter 4) are skills in managing with goals and objectives.

Management by Objectives is a refinement of the invaluable, widely used management cycle, originally outlined by Henri Fayol (see Figure 2.3). Although the number of specific steps in the cycle and their labels differ, depending on the preferences of the organization using the cycle, the fundamental steps of MBO are always the same and must always be used: *planning, organizing and implementing,* and *following-up.* These steps are essential for any project or activity to be completed successfully, whether or not the manager is aware that he/she is taking these steps. Setting goals corresponds to the first step, planning. Organization and implementation are essential functions that must be performed if a goal is to be reached. Follow-up is necessary to ensure that the goal has accomplished what was intended.

MANAGEMENT BY OBJECTIVES PROGRAMS

Most managers will agree that a day started without a plan—without some goals to achieve—results in less accomplishment than a day for which objectives have been set. The concept of goals and objectives* is a simple one. Setting appropriate goals with and for employees and lower-level managers clarifies what demands concentration and what is to be handled in a more routine manner. Goal setting helps managers think through the things that need to be

---

*For purposes of this text, the words *goal* and *objective* are used synonymously; the valid distinctions that exist between their various meanings are covered in the next section, entitled "The Hierarchy of Objectives."

done and thus helps to establish a regular habit of planning. Appropriate participation by staff members in setting goals can ensure that their knowledge, and not only the manager's, is applied to the problems and opportunities that face the team.

Goals represent specific targets. As such, they can give direction and can serve as a basis for the planning steps necessary to achieve a specific target. Individuals and organizations set goals for much the same reason: to provide direction. Generally, it is better for individuals and organizations to work with clearly defined goals than it is to work without them. This chapter explains how goals are set and how management can obtain employee cooperation and/or desire to achieve these goals.

The advantages of a regular goals program are extensive. They include better communication, setting priorities, establishing a clear view of respective responsibilities, and enhanced development of employees. These benefits are so significant that it would seem the concept of managing with objectives (or toward results) should have swept like wildfire through the industrialized nations to become the standard process everywhere. This, however, has not happened, primarily because competent management with goals is very difficult.

Objectives for Individuals

Everyone has goals. Even people who lead very simple lives have some general idea about where they would like to be in the future. For many, this is just daydreaming or wishful thinking. But for people who think seriously about the future and expect to accomplish something in life, goals are not merely guesses about the future: they are real and meaningful targets for which to strive.

Consider, as a simplified example of a goal, a high school student with a part-time job who wants to buy a stereo system by a certain date. This is a very clear and direct goal that requires the student to plan a budget so that a specific amount of money can be saved each week. Then, assuming that no emergency arises, the student should be able to purchase the stereo on the planned day. The student's goal is a comparatively easy goal to achieve. It is specific, clear, direct, and relatively short-term.

However, not all goals are as simple or as quickly accomplished. Many goals are not specific about the date they can be reached, or even about what is to be achieved. For example, consider a fire fighter whose career goal is to become a fire officer, possibly a chief. This goal is fairly clear, but not as specific as the student's goal to buy a stereo. This goal does not state exactly when or where the fire fighter wants to become an officer, nor whether the goal expectation is to become a fire officer or a chief. This long-range goal to become a fire department officer or chief involves many complex and intangible factors, including years of study, specialized training, work experience, and the development of skills and knowledge. Although all of these factors might be accomplished, there is still no guarantee that this long-range career goal will be reached. There are many factors, some of them unforeseeable and uncontrollable, that might be involved in realizing long-range personal goals.

Objectives for Organizations

Organizations set out to accomplish goals for many of the same reasons that individuals do — to provide direction and to get people involved in working toward the same purpose. Organizations set goals to satisfy their mission, to improve products or services, to increase sales, to speed up deliveries, etc.

To be effective, a goals system should not become an elaborate set of procedures that attempts to cover every facet of every activity. Such extensive and detailed planning usually turns out to be cumbersome and impractical, and often involves excessive amounts of undesirable paperwork. Conversely, goal systems cannot be superficial if they are to be paths to better performance. To be totally successful, goal systems require good management practices throughout the organization. For example, in the fire service this means that in order to achieve increasing levels of competence for the entire department, officers at all levels must constantly strive to improve their skills as leaders and managers. A goals system for a single organizational unit, such as a company, can work quite well, even though the department as a whole does not have a working goals program. All that is needed is for company officers to understand and practice the necessary skills. Although the basic principles involved in goal systems are similar in all organizations, the process of setting goals takes different forms in every organization.

Objectives for Fire Departments

If the chief of a department believes that the organization should have an MBO program, the process for starting it could follow the traditional goals commonly accepted by most fire departments as outlined in the *Fire Protection Handbook* and summarized below.[1]

1. Preventing fires from starting.
2. Preventing loss of life and property from fire.
3. Confining fire to its place of origin.
4. Extinguishing fires.

Whether documented or implied, these are likely to be primary goals in many fire departments. Each fire department, no matter what size, is encouraged to develop performance objectives that specify the results expected and the time required for achievement. The *Handbook*[1] also lists the following steps for Management by Objectives programs:

1. Develop performance objectives.
2. Develop a list of responsibilities.

3. Write a series of definite statements that describe desired measurable goals. These statements should be realistic and achievable, and include a time period for accomplishing the goal.

4. Establish standards of performance.

5. Monitor progress and evaluate progress.

This description follows the basic pattern of MBO programs but, of course, has been adapted to the specific needs of fire departments. It describes the process as it applies to entire departments, starting from the top and working down to lower organizational levels.

An Overview of Successful MBO Programs

To be successful, the goal-setting process in any organization requires cooperation and communication throughout the organization. Therefore, any successful goal-setting program must not only satisfy the needs of the organization, it must also simultaneously take into account the needs of each individual so that every employee will bring an interest to the organization's objectives and thus gain satisfaction from helping to achieve them. A goals program that ignores the desires and needs of the individual employee is often considered to be a device for getting people to work harder without providing benefits for them. Such benefits need not be in the form of additional money, but must be present in some form because the purpose of an MBO program is not efficiency as an end in itself, but greater overall effectiveness. This is not a play on words, because effectiveness has a broader meaning than efficiency. A manager who strives for greater efficiency usually is only concerned about getting more work and effort from people. A good MBO program seeks better output in the short term from better approaches — not from greater effort. The program also seeks to improve conditions for the future so that the organization can enjoy greater long-term success. Peter Drucker, a noted management consultant, summarized this concept with his now-famous statement: ". . . usually only 20 percent of a manager's work brings 80 percent of the desired results."[2] The key to effectiveness lies in that 20 percent of the manager's effort that involves planning and organizing for the near and distant future.

Thus, a successful MBO program helps avoid duplication of effort, helps prevent wrong starts and purposeless drifting, and provides better planning, better direction, and better coordination at all levels within an organization. A successful MBO program results in less wasted effort and significantly better overall decisions because more of the people who can contribute useful information and expertise become involved in decision making at all levels.

Although it might seem as though successful MBO programs involve extensive planning procedures plus all of the accompanying paperwork, this is only true in situations where planning has been inadequate. A successful goals program usually elicits better planning because the planning effort is concentrated in those areas where such effort will do the most good at a particular time. This kind of planning requires much more skill and judgment than planning that gives little attention to priorities.

The Hierarchy of Objectives

Most people who work with goals realize that there is a wide range in the types of goals. For example, goals range from the long-term type that describes the general direction in which an individual or organization wants to move (e.g., a fire fighter who plans to become fire chief) to the more immediate, short-term types that need to be achieved within days or weeks (e.g., the student who plans to purchase a stereo). Obviously, these types of goals differ not only in the time it takes to achieve them, but also in terms of the importance, or complexity, of the achievements they describe. Time, as well as quality, also distinguishes the two goals.

In Table 5.1, time refers to date of achievement, and scope refers to the complexity. Reading down on the time column indicates decreasing amounts of time, and reading down on the scope column indicates less complex accomplishments. In a general way these two scales parallel each other, except that, unlike the others, philosophical goals lack completion dates. Strategic goals generally take longer to achieve than operational goals because every strategic goal is supported by one or more operational goals. Nevertheless, the time relationship is not always proportional. Some operational goals take years, while some strategic goals can be accomplished in months.

Philosophical Goals — Mission Statements

In the hierarchy of objectives, philosophical goals (or mission statements) represent the highest-level goals for organizations. These goals are never completely achieved because they include such qualifying words as "best," "fastest," or "most"; philosophical goals aim far into the future. For example,

TABLE 5.1 Hierarchy of objectives.

In time

Long-term goals (objectives)
Short-term goals (objectives)
Action steps (explained in next section)

In scope

Philosophical goals or mission statements
  (objectives)
Strategic goals (objectives)
Operational goals (objectives)
Action steps (explained in next section)

a mission statement for a fire department might be: "With the resources provided by the community, the department will strive to achieve the fastest possible response time to all fires in its area." Obviously, this goal can never be achieved because improvement will always be possible. Philosophical goals describe in the broadest possible terms the primary aim of an organization or subunit. Individuals seldom are concerned directly with an organization's philosophical goals because the individual manager or employee can never achieve them. Individuals work on strategic and operational levels; as the goals at these levels are achieved, the entire organization moves closer toward the realization of its mission statement.

Although philosophical goals rarely are considered direct guides for action, they do offer a sense of direction. Frequently these goals do not appear in writing, or exist only in the form of general guidelines.

A fire department's goals can be explained by using the following example. The Anytown Fire Department has two fire stations, each with three companies. The department has eight paid fire fighters and four paid officers in each station. The other members of the department are volunteers. The staff decided at a departmental meeting to operate with a formal MBO program. A steering committee was established and charged with guiding the implementation of the MBO program. The committee was asked to recommend basic philosophical goals that would become the foundation for all other goals adopted by the department's organizational units.

The steering committee reported proposed philosophical goals at the next department meeting. These included goals for fire suppression, fire prevention, building location and size, apparatus requirements, and personnel policies. The fire prevention mission statement that was adopted at the department meeting read: "The department will establish, follow, and periodically update fire prevention policies and procedures to prevent all fires that a sound fire prevention program could prevent."

The general direction of an organization is set by the philosophical goals at the top—the departmental level. The more specific strategic goals translate the philosophical goals into meaningful, practical terms. The operational goals are the actual work performed at the lowest level of the organization. Thus, if all operational goals are met, strategic goals will be realized. If the strategic goals are accomplished, the organization will move toward its philosophical objectives.

Strategic Goals

Strategic goals are the specific goals toward which every department, division, company, platoon, bureau, or office is working. If a goals system exists, every member of the organizational unit should be aware of the strategic goals for the unit, and all officers are responsible for their share of such goals. The strategic goals are allocated to the various subunits in such a way that the organization's strategic goals will be accomplished if every subunit achieves its assigned goals.

Subunits do not do the work on the goals—it is the individuals in the unit who work on them. This means that if the employees in a subunit achieve a specific set of strategic goals, then the subunit will achieve its strategic goal. And if all subunits achieve the related strategic goals, then the unit will achieve its goal, and so on, up to the departmental goal (see Figure 5.1).

Note in Figure 5.1 that the departmental mission statement is supported by one or several departmental strategic goals. The strategic goals set for Station A, and the same or similar strategic goals for Station B, are needed to achieve each departmental strategic goal. If other stations exist, they would also need strategic goals in support of the overall departmental mission statement. Every strategic goal for an organizational unit requires that individual managers be assigned a share of the work to achieve a particular goal.

Figure 5.2 shows some of the Anytown Fire Department's strategic goals related to the fire prevention mission statement. The first strategic goal concerns annual inspections of buildings that are occupied by more than 20 people. Although not shown in Figure 5.2, the strategic goal would be

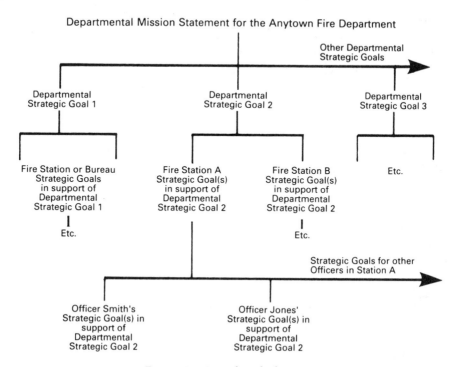

FIGURE 5.1 *Partial goals diagram.*

supported with both strategic and operational goals at all lower levels where work must be performed in order to achieve the goal.

The second strategic goal concerns prefire planning of all hazards where more than 20 people are employed. Supporting strategic goals are shown for two fire stations—A and B. Within Station A, the strategic goal has been further divided into strategic goals for three officers.

Other strategic goals of the department concerning matters of equal or greater importance, could be diagramed in the same way. In a real fire department, it is likely that substantially greater differences would exist among the strategic goals of the individual officers.

Not all departmental strategic goals have to be assigned to stations. In larger departments the responsibility for achieving strategic goals in fire and arson investigations, for instance, could be concentrated in a headquarters group. If so, a particular station might not have any responsibility with respect to that goal, or only a very limited routine responsibility that would not require a specific goal.

Operational Goals

Operational goals are primarily for people. These goals can be expressed in specific terms; they are directly measurable in scope and time factors (see Figure 5.2).

Operational goals are fairly specific and usually entail different work for different people, although some similarities exist when people work on similar types of jobs. The operational goals shown in Figure 5.2 are different for each of the officers listed. For example, if the Anytown Fire Department approves the use of a new set of symbols for its prefire plans, the first operational goal would be to familiarize all fire fighters with these new symbols in order for them to prepare accurate prefire sketches. Other operational goals cover different functions which must be completed if the officer is to achieve the team's strategic goal. In addition, each officer will have responsibilities in other operational areas. Such responsibilities might require goal setting for working inspections, drills and training, maintenance, emergency medical service, hazardous materials, and so on.

There are both long- and short-term strategic goals, and long- and short-term operational goals. Usually, it is not necessary to give much thought to whether a goal is a strategic goal or an operational goal. Sometimes that distinction is unclear, and other times it is unimportant. What does matter, though, is that all operational goals are clearly established with a specific completion date and a clear statement of the quantity or quality of the final outcome. Strategic goals usually cannot be given a specific date and quantity, but it is usually possible to set measurable subsidiary goals that must be accomplished so that the initial goal can be achieved.

Classifying goals as strategic or operational is not important because it resolves itself during the goal-setting step. On the other hand, understanding

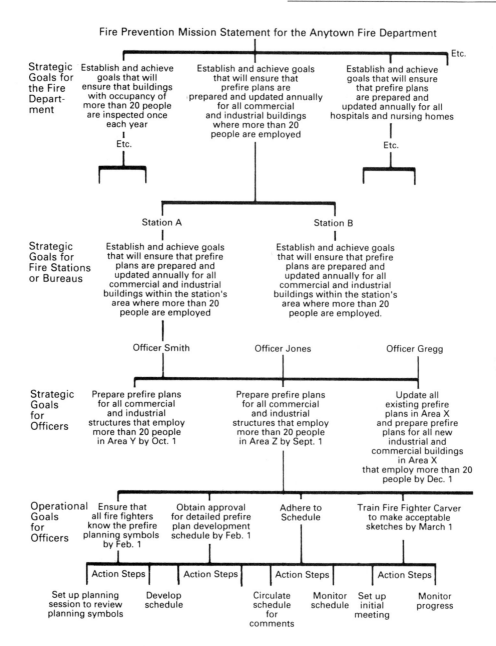

FIGURE 5.2 Portion of Anytown Fire Department's goals diagram, including action steps.

the distinction between operational goals and action steps (the subunit of activity) is of great importance in ensuring clear communication and having fire fighters and lower-level officer understand their responsibilities. There are major differences in the ways managers and their staff should view action steps, and such differences have implications of great significance in the success or failure of goals programs.

Action Steps — The Working End of a Goals Program

At the operational level, goals should always be measurable, attainable, and significant. Action steps are the specific steps that are necessary and desirable in order to either accomplish the goal or come as close as possible to accomplishing it. Action steps are rarely put in writing. However, whether in writing or not, they are expressed in the same terms as goals. An action step is distinct from a goal because an action step is under the control of the person who is responsible for carrying it out. Action steps can definitely be completed because, by definition, outside interferences are not involved. Therefore, someone can be held accountable for the completion of each action step.

Goals, because they are subject to external and uncontrollable events and circumstances, might never be achieved even if appropriate action steps are planned and carried out. In the earlier example of the student who wanted to buy a stereo, the action steps might be to save money from each pay check. These action steps would lead to the student's goal only if the student kept the job.

Action steps can be large or small, short term or long term; the length of time or the size of the task is not the key factor. What is distinctive is that the action step itself clearly is achievable by the person or persons involved (see Figure 5.2).

Following is a list of action steps leading to Anytown Fire Department's operational goal of ensuring that all fire fighters know the prefire planning symbols by February 1. Rarely is there a need to prepare a formal listing of such action steps because competent officers usually are well acquainted with the action steps that are necessary to achieve specific operational goals (see Tables 8.1 and 8.2 for further examples).

1. Set up a training session for all fire fighters next Monday.
2. Prepare copies of all symbols and distribute them before the training session.
3. Discuss all symbols at the training session.
4. Give practice samples at the training session.
5. Give tests after the training session.
6. Meet with each fire fighter individually before the end of the week to discuss the results of the tests.
7. Administer additional practice assignments within two weeks to those fire fighters who had difficulty with the tests.

Making MBO Programs Successful

There are no instant solutions that help make MBO programs successful, nor are there any exact formulas available or answers that can be suitably adapted to all organizational situations and structures. Organizations become more effective by significantly improving performance and on-the-job satisfaction for employees. To accomplish this, MBO programs must provide satisfactory answers to the following eight questions. Only when all staff members understand the deeper meaning of these eight questions, (see Figure 5.3) and find satisfactory solutions to the problems involved, can a goals program come close to achieving its potential.

1. **How many goals should be set for each person? (*Extent*)**

>   A fire department must decide how many of the ongoing or special responsibilities of each officer, or possibly even of each fire fighter, should be given special emphasis during the coming months, quarter, or year.

2. **How can quality of goals and goal statements be judged? (*Quality*)**

>   Are the goals both challenging and realistically achievable? Are they set on the most important matters? Do goals statements include quantity and quality of achievement, and time, where appropriate?

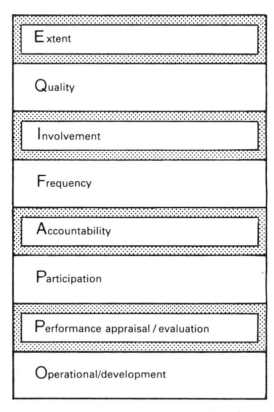

FIGURE 5.3 *Potential problem areas in Management by Objectives programs.*

3. **How extensively should a manager be involved in his/her staff members' work toward achieving goals?** (*Involvement*)

> How often should the chief check and discuss with an officer how well the drills are being performed, or when the hose-drying program starts, or what inspection schedule is planned? How often should the captain check on the way a fire fighter carries out an assignment?

4. **How frequently should progress toward goals be reviewed and how frequently should new goals be set?** (*Frequency*)

> How often should an officer meet with individual staff members to discuss what has been achieved since the last time goals were set? Which goals should be revised, which ones should be dropped, and which new ones should be considered? What kind of help do the staff members need from the officer?

5. **How should performance be evaluated with respect to achieving goals?** (*Accountability*)

> Should performance be judged solely on the basis of how many goals were achieved? What should be done when a goal is almost achieved, if a goal cannot be achieved because of external circumstances, or when more than the goal is achieved? For what should officers or fire fighters be held accountable beyond the accomplishment of routine duties?

6. **How much should staff members be involved in setting goals?** (*Participation*)

> Who should be involved in setting goals and when? If a new piece of apparatus is going to be purchased, who should be asked to contribute ideas, at which point in the decision should they be involved, and how much weight should be given to their opinions? Who should decide on the drill schedule, the drill topics, and the inspection program?

7. **What should be the role of performance appraisals and evaluations?** (*Performance appraisal/evaluation*)

> Is there a performance appraisal system in the department? Does the appraisal system relate to the MBO program? Is goal achievement given appropriate weight?

8. **How should personal development and career planning be handled?** (*Operational/development*)

> What goals can be set for individuals so that they will gain greater satisfaction from their work and from the direction of their careers?

The remainder of this chapter explores the eight problem areas that usually arise in MBO programs, and discusses how these particular areas might apply to both managers and individuals (i.e., fire service officers and fire fighters) in a fire department. Fire service officers need to know how to cope with these problem areas if they are to achieve smoothly operating goals programs, along with higher morale and better performance.

Each decision an officer makes should be guided by the following three considerations:

1. The officer's capabilities,
2. The capabilities and competence of the staff members, and
3. The particular situation.

Guidance by these three considerations is especially necessary with respect to all skills involved in overcoming the eight problem areas in goal programs.

Extent of Setting Goals

Setting an appropriate number of goals involves several challenges for the officer. For every time period, departmental officers must determine for themselves, and jointly with each staff member, how many programs or activities on which to focus.

Goals should concentrate on those areas where they will either bring improvement in operations or lay the foundation for requirements that will have to be met in the future. No matter how many goals are set, every fire fighter still has to work on all the duties that are part of the job. However, during any single period there should also be one or several tasks or responsibilities that deserve highest priority. These tasks or responsibilities are the ones on which goals should be set.

There often are great pressures to set many goals to cover all the areas where improvement might be desirable. Yet if too many goals are set, people cannot cope with both the complexity and time demands of the goals and their regular work. For example, when an individual fire officer is expected to simultaneously achieve challenging goals to improve inspections, to improve prefire planning, to improve training, and to enhance personal competence, all while attending diligently to regular duties, the officer is likely to face an impossible task and probably will resent the goals program.

Furthermore, the entire goal-setting process could become enmeshed in a maze of paperwork. Too much detail in the goals program means that a considerable amount of time is wasted with what might appear to be unnecessary "busy work." That, too, can prevent the MBO program from generating the enthusiasm it needs to succeed.

If too few goals are set the program will not involve people sufficiently enough to challenge them, nor will the program help them to realize the benefits that can result, such as greater success and higher job satisfaction. Because the capabilities of fire fighters and officers vary, some can work on multiple goals simultaneously, while others can only work on a single goal at one time. For these reasons, among others, determining how many goals to set for a particular staff member can be as important as determining what goals to set and who should set the goals.

There is no foolproof or exact way to determine how many goals to set with a particular person at a specific time. However, there are two concepts that can provide some guidance: the Life Cycle Theory of Leadership and the Importance/Urgency diagram. The Life Cycle Theory of Leadership provides guidance on the number of goals an individual can accept and work with, based on his/her level of experience and work maturity. The Importance/Urgency diagram helps a manager decide which goals are important enough to deserve a place among the limited number of goals that can be set.

Life Cycle Theory of Leadership: Drs. Paul Hersey and Kenneth Blanchard developed the Life Cycle Theory of Leadership while they were professors at Ohio State University (see Figure 5.4). In this diagram, the horizontal axis depicts the extent to which an officer or a manager assigns tasks. The vertical axis represents the leader's concern for establishing a good working relationship. If a point is plotted at the bottom of the diagram, the leader has little concern about how well the staff member likes the decisions that are made. If a point is

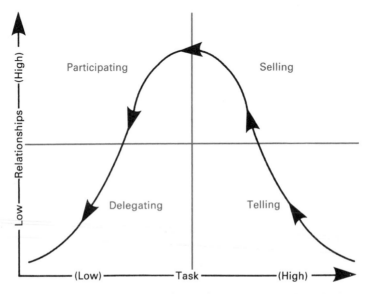

FIGURE 5.4 A representation of the Life Cycle Theory of Leadership.
(Source: *Training and Development Journal*, 1974[3])

plotted at the top of the diagram, the leader has maximum concern about the way the decisions or work arrangements are accepted by the staff member.

In the fire service, a rookie must be introduced to the job, the rules of the organization, and the procedures that are being used. The rookie must accept these rules and requirements without taking part in the decision making. But as the rookie acquires job experience, the fire officer will find it advisable and necessary to explain the reasons for decisions so the fire fighter will perform well in emergency situations. Depending on previous experience and personal capabilities, a new fire fighter moves up the curve more or less rapidly (see Figure 5.4). At the same time, fire officers can relinquish control proportionate to a fire fighter's capabilities so that assignment of tasks is less specific, and trust and confidence in the fire fighter's ability to act competently without specific instructions increases. Each fire fighter is different, and the speed at which relinquishment of close guidance occurs depends on individual capabilities.

Although the fire fighters must be trained to deal with all types of emergencies, fire officers cannot be expected to constantly oversee operations because of the nature of the work. Therefore, fire fighters are located primarily on the left side of the curve (see Figure 5.4); they are capable of accepting assignments in general terms because they usually make more of the decisions about what they should do, when it should be done, and how it should be done. Fire fighters usually establish their own goals in consultation with their managers, but they often work independently to achieve them.

Since they originally described the Life Cycle Theory of Leadership, Drs. Hersey and Blanchard added four fundamental supervisory styles to their diagram (Figure 5.4): telling, selling, participating, and delegating.

The capabilities of the officer in charge and the situation at hand are two other factors that need to be considered when setting goals and the priorities for those goals. Four factors to consider when setting priorities for goals are:

1. **The urgency of the goals.** Although an organization might have many important goals to accomplish, there are times when the urgency of one particular goal takes precedence.

2. **The importance of the goals.** Sometimes several tasks occur simultaneously and require particular actions or responses that are part of one goal. For example, returning administrative telephone calls is a major goal of good departmental communications. If many telephone calls were received in one day, answering these calls should be ranked by priority. A call to announce an emergency would, of course, be the highest priority and receive immediate attention; next might be complaints from citizens, or a call from a union representative concerning a grievance; and, finally, a low priority might be a call from a fire apparatus salesperson.

3. **How quickly a particular goal can be completed.** Often there is a desire to complete those goals that can be finished quickly in order to simplify scheduling and to allow full concentration on those goals that are more time-consuming. However, if the time-consuming goals are of great importance, work on them must receive primary attention or run concurrently with goals that can be accomplished quickly.

4. **The relationship between the completion of one goal with the completion of others.** If a series of inspections has to be made in the same time frame as prefire plans must be drawn, the inspections should be done first so that the prefire plans could be based on the results of the inspections, without duplicating effort. Figure 5.5 helps catagorize the relative urgency and importance of tasks in deciding on the priority of goals.

The Importance/Urgency Diagram: Although, in practice, managers have a tendency to favor relatively urgent tasks for setting goals, it is more efficient to think of the relationship between urgency and importance when deciding on goals. Adding this component can enhance the goal-setting process by ensuring that the limited number of goals that can be set for any one period are placed where they will do the most good. At the same time, considering both importance and urgency can help to ensure that matters that are important, but not urgent, receive proper attention so that they will not result in crises at a later time. Figure 5.5 is divided into four quadrants that represent relative urgency and importance. Consideration of these four quadrants helps prioritize goals and maximize the effectiveness of available resources.

Area A in Figure 5.5 represents tasks that are urgent but not of primary importance. These tasks might even be very urgent, but they are less important than projects in areas B or D. Area A might include returning telephone calls or

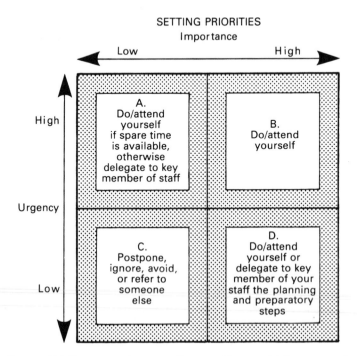

FIGURE 5.5 *Importance/urgency diagram.* (Source: Lieberman and Rausch, 1971, and Rausch, 1984[4,5])

altering plans for a fund-raising picnic. It is not really possible to set goals in this area, because the tasks are usually too immediate and not important enough to require goals.

Area B represents those matters and tasks that are both important and urgent, and should receive first priority. Tasks in Area B are so urgent that there is little time for goal setting. Examples of such tasks include: responding to an alarm, developing procedures to maintain rapid response time in areas under-going road construction, or improving relations with a community upset over a fatal fire incident that was described unfairly by the press as having been managed ineptly.

Tasks that are neither important nor urgent are located in Area C. These might include reading fire service magazines, updating unimportant depart-mental records, or cleaning a storage area filled with obsolete materials. These tasks should be accomplished only after the tasks in Areas A, B, and D have been achieved. The tasks in Area C can be postponed until there is spare time. A checklist containing these tasks can be prepared for use when no other work has to be done.

The most critical decisions with regard to priorities must be made for tasks that are classified in Area D because this high importance/low urgency area is the breeding ground of crises. These are matters that are important, but not as urgent as those in Area B. If a manager does not assign tasks in this quadrant a reasonably high priority, sooner or later they will have to be performed on a crash basis, or they might even reach crisis proportions. This is the area where goal-setting is most important; action plans must be prepared so that progress is made continually on these matters. In fact, this is the only area where setting goals is truly crucial.

Tasks in Area D might involve a training program for a sophisticated new apparatus, or developing plans and proposals for a new fire station that will be needed to serve a new development. These tasks usually involve planning and preparation steps for important results that will have to be achieved at some future time. When goals are assigned for such tasks, the preparatory steps are likely to receive the same priority as other, more urgent tasks.

The conclusion from Figure 5.5 is: When setting goals, all tasks that deserve consideration should be classified as belonging in Areas A, B, or D; tasks in Area C need not be considered. The tasks in Area D should be assigned goals and action plans with specific target dates assigned for the various steps. This sometimes requires difficult analyses, but can lead to meaningful long-range planning and continual operational improvement.

Quality of Goals and Goal Statements

All goals must be relevant to the overall mission of the organization and the purposes of the staff. Goals must help bring improvement in some aspect of the work or the employee's competence, and they should add to the motivational climate. This requires that, while being realistic, goals should be demanding and challenging for each individual. Goals must be set high, but not so high that they are beyond achievement. For example, to set a goal of a response time that would mean traveling at excessive speed is clearly unrealistic. On the other hand, to work toward a reduction in turnout time by 10 percent or even 20 percent can be challenging, yet realistic.

It is important to understand that goals are based on forecasts or estimates of what can be accomplished. A forecast, by definition, can never be assumed accurate; the best that can be done in setting goals is to reach for something that appears achievable. For example, if it appears as though ten inspections a month are possible but difficult, then that could be a realistic goal for a company. Yet, if it is clear that ten inspections have never been accomplished even during the best periods, then that goal might be unrealistic. When goals are clearly set too high, they are not challenging because people either do not take them seriously or they become discouraged by them. In contrast, if a goal is certain of accomplishment without extra effort, it is hardly worthwhile to spend time on setting it.

For goals to be part of an effective management process, not only must they be challenging and realistic, they must be worded so that they communicate clearly what is to be accomplished and by when. This clarity of goal statements means that goals will be measurable. To be measurable, operational goals must not only specify what is to be accomplished, but they must also indicate a completion date. For example, a goal that states: "We will prepare three prefire plans" is not definite enough, even though the quantity of the work is clearly implied. A more appropriate goal statement would be more specific, such as: "We will prepare a prefire plan for block A by September 1, and for enclosed mall buildings by January 12." So stated, the goal is measurable if everyone clearly understands what details are included in the plan.

Another example of a vaguely stated goal is: "We will train all fire fighters in prefire planning." This goal statement fails to indicate what subject is to be mastered and how thoroughly it is to be achieved. However, if the goal statement included specifics, it would then be measurable: "By the end of June, every fire fighter in the company will be able to draw a sketch of a one-story building with all pertinent sections noted and with the proper symbols used in prefire planning."

Officer Involvement

An officer should keep in mind the Life Cycle Theory of Leadership when deciding how deeply to become involved in helping lower-level officers or fire fighters, or in checking how they approach their assignments (see Figure 5.4). Those fire fighters or even newly appointed officers who either have limited experience or limited capabilities usually require fairly careful checking to see that they are approaching their assignments in a competent way.

In fire departments, company officers usually work closely with the fire fighters in jointly carrying out goals. This is particularly true in fire fighter training and education. For example, if it is decided that a fire fighter will enroll in a tactics course in a community college, the company officer should become involved to ensure that the fire fighter really learns the course. With a highly motivated and mature fire fighter, it might only be necessary to discuss how the course is progressing. With an individual who is less motivated or learns more slowly, the officer might help explain portions of the course.

Whether or not an MBO program is successful often is determined by the type and amount of involvement by the manager. Detailed involvement with a more competent fire fighter could be interpreted as interference and could dampen motivation. On the other hand, less competent or less experienced individuals could possibly appreciate this assistance, thereby increasing motivation. To be most effective, fire officers must permit fire fighters and lower-level officers the freedom, within reason, to do their jobs the way they feel the jobs should be done. At the same time the managers must be available for questions or help when needed.

Frequency of Reviews

In order for an MBO program to be successful, regular reviews are necessary. Reviews should be well-planned because they are important two-way communication tools that allow both sides to know what is happening. These reviews have seven primary purposes:

1. To evaluate where the manager should provide additional help or support to enable completion of goals that are not being achieved satisfactorily, and to discuss what form such help or support should take.
2. To keep the manager informed of progress on goals where work is proceeding smoothly.
3. To plan goals for the upcoming period.
4. To discuss which goals have become unrealistic and require modification.
5. To help overcome staff members' complaints that supervisors do not really know what they are accomplishing or contributing to achievement of the organization's goals.
6. To provide evidence that goals programs are serious in intent, that the managers support them, and that they are not merely routines to satisfy some requirement of higher-level managers.
7. To provide opportunities for supervisors to obtain additional knowledge about the capabilities and potentials of their staff members, thus enabling the supervisors to help their staff develop greater competence and success.

To be as effective as possible, reviews should be carried out on a one-to-one, face-to-face basis. Regular, written reporting or correspondence procedures should be incorporated if such procedures are helpful.

Although reviews should be regular, what is considered regular for one individual might not be regular for another, depending on an individual's competency, experience, needs, and maturity. Most people would probably agree that daily reviews are too frequent and that yearly reviews might not be frequent enough. Organizations that have reasonably effective goal programs generally require their managers to hold goal reviews, with each staff member reporting to them at least once every three months.

In a fire department, the chief might hold sessions with lower-level officers once a month to review goals. On the other hand, the company officer who works regularly with each fire fighter might only review goals on a formal basis each quarter.

One problem that often confuses managers about the frequency of goal programs — particularly when there is discussion about reviewing goals once every few months — is the fact that many goals are of short duration. These short-term goals should, however, be viewed as steps toward long-term goals. For instance, to complete a certain number of inspections in the course of a week is part of a goal to complete a much larger number in the course of a year. Similarly, a goal to make a revision in the way the hosebed is laid out is part of a larger goal to achieve increased apparatus efficiency. Goals, however, do not need to be assigned to every activity; if it is an accepted routine to inspect a given number of call boxes in the course of every week, there is no need for a goal.

Accountability

Accountability involves the extent to which an individual can be expected to achieve a goal, as well as how performance can be judged if the goal is not reached. For example, in the event that unexpected and extensive fires and emergencies require much more time than originally had been anticipated, to what extent might Officer Jones be considered accountable for fulfilling a goal? Did Officer Jones do a good job during this period by completing half the prefire plans, or did Officer Jones do a poor job by completing only half of the prefire plans? More simply stated, accountability is concerned with:

1. Whose fault is it when goals are not achieved?

2. Who should be held responsible, and to what extent?

3. What is considered fair, and what is considered subjective?

Failure to deal effectively with this specific problem area is one of the most common reasons that goal programs do not achieve their potential for improving control, organizational competence, and climate (the Three Cs of Management described in Chapter 4).

Because goals primarily are forecasts and because they might not be achieved even with the most careful planning and sound implementation, it does not seem useful to hold individuals responsible for the actual achievement of goals.

It is meaningless to observe that 80 percent of a goal has been achieved, or to note that the goal has been achieved on schedule, a few days earlier than scheduled, or two weeks or a month later than scheduled. The original goal might have been totally unrealistic and impossible to achieve, or it might have been very easy. Following are eight performance areas in which staff members can be evaluated factually and fairly.

1. Setting Challenging Goals: Participation by staff members is desirable when setting goals; however, setting goals is meaningful only if these staff members are sincere in helping to establish goals that are both realistic and challenging. If a lower-level fire officer or a fire fighter is forced to play a game to obtain the lowest possible goal so that the least amount of effort is required to achieve it, then mutual goal setting is not effective. Managers, therefore, need the cooperation of the members of their staff in helping to set challenging and realistic goals.

If a program exists to set goals and the manager wants it to become a way of life rather than a theoretical program, then obviously the manager cannot expect people to set challenging goals if they are punished when they do not achieve them. A manager who requires that staff members set challenging goals must be prepared to look at goals as predictions of achievement and to expect serious efforts to be made to attain them. Some goals, however, might not be achieved even with the best action program and the most untiring effort. If a fire officer accepts this fact, then fire fighters and lower-level fire officers can be held accountable for setting realistic goals that are also challenging.

2. Action Steps: An employee working on goals should always be aware of what action steps are necessary to come as close to achieving that goal as possible. Even though a manager would not frequently ask competent staff members what progress is being made toward the accomplishment of a goal or what actual steps are being taken, the staff members should know what these steps are. The manager can, therefore, hold staff members accountable for having appropriate and adequate action steps for their goals.

3. Planning: Lower-level officers and fire fighters are accountable for competent, thorough planning. Planning is an ongoing process. A competent person, working toward reaching goals, will think of goals at all times and the plans to achieve those goals.

4. Quality of Effort: When looking at the action steps that a lower-level officer or fire fighter takes, the manager obviously must evaluate them to see whether they are the best that can be taken. A staff member who regularly takes action steps that show improvement certainly deserves to be commended; one who takes inadequate action steps should be held accountable. If inadequate steps are being taken, performance should be viewed against the training that the staff member has received. A lack of quality could be related to inadequate training.

5. Achievement of Completion Dates: If a lower-level fire officer or fire fighter agrees to complete a certain action step by a certain time and does not accomplish it in that time even though it was possible, he or she should be held accountable. The same is true of all action steps leading to goals. Once they commit themselves to a plan of action, fire fighters and/or lower-level officers should implement that plan as decided and should be deterred from it only by matters beyond their control.

6. Viability of Action Steps: When someone accepts responsibility for a goal, develops a set of workable action steps, and takes those action steps, it might sometimes become apparent that the action steps will not lead to achieving the goal. When that happens, the person working toward achievement of the goal should be expected to immediately reevaluate the action steps and make necessary adjustments.

7. Notification of Obstacles: Once an organization understands how to work with a goals system, everyone should know that it is essential to notify the manager as soon as it becomes clear that a goal will not be achieved. This gives the manager an opportunity to provide additional resources or help to enable achievement of the goal. The manager can also change the goal if it appears that all has been done to achieve it, yet it cannot be achieved with the effort or the resources being devoted to it. For example, a lower-level fire officer might have the goal of investigating hose evolutions. The officer has been committed to completing the trials by a certain date but, as time progresses, finds that more urgent matters have come up and the tests cannot be completed in time. At that point, the officer should inform the higher-level officer that the goal will not be achieved unless more time is allocated or unless others can be assigned to the project. If there is still time to achieve the goal, the officer then has the opportunity to rescue the goal or to let it be completed at a later date. If everyone in an organization accepts the responsibility to provide timely notification when a goal is in jeopardy of being completed, then there is greater likelihood that goals will be achieved in time.

8. Relationship with Others: Fire officers and fire fighters can be judged on the extent to which they are able to obtain cooperation from others, to achieve their goals, and provide cooperation to others in return.

These eight issues, for which fire officers and fire fighters can be held accountable, are, of course, far more complicated than simply checking how well goals have been achieved. Nevertheless, holding them responsible on the basis of the eight evaluation criteria discussed above is a far more sensible and effective way to evaluate performance than by simply looking at the extent to which goals were actually achieved.

Participation

The most important step in bringing satisfaction to fire officers and fire fighters concerns the amount of participation they have in the goal-setting process. Every individual wants an opportunity to influence the decisions that will affect individual working conditions, as well as the work itself. It should be clearly understood that the concerns that apply to participation in the setting of goals apply to all decisions affecting people. Setting goals is just one specific type of decision.

In most decision-making situations, it is necessary to answer three questions: 1) Which people should participate? 2) To what extent should those people be involved?, and 3) At what point in the process should they participate? Participation of all staff in making goal decisions certainly is not necessary or even desirable. At a fire scene, for example, the ranking officer takes command and assumes a dominant role in all decisions.

Strategic goals, such as conducting inspections, checking alarm boxes regularly, and removing snow or obstacles in front of hydrants, are basic to the existence and effectiveness of the fire department. Only the operational goals within these strategic goals are subject to discussion.

In some decision-making situations, all of the people who will be affected by the decision can—and should—take part. In other situations, the persons who should take part in making decisions should only be those who have expertise in the particular topic for which a decision will be made. Sometimes it is preferable that everyone participate right from the beginning; in other cases such involvement might be necessary only at a certain time or only for a segment of the total decision, such as with the implementation aspects of a decision.

There are many levels at which people can participate in the setting of goals. For example, an officer might ask: "We're going to make a prefire plan for this whole block. Where shall we start?" Or, "What should be preplanned?" Or even, "How should we organize ourselves to do this preplanning?" Each successive question requires a broader and more significant level of participation. Because there are many kinds of levels and possibilities, the question of participation in the decision-making process is a complicated and widely misunderstood one.

Behavioral scientists have devoted considerable effort toward investigating the way participation should be used. One important theory, Tannenbaum and Schmidt's "Continuum of Leadership Behavior" (see Figure 3.3), provides at least some limited guidelines to action for the officer who wishes to create the best possible motivational climate. Tannenbaum and Schmidt posed a difficult question: At what point along the range of possible participation choices should the manager aim for a specific situation? There are two general guidelines that can be used. First, participation depends on the competencies and capabilities of the fire fighters and lower-level officers. The more competent and capable a staff member is, the more extensive the level of participation should be that is likely to lead to favorable results.

Secondly, when in doubt, a manager is likely to fare better by allowing somewhat greater participation because greater participation will usually lead to more information for the manager. This information will, in turn, help fix the level of optimal participation that will lead to the best decisions. The better the decisions, the more success is achieved, and success leads to greater satisfaction;

staff members share in both the satisfaction of having participated and the satisfaction of realizing a successful outcome.

When a manager or officer uses employee participation appropriately, consideration usually is given to three characteristics of the staff member in determining the amount or quality of participation:

1. Attitudes and maturity.

2. Willingness or interest in becoming involved.

3. Knowledge of subject matter related to a goal.

These characteristics correspond in a rough way to the individual's position on the Life Cycle curve (Figure 5.4).

Attitudes and maturity concern the extent to which an individual is willing and able to accept responsibility and to devote extra effort when required, the level of judgment that the person can apply, the willingness to accept the direction in which the goal takes the group, and so on. If a person generally makes decisions based on emotional rather than factual considerations and does not analyze the facts carefully, then that person cannot participate at the same level, or in the same manner, as someone who has a more objective, rational, and careful approach.

The extent to which a staff member wants to be involved also is important. There are many reasons why a staff member might not wish to participate in setting a particular goal. One reason involves the attitudes that the staff member might have toward the goal. If he or she thinks that the manager or officer merely wants participation in order to have others share responsibility, then there might be a negative attitude toward participation. Similarly, if a staff member believes that a manager asks for participation only on a token basis and does not really want opinions or help to make a decision or set a goal, then he or she often does not want to participate.

Finally, a thorough knowledge of the subject matter involved is required. If a staff member has little technical knowledge in the subject of a goal, then it would not be wise to give that person a large voice in a decision related to that subject. A fire fighter who knows little about apparatus requirements could not contribute significantly in the selection of new auxiliary apparatus; furthermore, this fire fighter might not want to be involved in such a decision because of a lack of knowledge.

There is another point to be considered in deciding the level of participation. It concerns the requirements of the decision or the goal itself. In order to make a decision or to set a goal in the best possible way, two things have to be considered: 1) technical quality or the knowledge that is required to make a successful decision or to set a high-quality goal, and 2) acceptance quality or the extent to which successful implementation of a decision or achievement of a goal requires acceptance on the part of the people who are affected (see Figure

3.4). Which participation level to use is easiest to decide when technical quality requirements are high and the acceptance need is low. Such decisions can be made without much involvement and then announced or explained to staff members. The selection of a new piece of apparatus is an example of this type of decision.

Decisions that require neither high technical knowledge nor widespread acceptance are rare, yet they generally are decisions where nobody really cares which way they are made. An example involves keeping a fire station's facilities clean. Not many fire fighters care to make the decision about who should take out the garbage on a specific day, as long as that work assignment is fair.

Decisions that require high acceptance for success include increasing drill time or training time, conducting more inspections, and preparing additional prefire plans. Most matters involving a significant amount of effort would be in this area, except for those decisions or goals that, in addition to acceptance, also require high technical knowledge. For example, a decision to hold more drills does not require technical knowledge. Everyone knows what is involved if more drills are held. Any goal or decision that requires employee contribution and that affects employees directly requires a high level of participation. Good skills are needed by the manager to lead the group to a joint decision so that there will be no resentment and so that everyone will exert the greatest effort toward making a good decision.

Finally, goals and decisions where many technical problems are involved and where high acceptance is needed also require the greatest skill on the part of the manager. A goal to reduce the time required to lay a specified amount of hose and to charge it might require considerable technical knowledge if the goal is to be set realistically. In addition, for successful implementation a high level of acceptance is also necessary.

For example, perhaps a fire chief decides that attack time must be improved. One officer will be asked to investigate and recommend hosebed layout for the 2½-in. hose that would allow the most rapid straight and reverse lay of 250 ft, and then let the chief know when the investigation will be completed. If a new recommendation is accepted, the best time would be set as a goal for all companies that could be converted to the layout. To forecast how long it would take to study the situation and make an estimate of the implementation time requires considerable knowledge about time studies and how to make them, as well as about the time that is required for development. On the other hand, to successfully implement the tests and to get accurate time values while the tests are being run requires the cooperation of every fire fighter involved.

Decisions of this type are most difficult. Technical knowledge on the part of the decision maker and a high degree of acceptance on the part of those who have to implement the decision are necessary. The following three guidelines are useful in deciding on the optimal level of participation when setting any goals or making any decisions:

1. Decide what level of participation will lead to greatest success. This automatically ensures that the choice of participation level will receive serious consideration.
2. Consider the technical quality requirement as well as the acceptance quality requirement of the decision or goal to help narrow the choice of participation level and provide direction.
3. Weigh the capabilities and other factors related to the staff member(s), including emotional maturity and attitudes, willingness to participate, and knowledge of subject matter, to help pinpoint the best level of participation.

After determining answers to these guidelines, a manager or officer should be able to apply one or more of the participatory styles depicted in Figure 3.3. A manager should neither be seen as autocratic nor democratic; rather, a manager should select from the great variety of leadership styles depending on the needs of the situation and the staff member(s) at a given time. At one time a manager could rely on others to supply answers and decisions, or the manager could inform staff members of a decision. At another time the manager could be highly supportive and provide help, or might insist on strict compliance with previous requests without offering additional resources. However, such flexibility to adapt to the needs of a situation could be mistaken for unreliable behavior. It is, therefore, important that the manager base his or her choice of leadership style soundly on the factors explained here. Reasons should be communicated clearly whenever appropriate. No manager can be consistently competent in these leadership style selections; however, the manager who develops a good rapport with staff members and then provides evidence of trying to satisfy the needs of the situation will be a much more competent manager than one who attempts to stick rigidly to one style.

Performance Appraisal and Evaluation

Most employees, including fire fighters, are concerned with what their supervisors think of the quality and quantity of their work. They want to know how they are progressing in relation to their own future and in terms of their contribution to the overall success of the organizational unit. Information about performance or specific assignments should be made available to the individual on a regular basis and should cover both positive and negative aspects of progress. From time to time, however, there should be a formal review that clarifies how the manager perceives the staff member's overall performance, suggests ways in which the staff member's performance can be improved, and explains how the manager can help the staff member reach personal work and career goals. Such reviews are usually called performance appraisals or performance evaluations, and they serve three basic functions in a fire department:

1. To inform fire fighters and lower-level officers how they are performing and that their managers are aware of that performance.
2. To give officers a more factual way to look at performance so they will rely less on personal preferences and aspirations.
3. To identify and allow correction of deficiencies in knowledge and skills.

A major concern of many managers involved with the conduct of performance appraisals is how to keep such appraisals as objective as possible. Supervisors need to be as factual as possible in their evaluations of people, even though they might have personal preferences for certain strengths and personal dislikes for certain weaknesses. The approach of establishing clear accountabilities, based on goals and steps leading to the goals, can help to overcome many of the obstacles that arise when one person evaluates another. An objective, and thus fair, evaluation usually can be based on all or most of the eight performance areas discussed on pages 123 and 124. Goal achievement can be blocked, whereas achievement of action steps, as represented by the eight areas, is almost always possible.

Even when using these eight areas for performance evaluation, there is still a great deal left to personal feelings and to the opinion that a manager has about any individual staff member. Obviously, there will never be a system that can completely eliminate these defects. However, a performance appraisal system that is based on accountabilities and on the opportunity for the fire fighter or lower-level officer to participate in the process has the greatest chance to be fair to the organization and to the individuals involved. This system concentrates on the efforts that people devote toward the achievement of goals and on the quality of that effort. For additional information, consult *Win-win performance management/appraisal.*[6]

The best performance appraisals are joint activities in which the manager and the staff member both complete the required forms and then discuss any differences in the way they perceive the staff member's performance in each category of accountability. These performance reviews also serve as an excellent foundation for deciding what knowledge or skills a fire fighter or lower-level officer needs for better performance and as preparation for possible promotion.

One question that often arises concerns the similarities and differences between performance appraisals and goal reviews. The two are similar because both are explicit contacts between a manager and a staff member. Both provide an opportunity for the manager to learn more about the interests, views, and aspirations of each staff member. However, during a performance appraisal, the manager does the evaluating and the staff member is evaluated. Although the staff member's views receive a full hearing, the evaluator/evaluatee relationship remains, and the evaluator makes the final decisions on salary increase, promotion, and so on.

When reviewing goals, on the other hand, the discussion should be between two people, each of whom has something to contribute to the achievement of the goal. The discussion does not center on what was done well and where there were shortcomings. Instead, it concentrates on what else is needed to achieve goals that have been set, what new goals should be set, what goals can be dropped, and, most importantly, how a manager can help solve any problems a staff member might have.

Operational/Developmental Goals

Developmental goals are a form of operational goals that, together with the action steps supporting them, are concerned with increasing the competence of individuals. A goals program that covers only operational goals that are concerned with performance objectives is not complete. Employees need to see that the manager or officer will include some goals that are intended not just for the organizational unit, but also for the individual staff member. Such goals can involve development toward a personal career goal, assignments that provide satisfaction to the staff member, or help with existing job problems. A manager or officer who attempts to create a workable goals program has many opportunities to determine what the personal needs and aspirations of staff members are and what specific knowledge or skills would most help improve their performance. Developmental goals thus become a regular part of the goals program and provide chances for officers to be supportive. In this way, the organization and the manager prove that they do not consider the goals program as a one-way street toward greater output, but rather as a way to fulfill employee needs and provide for the quantity and quality of work that needs to be done.

The professional development of personnel through training is a major factor in achieving competence, one of the Three Cs of Management (see Chapter 4). Such development enables personnel to become more competent in their current jobs and to become better qualified to accept the responsibilities of higher-level positions when openings occur. An organization composed of skilled and competent personnel who are continuing to develop themselves toward even higher levels of competency is more likely to achieve its goals than is the organization that has little or no concern for the professional growth of its personnel.

Multiunit Goals

Although not generally considered equal in importance to the eight problem areas shown in Figure 5.3, a challenge often encountered at various organizational levels concerns multiunit goals that cut across departmental or divisional lines. This challenge occurs when several units in an organization share a common goal that cannot be accomplished without the combined efforts of the units involved. Multiunit goals are of concern to the fire service when departmental goals are set that affect all units—divisions, battalions, and companies—within the overall organization.

Although multiunit goals should be the primary responsibility of a higher level, this is not always practical, so the problems inherent in them must then be solved at lower levels. Only when the goals process is thoroughly understood by an organization can such problems be resolved readily. One solution is to charge a manager with leading and coordinating the efforts of the different units involved. In such a case, the manager helps plan the action steps needed by each unit in order to help the organization accomplish the goal. The manager also works directly with all personnel involved so that the plan can be changed and adapted as needed to suit the requirements of the various participating units.

Motivational Impact of Goal Setting on Employees

Many managers believe that their function is to motivate their staff members, and many believe that they can do so by being good leaders. Most people, however, are not motivated by managerial action when the obvious intent is to get them to do more work. Therefore, modern management concepts suggest that managers should not try to motivate their staff members, but rather should emphasize creating a climate that will encourage motivation to develop.

A manager or officer who tries to provide for many needs of employees and tries to help them attain greater satisfaction from their work usually finds that people gain higher levels of motivation. Individuals vary greatly in the extent of motivation they can bring to a specific type of work. When a manager creates a very positive climate, there are some staff members who will react very favorably. However, it is also likely that some individuals will not be stimulated at all.

In summary, a well-operating goals program can help to produce a working climate in which people find motivation. Some of the elements that make a program successful include:

- An appropriate number of goals that effectively challenge staff members, and selection of priorities that satisfy the desire to accomplish something worthwhile.

- Quality goals that are appropriate and realistic, and statements that eliminate uncertainties, questions, and confusion about what is really expected. Well-planned goals give a feeling of direction that anyone can share.

- Exercise of good judgment by managers who provide help when needed and refrain from becoming involved when staff members can accomplish a goal independently.

- Review of progress on a fairly regular basis and assistance, when needed, to achieve assigned or individual goals.

- Managers who hold people accountable for the things they can achieve, and do not place blame or give credit for things they have no control over.

The right amount of participation in setting goals gives staff members a feeling that they have influence over their work and their future. They know that they have a voice in deciding how the work is to be done, and that knowledge contributes greatly to work satisfaction and to confidence in their organization and their managers.

Links Between Linking Elements

Management by Objectives, which is a key factor in the control linking element (see Figure 4.1), influences and is interrelated to the other linking elements described in Chapter 4. If the various linking elements—the skills of managers—are applied competently, they reinforce each other in numerous ways by providing even better *control*, leading to higher levels of *competence*, and creating a greatly improved *climate* (The Three Cs of Management).

ACTIVITIES

1. Describe the benefits to managers of working with goals/objectives.
2. Describe the purpose of the following terms in relation to Management by Objectives:
    (a) A goals program.
    (b) Organizing.
    (c) Follow-up.
    (d) Implementation.
    (e) Review.
    (f) Planning.
3. You have decided that your individual long-term goal is to become a fire service specialist in the field of extinguishing systems. What short-term goals and action steps would you need to take to accomplish this goal? How would these steps differ from those needed to achieve a goal such as the preparation of a 20-page research paper that must be completed in a month?
4. Explain why it is necessary that, in order to be successful, a goal-setting program must satisfy both the needs of the organization and the needs of the employees. What are some of the general guidelines that an organization can make use of to fulfill the needs of both the organization and its employees?
5. Review the eight problem areas most often found in MBO goal programs (see Figure 5.3). Then, with other members of your class, discuss the particular problems that could arise in the process of attaining each of the following goals. For each goal, write a summary statement that explains how your group thinks it could best alleviate these problems.

(a) The preparation of two prefire plans.
(b) Maintenance of state facilities.
(c) Reduction of total response time.
(d) Inspection of all industrial occupancies during the next three years.

6. How can the importance-urgency diagram (Figure 5.5) help a fire officer more effectively select which tasks or functions require goals?

7. Explain the advantanges of scheduled reviews in a goals program. What are the most effective ways of carrying out these reviews?

8. In addition to their routine duties, fire fighters have been assigned the goal of completing a six-month physical fitness program. After six months, only half of the program has been completed. What factors should be considered when determining accountability for the goal not being fulfilled?

9. Do you think an emergency situation requires joint decision making, authoritarian decision making, or a combination of the two? Explain your reasoning, and describe some of the problems that might occur if a fire officer felt that extensive joint decision making would be desirable at the fire scene.

10. Describe the eight criteria used to evaluate performance of fire fighters and lower-level officers.

11. Describe the differences between operational goals and developmental goals. Explain why it is important for organizational leaders to provide both types within a goals program.

12. Explain how each of the following factors can be used to create a climate in which employees can find enhanced motivation for goal achievement.
(a) Number of goals.
(b) Quality of goals.
(c) Goal reviews.
(d) Accountability for goals.

13. Describe ways in which the linking elements of the Three Cs of Management reinforce each other to bring better alignment between staff members and the fire fighting organizational unit?

REFERENCES

[1]Cote, A. E., ed., *Fire Protection Handbook*, 16th edition, National Fire Protection Association, Quincy, MA, 1986, pp. 15-3, 15-4, 15-5.

[2]Drucker, Peter, *Management: Tasks, Responsibilities, Practices*, Harper & Row, New York, 1974.

[3]Reproduced by special permission from *Training and Development Journal*, February 1974, Copyright © 1974 by the American Society for Training and Development, Inc.

[4]Lieberman, H. R., and Rausch, Erwin, *Managing and Allocating Time*, Didactic Systems, Inc., Cranford, NJ, 1971.

[5]Rausch, Erwin, *Balancing Needs of People and Organizations*, Bureau of National Affairs, Washington, D.C., 1978; Didactic Systems, Inc., Cranford, NJ, 1984.

[6]Rausch, Erwin, *Win-Win Performance Management/Appraisal*, John Wiley & Sons, New York, 1985.

6

Management Functions in the Fire Service

Chapters 1 through 5 primarily discussed fundamental concepts and principles of modern management theory. The remaining chapters emphasize fire service managerial issues, including fire prevention, fireground command, physical resources, personnel, and training.

This chapter provides both an overview and the foundation for further detailed treatment of management functions unique to the fire service. A brief history of the development of public fire protection is presented, followed by a discussion of a fire department's organization, areas of management responsibility, and management roles of a department's administration.

Although the fire service has unique functions, it is, nonetheless, a work organization. Thus, general management principles are fully applicable. To be an effective officer in today's fire service one should be skilled in applying modern management principles to the fire service. The quality of fire protection an organization delivers to the community is directly related to an officer's competence as a fire resource manager.

EFFECTIVE MANAGEMENT IN THE FIRE SERVICE

Appropriate objectives are the primary foundation of effective management in the fire service as well as in other organizations. Traditional objectives that are commonly accepted by most fire departments include:[1]

1. Preventing fires from starting.
2. Preventing loss of life and property when fire starts.
3. Confining fire to its place of origin.
4. Extinguishing fires.

Although the intent of these objectives has remained the same, the scope has changed over the years because people realized the necessity for communal and organized fire fighting. In addition, the scope of responsibilities within the fire department has also changed. Highly trained medical professionals in fire departments have broadened responsibilities which include saving lives in disasters other than fires, such as airport crashes or automobile accidents. Hazardous materials response teams now play a growing role in many fire departments. Today's fire chiefs and officers are no longer only fire-scene leaders: they must also know how to train personnel, how to manage both physical and economic resources, and how to manage an entire fire unit effectively. All of these changes in roles and in fire department responsibility have evolved from years of increased technological development in the fire sciences.

In order to meet the objectives listed above, a fire department must be structured to perform a wide range of tasks. Fire prevention includes controlling the amount and storage of combustibles that are found in every jurisdiction. A fire department must ensure that inspectors routinely inspect the hazards in the community and that sufficient enforcement personnel promote fire prevention and adherence to building codes. These personnel must also be available to advise people in the community who have firesafety-related problems and questions.

Modern fire service practice dictates that public firesafety education be an integral element in fire prevention. After firesafety needs have been identified in a community, an educational program must be developed to address those needs, and sufficient resources must be allocated to do the job correctly.

The maintenance of a well-trained and properly equipped fire suppression force lies at the heart of preventing loss of life and property when fire starts. This objective involves a number of important tasks that help to confine and extinguish fires, such as planning for operational contingencies and devoting sufficient time and talent to pre-fire planning. The hazards in a community must be identified, and plans for delivering protection in the event of fire must be developed. Tactical tasks and long-range planning must be addressed to ensure future fire fighting success, such as mutual aid to alleviate specific or temporary shortfalls in personnel and equipment.

History of Fire Departments: A Brief Overview

In 1648, New Amsterdam (now New York City) appointed five municipal fire wardens who had general fire prevention responsibilities. This is often considered to have been the first public fire department in North America. Thirty-one years later, Boston experienced a devastating conflagration that destroyed 155 buildings and led to the establishment of the first paid municipal fire department. Boston obtained a fire engine from England, and employed 12 fire fighters and a fire chief. From its inception, the department used municipal fire fighters on an on-call basis; by 1711 fire wardens were appointed to respond to fires, and by 1715 Boston had six fire companies complete with English-manufactured engines. The concept of mutual aid also had its beginning in Boston: Affluent citizens banded together to assist each other in salvaging valuables from fires in their businesses and homes.

In the latter half of the 19th century, fire departments developed further techniques for reducing water damage and increasing salvage from fires. Technological advances in manufacturing methods led to improvements, such as the development of more effective fire hoses, automatically raised ladders, progress in the area of hydraulics, and increased use of mechanized apparatus. In turn, such improvements led to the need for specific organizational and training techniques within fire departments. Thus, in 1889, Boston established a drill school; in 1914, New York City established a fire college. Additional developments increased the efficiency of fire departments in the post-World War II period, including spray nozzles and radio communications. In 1976, a National Fire Academy, sponsored by the federal government, became a reality.

Fire attack techniques have been improved greatly through the use of preconnected attack hoselines, self-contained breathing apparatus, and large-diameter water supply hose. In areas remote from water supply sources, large pumper tankers have been developed to transport water to the fire.

More recent developments include the use of computers for standard departmental record keeping, alarm dispatching, and fire prevention inspections. A number of fire departments now have equipment that allows fire inspectors to type their findings into a hand-held portable computer unit. At the end of the work day, the inspector places this unit into a terminal module that automatically sends the data to the departmental computer for future use.

Although developments and improvements in apparatus and fire fighting techniques can elevate a department's overall efficiency, a department cannot effectively employ such developments without proper organization. Although fire departments had small and simple beginnings, their early years reflected the need for internal organization. For example, Boston fire wardens in 1711 had, as their main duty, the supervision of citizen bucket brigades. Even though the fire fighting equipment used in colonial times (see Figure 2.1) seems simple when compared to modern equipment, those fire fighters still had to have an overall organizational plan, or a leader, to provide direction and attempt efficient operation.

Organizational Components of a Fire Department

The work of a modern fire department has far exceeded the traditional fire-related objectives of what was once expected from municipal fire agencies. Current trends in fire protection call for a wider range of emergency services to the community than ever before, including:

- Hazardous materials emergency response capability.
- Rescue and emergency medical services.
- Disaster planning against such diverse emergencies as floods, earthquakes, and hurricanes.

These services, among others, must be accompanied by written local plans which can increase effective delivery of emergency services during times of disaster.

A fire department, like any other organization, must have some form of external structure. In addition, there should be an internal structure, usually in the form of ranks or roles, in order to achieve the purposes of the organizational unit.

External Structure of a Fire Department

The external organization of a fire department is the relationship among the operating divisions of the total organization. Figures 6.1, 6.2, and 6.3 show typical examples of the organizational structures of small, medium, and large fire departments, respectively.

Internal Structure of a Fire Department

The internal organizational structure of a fire department can be illustrated by two components: one is the organizational principles, and the other is the roles of the individuals within the organization (discussed in this chapter).

The internal structure of a fire department is based on the following four organizational principles: 1) division of work, 2) coordination, 3) clearly established lines of authority, and 4) unity of command.

Division of Work: The most basic organizational principle for a fire department is the division of work according to a well-arranged plan, both among the individuals in the department and in the operating units. The plan should be based on the functions that must be performed according to a fire department's purpose and duties, such as fire prevention, training, communications, and so on.

Coordination: There is more need for internal coordination as a department increases in size and complexity. A small department usually has a simple organizational structure that allows frequent personal contact among individuals, thus ensuring efficient coordination. However, because the structure of a larger department does not allow such frequent personal contact, more extensive coordination of the operating units is necessary.

Established lines of authority: These define the individual's relationship to the total department. A broader organization line shows each operational unit or division with its relationship to the total department. The principle of lines of authority also includes the extent of an individual's input into the decision-making process and the individual's independence when working on assigned tasks. In many cases, individuals are given the responsibility of performing

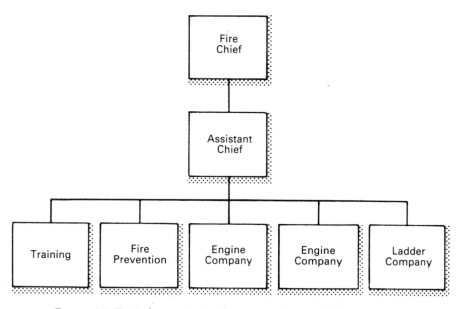

FIGURE 6.1 *Typical organizational structure of a small fire department.*

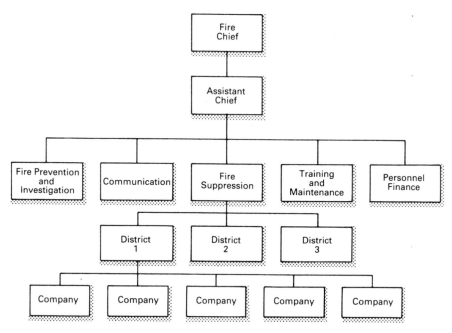

FIGURE 6.2 *Typical organizational structure of a medium-sized fire department.*

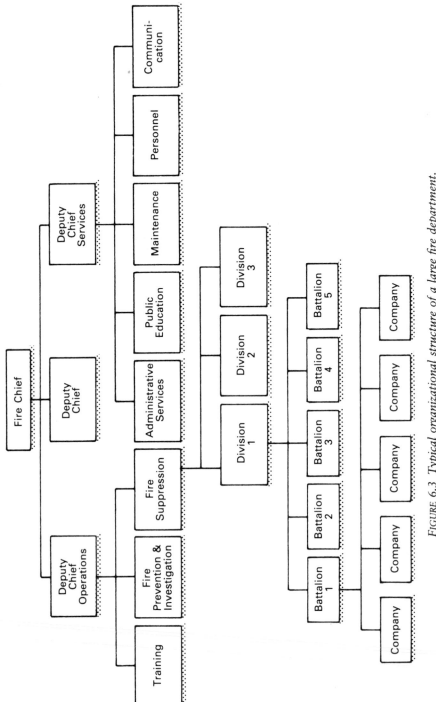

FIGURE 6.3 Typical organizational structure of a large fire department.

certain tasks, but are not given the authority to make some of the decisions necessary to complete the tasks. This policy tends to restrict the performance of the department because these individuals must constantly consult their immediate supervisors when decisions have to be made.

Unity of Command: This concept states that each member of the organization reports to only one superior. It is important in the departmental structure because conflicting orders from several superiors can result in confusion and inefficiency. A fire fighter who receives orders from only one superior usually can perform more efficiently. Likewise, similar situations can arise for supervisors who guide too many individuals. In such instances the leaders sometimes commit a major portion of their time to supervising subordinates, thereby ignoring other important managerial duties.

Areas of Management Responsibility

As stated earlier, the fire service has many unique functions. These functions range from the requirement of a distinct team spirit to the need to deal with the public in both minor and major crisis situations. Accordingly, these unique problems require special management styles and capabilities.

The specific functions of an individual fire department and the reporting relationship to other governmental bodies are established by state or provincial legislation. This legislation generally places the fire department under the jurisdiction of a county government, a municipal government, or a special district that is empowered by statute to perform the functions of a governmental unit.

The operation of a fire department is usually a function of local government (in the case of a fire district, possibly the only function) that supports the service and is responsible for the level of service rendered. According to the *Fire Protection Handbook*, the operation of the fire department involves three major areas of responsibility for the governing body:[2]

> . . . (1) fiscal management, (2) personnel management, and (3) productivity. In general, *fiscal management* practices follow those used by the government agency supporting the department and include budgeting, cost accounting, personnel costs (including payroll), and purchasing or procurement costs.
>
> . . . Fire department *personnel management* is involved to some degree in the recruitment, selection, and promotion of personnel needed to fill various positions in the organization. Largely, these matters are governed by local and/or state law; by personnel agencies, including civil service authorities; and by direct decisions of the governmental agency operating the fire department . . . [See Chapter 13 for more detailed discussion of personnel management functions in the fire service.]
>
> *Productivity* in the fire service is the most difficult ingredient for management to measure. The basic objective of the fire service is the protection of life and property, [which] involves two major activities: (1) control of hazards to minimize fire losses and to prevent fires, and (2)

dealing with actual fires and emergencies to minimize suffering and losses. It is difficult to assess the number of fires and the suffering that have been prevented by fire department activities; however, experience has demonstrated that lack of effective fire prevention and control measures invites disastrous experiences. Likewise, the fact that most fires are suppressed with minimum losses and injuries does not indicate conclusively that an adequate level of fire department service has been provided. Experience shows that major fires and emergencies arise from combinations of circumstances beyond the immediate control of fire department management, but which must be dealt with effectively to protect the public . . .

Productivity can be measured, to some extent, by comparison of key achievements between departments of similar size in similar situations. Fire department management is responsible for maintaining highly trained and efficient operational units to perform assigned tasks both in the prevention and suppression of fires.

Fire departments are becoming more creative in issuing positive statements about the level of productivity. Rather than reporting a loss of $9,000 on a structural fire in a $150,000 home, a figure of $141,000 can be reported as the amount not damaged by fire. This type of reporting often reflects more realistically the effectiveness of a particular fire department.

Fiscal Management

Fiscal management refers to the economic factors involved in the operation of a fire department. Although it is obvious that accounting and budgeting are fiscal management functions, there are also a great deal of planning and research functions, which are needed for assessing current and future developments and needs before budget proposals can be formulated. After the actual budget is submitted, fiscal management also includes wise decisions about purchasing equipment and supplies and the storage of these supplies.

Planning and Research: The responsibility for planning varies in a fire department. For example, in some jurisdictions, all department heads are required to submit in advance estimates of capital equipment needs for five years. In rapidly developing communities, some of the larger fire departments have planning staffs to assist in the planning of new fire stations, the replacement and possible relocation of old stations, and also for replacement of apparatus. However, in the vast majority of communities, planning is much less sophisticated. City administrators might approve citizens' demands for better protection of areas remote from existing fire stations, and the fire department might merely be consulted about a suitable location. Outside consultants might also be employed to recommend relocation and consolidation of fire stations, using fire department annual reports as a basis for recommending various improvements.

Planning for the future needs of a fire department is the fire department manager's most important task. Without adequate planning, an administrator will be handling one crisis after another. All departments need to develop long-range plans, and these plans need to be flexible and reflect change in the local community.[3] To do this, fire departments should maintain a close working relationship with local and regional planning groups.

Good planning should be based substantially on research that reveals needs for planning or budgeting in particular areas. Few departments, however, are adequately staffed or financed to support significant research activity. Research is limited because most fire departments are relatively small organizations that lack sufficient personnel to plan the on-going obligations for furnishing fire protection. True research into such areas as efficient equipment design or improved turnout equipment generally is beyond the capability of most fire departments.

There are many ways, however, of using research in a fire department. One is to compile tables, flow charts, or graphs in order to discern areas of need or expansion. Table 6.1 shows a breakdown by percentage of fire department calls and a classification of fires that could be used for apparatus planning and procurement, or for allocation of inspection resources to properties that are fire risks in the community.

Other research sources are available to fire department managers, including a fire record program entitled *Uniform Fire Incident Reporting System* (UFIRS),[4] which was developed by NFPA in cooperation with a selected group of fire departments. The NFPA's research division also can be of direct help and benefit to fire departments.

Accounting and Budgeting: Competently managed departments have a system of accounts for financial administration. An efficient system maintains a record of funds received by the department and funds expended, and provides data for continually analyzing how the department's funds are being spent. The more

TABLE 6.1 Sample of statistical research for fire department management.

Fire department calls	Percent	Classification of fires	Percent
Structural fires	25.0	Dwellings	35.2
Emergencies other than fires	12.0	Other buildings	10.2
EMS response	56.0	Rubbish outdoors	10.8
Hazardous materials incidents	2.0	Trees, brush, grass	21.0
False alarms	5.0	Miscellaneous fires outdoors	5.0
	100.0	Vehicles	17.5
		Aircraft	0.2
		Ships and boats	0.1
			100.0

thorough and relevant this analysis, the more effective fire department management will be in gaining full use of available financial resources. To provide for constant monitoring of resources, a fire department has to move away from traditional financial control systems whose primary purpose is simply to monitor public funds to prevent careless or inappropriate spending.

Budgets are an important element of a dynamic system. They outline the financial plans of the fire department. In a complete budget, one part lists the services, activities, and projects for the department with the appropriate or projected expense of each. The other part lists the income to be used to meet the total expense. Financial controls and budgeting are covered in greater detail in Chapter 12.

Purchasing and Storing: In most municipalities, fire department equipment and supplies are procured through purchasing departments. Records of procurement must be maintained and storage of acquisitions must be authorized when necessary. Common items are usually requisitioned from the purchasing agency and charged to the appropriate fire department account. Items of a specialized nature, however, require the preparation of purchasing specifications by the fire department, approval from the purchasing department, and advertisement for bids. The fire chief, with the advice of the apparatus and equipment superintendent, should determine whether or not proposals submitted by bidders meet specifications adequately.

Even when emergency purchases must be made, most departments still require estimates from several suppliers. If the expenditure is small and if funds are available in the budget, the chief can authorize the expenditure. If funds are not available in the budget or if the amount exceeds a statuatory level, authorization and funds must be obtained from the municipal manager or finance officer.

Management of Fire Department Personnel

In order for a fire department to operate effectively and efficiently, personnel who meet the appropriate standards should be hired. Normally, recruitment of personnel is not a career fire department responsibility because it is handled by the local governmental personnel agency. NFPA 1201, *Recommendations for the Organization for Fire Services,*[5] recommends that the fire chief prepare the personnel policies and standards for the department and issue the orders necessary for administering personnel procedures. In some departments the chief might decide that an assistant chief should specialize in personnel matters and designate that officer to be department personnel officer.

The specific personnel activities that might be conducted by a fire department depend on the scope of personnel services provided by municipal, state personnel, or civil service agencies. State, provincial, and civil service commission legislation might set specific standards of pay, hours, working conditions, working schedules, and other features of personnel policy that would limit the authority of the municipality and the fire department. (See Chapter 13 for a more detailed description of the effect of authority as it relates to personnel matters.)

Personnel Standards: The personnel standards of a fire department should be designed to establish and maintain a competent and well-trained force by recruiting highly qualified individuals and by providing an interesting and useful career from recruitment to retirement.

After recruiting and hiring have been accomplished, there are various areas where personnel policies, standards, and procedures are applied. These are summarized in NFPA 1201:[6]

- Attendance and duties.
- Annual physical examination.
- Health maintenance.
- Safety.
- A system of ranks.
- Disciplinary action.

Selection, Recruitment, and Promotion: Management's responsibility in these functions can best be summarized as the selection of the most qualified candidate for every opening, within the department's policies and procedures. A detailed discussion of the selection process for management, including procedures for management responsibility from the initial interview to salary administration, training and development, and career development can be found in Chapter 13 under "Personnel Management Functions."

Promotion within a department's ranks should be accomplished with the same overall objective as selection. NFPA 1201 suggests that the following steps be utilized by the fire chief in a fire department's promotional program:[7]

- Establish a formal procedure that requires supervisors to evaluate and report on competency, participation, and ability of department members for the purpose of evaluating their qualifications for promotion.
- Identify department members who are qualified for in-service training to develop competencies necessary for promotion to company officer, chief officer, and to positions requiring special qualifications.
- Require identified candidates to complete an in-service training program (based on a job analysis for each position) and pass an examination on such training.
- Arrange assignments so that the officer candidates have a variety of duties and experience in various aspects of staff work.
- Arrange assignments so that interested members can pursue courses for academic credit or college degrees at accredited and approved colleges and schools.
- Appoint candidates to appropriate positions when procedures of the department, as well as those of personnel jurisdictions, have been met.

Retirement Procedures: This is the final area of responsibility in personnel management. A compulsory retirement age, consistent with state and local law, should be established. Ideally, a sound retirement system would provide for retirement on the basis of age, years of service, and physical and mental condition of members as related to the members' duties.

Productivity Management

As stated ealier in this chapter, productivity is an area of management responsibility that is difficult to measure or define. Productivity can encompass not only the effectiveness of the fire department, but also the public image of the department. Therefore, management's area of responsibility in obtaining the productivity essential to successful fire department operation is to ensure that a department operates as efficiently and effectively as possible in spite of any limitations in personnel or equipment, or any obstacles that exist while responding to fires in a municipality. Although this might seem to be a difficult task, there are many ways a fire department manager can ensure high productivity, starting with those outlined below.

Records and Reports: An effective and efficient record-keeping system is the basis for all planning, budgeting, and risk analysis programs. The modern fire department needs a computerized record-keeping system that meets both current and anticipated needs. This system must provide the data for evaluating the department's effectiveness in all phases of its operation, including data for development of reports on accomplishments and other performance elements and recommendations on organizational changes and capital investments to local government officials. The same data, of course, can be useful for press releases.

It is important to remember that no matter what type of record-keeping system is implemented, it must satisfy the legal requirements for the particular state or province. Chapter 9 provides examples of typical management records and reports.

Water Procedures: NFPA 1201, *Recommendations for the Organization for Fire Services*, recommends the following with regard to productivity:[8]

1. The fire department should establish minimum fire flow requirements for representative locations in the municipality or fire protection district.

2. Water flows for new construction proposed for the district should be determined and a mechanism for their delivery specified.

3. The fire chief should assign a water officer to maintain regular contact with the managers of public and private water supply systems. This officer must keep the fire department apprised of all water supply sources available for use and recommend new facilities as determined through the municipal risk analysis system.

4. Training must be provided to all personnel in the use of water supply system equipment and facilities, and regularly scheduled drills should

be conducted to develop a working knowledge of the system's capabilities.

NFPA 1201 also specifies that each company in the fire department maintain a water resources map for the respective first-due area, which indicates the following:[9]

- Location and size of mains.
- Areas of insufficient flow and/or pressure.
- Areas requiring special operations to supply water.
- Hydrant locations and capacities.
- Information on location, capacity, and accessibility of auxiliary water supply systems.

A department training program should include information and instructions on available water sources, or field exercises that would educate fire fighters in hydrant locations for fighting potential fires.

Operational Procedures: Recommendations for fire department operational procedures such as duty schedules, standard operating procedures (SOPs), and response procedures, can also be found in NFPA 1201. In order to meet the changing needs of the department, best results will be obtained where these procedures are regularly reviewed, revised, and thoroughly communicated to all department members.

Fire Investigation: The investigation of fires is basic to good fire department management because it identifies factors that can be used to lessen the number and severity of fires in the future. Data from fire investigations help to enhance inspection procedures, public education programs, and fire suppression activities. When recorded in the department's management information system, the data are quickly available and comprehensive.

Training: Training is an integral part of any fire department's operational scheme. It is an invaluable tool for developing the human resources of the department to meet the challenges of providing effective fire protection. A comprehensive fire department training program includes at least the following topics in which competency, knowledge, and skill are covered:

- Entry-level recruit training.
- Fire prevention.
- Tactical operations.
- Maintenance procedures.
- Inspection procedures.
- Prefire planning.
- Fire cause determination.
- First-level supervisory training.
- Instructor training.
- Incident command procedures.
- Company management.

Additional guidance for training is available from various NFPA professional qualifications standards (see Chapter 14).

Communications: Communications for a fire department involves not only emergency calls from the public, but also *en route* and fireground communications among fire department personnel, alarm and signaling systems from individual properties, and street box alarm signals. Regular testing and inspection of all means of communications systems can ensure adequate response time for effective fireground activity (see Chapter 11 for a more detailed discussion of this topic).

Equipment and Buildings: Fire department managers are considered to be responsible for evaluating and upgrading department facilities, apparatus, and personnel equipment, in order to ensure good performance and safety on the job. (See Chapter 11 for an explanation of management's responsibility in assessing and providing adequate facilities and equipment for effective department operation.)

Public Relations: Fire departments must devote both time and talent to promoting and maintaining a public awareness of the benefits obtained from expenditures on fire protection in the community. As a public agency supported by public funds, the fire department needs public support. The public's understanding and cooperation can enhance fire department programs and enable the department to perform effectively within the political environment of a particular community. Public information and community relations programs are, therefore, an important management activity.

Two main areas of responsibility exist in a good public information program: 1) promoting public awareness of the fire department, and 2) promoting public understanding of fire. An effective public relations program sets up procedures to keep the public informed of department operations. Important developments and newsworthy events should be transmitted regularly to the public through newspaper releases and other media. To gain maximum readership, information should be delivered in a lively and informative manner, geared to the target audience in the community.

Community relations is a year-round activity, and the department's efforts will bring the best results if they are targeted to the public's actual needs. For example, the Newark, New Jersey, Fire Department has a community relations division with a community firesafety center to meet the firesafety needs of the neighborhoods. Their public firesafety educational programs are available for all age groups. Interested business people receive fire training sessions designed for their specific organization. Code consultation is available through a staff member. The financial support for this center comes from both budgeted funds and donations from the business community.

Public Firesafety Education: An emerging area of great importance is the development of truly effective public firesafety education programs. Citizens do not know enough about how to live in a firesafe manner or how to act appropriately in case of fire. By providing continuing educational messages in various ways, the knowledge level can be raised. Where these programs have been used, there have been fewer fires, less injury to people, and less damage to property. Public firesafety education differs from community relations because it goes beyond making people aware of fire department activities; it arms them with ways to prevent fires, save lives, and minimize damage. Firesafety education is discussed more thoroughly in Chapter 8.

Administrative Management

To be efficient, an organization must delegate various roles and individual responsibilities to ensure a proper division of labor. This requires a knowledge of a member's relationship with the department and with its management. In the same way that industry or business managers have assistant managers or department heads to aid them in their decision-making and leadership techniques, fire chiefs are assisted by officers and aides in making decisions for fire departments. The fire chief of a fire department usually is assisted by three classifications of personnel: 1) chief officers, 2) chiefs' aides, and 3) company officers. Each of these has an important role to play in the efficient operation of a fire department.

Chief Officers

At least one deputy chief is needed in all fire departments who is responsible in the absence of the chief officer and who assists in overall operational command at fires. In some small, paid fire departments, the deputy chief is in command of one of the regular work shifts, while platoon captains oversee the other work shifts, thus performing dual roles as company officers and duty-shift commanders. Other departments designate the platoon chief to be in charge of each duty shift, supervising the various fire companies through their officers, and responding from a command car to all alarms for structural fires and other working fires. In addition, the platoon chief also is in charge of operations and has the authority to call off-shift help when needed, or to request additional mutual aid assistance. A senior platoon chief or deputy chief would be in charge of a department in the absence of the fire chief, unless there is a higher-ranking administrative deputy chief designated for this responsibility.

Chiefs' Aides

One of the most important positions for fire department efficiency is that of chiefs' aides or assistants. Aides are experienced officers or fire fighters who are assigned to work directly as assistants to various chief officers rather than as members of a company team. Aides are administrative assistants in the operation of the command. Generally, aides operate the command car, handle and channel most fireground radio communications with the alarm center, and assist the chief in numerous other ways, including helping to assess a fire and placing fire companies as determined by the chief. The aide is essential to efficient management and operations because the chief officers they work for must prepare hundreds of fire, personnel, and inspection reports while also answering alarms and supervising the administration of companies in their districts.

Company Officers

Every fire company or similar fire fighting unit should be under the supervision of a qualified company officer when in quarters, when responding to alarms, or when making in-service inspections. In many fire departments company officers hold the rank of fire captain, and there is a fire captain assigned to each duty shift of each fire company. The captains also are used as relief chiefs when one or more of the chiefs on the duty platoon is absent, and as station commander and coordinator of operations in the absence of a chief officer.

Other departments have a number of lieutenants reporting to a captain, who is responsible for overall company performance. Some fire departments also have a rank of sergeant for fire officers. Sergeants are officers who are in charge of work shifts in their assigned companies. While sergeants often function as lieutenants by doing the work of lieutenants, they rank below lieutenants in the chain of command, both in quarters and on the fireground.

Role of Fire Service Officers in Management by Objectives Programs

Chapter 5 detailed the goals and stages in a Management by Objectives (MBO) program. In this chapter the roles of the chief, the intermediate-level officers, and the company officers in a successful MBO program are discussed. This discussion forms the basis of the detailed presentation of fire service management activities in the remainder of the text.

The Chief

First and foremost, the chief of a fire department (Figure 6.4) provides direction for the members of the department and for the operation of each unit. This means that the chief should, in conjunction with the community administrators, determine the long-range goals for the activities of the department. In order to do this, the chief must have the ability to foresee the operational future of the department by preparing for the problems and the needs that could occur in years to come. In this way the entire department gradually can take the necessary steps and lay the foundation for needed changes. For example, a new fire station might take years to build after the department recognizes a need for

FIGURE 6.4 *Fire Chief Lowell F. Jones runs the multi-million-dollar fire department in Newark, New Jersey.* (Courtesy of Harry Carter)

it. Or, a department might have to wait three to six years before large pieces of apparatus are delivered. The chief, then, should be able to plan for these needs and be able to cope with deficiencies in the existing facilities or equipment in order to ensure stable operations.

Setting Goals: Obviously, long-range planning is not the only thing a chief has to do. Long-range plans need strategic and operational goals at all department levels to support them. To achieve the desired results, the chief should guide and lead the department members to establishing and achieving these goals.

An example is constructing a new fire station, staffing it, and equipping it with apparatus. During the year when approval is sought for the new station, the chief would obtain proposals from consultants to determine where the new station should be located. A series of goals would be needed at the chief's level and at lower levels to acquaint the community with the reasons for building another station and the benefits for the community. Such goals might involve only a few officers, or they might lead to involvement of all companies. Members could conduct fire station tours, maintain contact with the community through the news media, or direct education efforts to neighbors, friends, and acquaintances. In later years, goals involving decisions about specific pieces of apparatus and station equipment would be needed.

Using Linking Elements: The chief's role in planning, organizing, and implementing through the goal-setting process requires familiarity and use of the Linking Elements concept discussed in Chapters 4 and 5 (see Figure 4.1). It is the chief's role to ensure coordination and cooperation between the different divisions in the department, particularly if there are staff divisions that are concerned with matters affecting maintenance, equipment decisions, and so on.

Coordinating rules for the organization is important, especially when they pertain to the maintenance and use of equipment and apparatus. These rules should be reviewed from time to time to ensure that they still are appropriate for the department's needs and its members. The chief should take an active role in ensuring that such a review takes place from time to time, that any recommended rule changes are approved or revised, and that all rules are observed.

The chief should also be concerned with the total development of the department's human resources. The chief's role is to set policy with respect to training and to help the various units develop their training goals. The training should be done to ensure that each unit keeps abreast of the changes and developments in technology. This role is also involved in apparatus and station house maintenance and equipment usage.

If apparatus, facilities, and equipment are involved in long-range plans, there might be ways to provide tangible rewards (pay) to staff members who spend time planning and organizing such purchases. However, hidden tangible rewards, such as allocating responsibilities for equipment, exist among different fire stations and companies. New apparatus should be assigned to the members of a department, and decisions involving re-equipping or obtaining new equipment should be shared. The assignment and procurement of these materials can have a significant impact not only on an individual's tangible needs, but also on the morale of all personnel involved. The motivational climate in a department will be affected by the way decisions are made and by the image or pride that is evoked from obtaining new equipment or a new building.

Intermediate-Level Officers

Deputy chiefs, battalion chiefs, and officers in staff positions, such as those in bureaus concerned with buildings or apparatus, have important roles in helping a department achieve its goals. These intermediate-level officers should help provide direction and recommendations, and should perform their functions competently in order for a department to achieve the highest possible level of performance. This means that all deputy and battalion chiefs who are involved with the chief in all major aspects of a building program or in the purchase of apparatus in their respective units should also apply the Linking Elements concept to their decisions and leadership techniques (see Chapter 4). Not only should these officers be involved in some of the goals of the department, but they should also be involved in coordinating and providing psychological satisfaction.

Intermediate-level officers are of utmost importance to the chief's overall decisions. The chief can use these specialists for training sessions to acquaint officers and fire fighters with the facts and respective advantages and disadvantages of equipment that might be considered. Officers and fire fighters would thus be better prepared to participate in the formation of decisions. The positive results from sharing information include greater exchange of ideas between staff and line officers, better decisions because of the participation from more fully informed staff members, and greater personal satisfaction from participating in the decision-making process.

Company Officers

Company officers have the task of translating some of the strategic and operational goals into action steps. This applies not only to the operational goals of the specific aspects of the equipment and maintenance decisions, but also to the training and development goals. The specialists in the staff departments, the training officer, and knowledgable representatives of the equipment manufacturers can be brought in to help increase the knowledge level of a company's members so that they can gain maximum benefit from new equipment, supplies, and techniques. At the same time, the company officer has major responsibilities for helping fire fighters gain psychological rewards from their work on maintenance, housekeeping, etc., and in the use and purchase of equipment and supplies. This may seem to be a difficult task, but opportunities for providing social satisfaction and higher esteem are widespread when allocating work assignments that are seen as desirable, in giving recognition through appropriate participation in decisions, and in giving the general public and special groups opportunities to inspect the station and equipment during Fire Prevention Week or at other times.

Officer Management of a Goals Program

Every fire department needs to accomplish multiple goals during any given period and, from period to period, the goals change. To outline a comprehensive set of strategic and operational goals that could have wide application is impossible. However, a hypothetical list of goals with their appropriate organizational-level goals should help in detailing officer roles in MBO programs.

- **Examples of Department Mission Statements**
    1. Locate sufficient stations to provide the best possible protection of life and to minimize damage to property.
    2. Provide the necessary apparatus and equipment for fire fighters to carry out their responsibilities in the protection of life and property.
    3. Minimize cost to taxpayers.

- **Examples of Chiefs' Strategic Goals**
    1. Establish and achieve apparatus and equipment performance goals.
    2. Establish and achieve goals related to new apparatus and to location and structure of fire stations.
    3. Establish and achieve public information goals on need for apparatus or equipment.
    4. Establish and achieve stringent, but realistic, budgets.
    5. Establish procedures to assess community impact upon fire protection requirements.

- **Examples of Station Strategic Goals (for officer in charge of station)**
    1. Establish and achieve goals related to adapting of apparatus and equipment to the district's needs.
    2. Establish and achieve goals related to reducing turnout time.
    3. Establish and achieve building maintenance goals.
    4. Establish and achieve goals relating to greater efficiency in attack preparation.

- **Examples of Chiefs' Operational Goals**
    1. Ensure that tests to evaluate alternative hose loadings and breathing apparatus mountings are completed by (date).
    2. Obtain agreement of department officers to request new apparatus by (date).
    3. Arrange to publish three articles on firesafety in local newspapers before Fire Prevention Week.
    4. Achieve agreement with municipal manager on department budgetary needs by the end of next month.
    5. Ensure that a report on the impact of the proposed new hospital on department fire protection capability is submitted by (date).

- **Examples of Station Operational Goals (for officer in charge of station)**
    1. Analyze available breathing equipment and recommend specifications by (date).
    2. Obtain agreement to reduce turnout time.
    3. Without reducing cleanliness or building operation efficiency, reduce building housekeeping and maintenance time by 10 percent by (date).
    4. Obtain data and prepare specific recommendations on changes in the layout of the crew's quarters by (date).

- **Examples of Company Officer Operational Goals**
    1. Finish three time study tests of experimental hose layout changes by (date).
    2. Reduce turnout time by 20 seconds before (date).
    3. Ensure that fire fighter Smith thoroughly understands revised prefire planning symbols by (date).
    4. Take a course in advanced fire tactics and obtain a grade of B or better by (date).

- **Examples of Company Officer Action Steps**
  1. Write and submit report on time study tests by (date).
  2. Meet with each company member individually by (date) for suggestions on changes in quarters.
  3. Have fire fighter Smith study prefire planning symbols on Wednesday afternoon. Prepare an exam, and set up another study session if Smith does not score at least 80 percent on the test.
  4. Register for an advanced fire tactics class at an accredited college on (date).

Officers rarely write out a complete set of goals and action steps, except possibly when using a goals program for the first time. Usually, only two or three goals are in writing and only important action steps are noted on a calendar or in a notebook. If working with goals is to be a way of life, the mechanical aspects must be informal and the paperwork minimal.

In summary, the main topics discussed in this chapter—organizational components of a fire department, areas of management responsibility, administrative management, and roles of fire service officers in MBO programs—are intended to be an overview and serve as the basis for the remaining chapters of this text. The subjects dealt with in this chapter will be discussed in greater detail in Chapters 7 through 14. To understand the uniqueness of the management functions of the fire service, it is also important to keep in mind the organizational principles of management and the development of various management concepts discussed in Chapters 1 through 5.

ACTIVITIES

1. In what ways have the traditional objectives of a fire department been revised and expanded?
2. What are the primary purposes of a fire department?
3. Briefly explain the external and the internal structure of a fire department. How is each structural form important to the overall organizational structure of a fire department?
4. Why is productivity management difficult to define? In what ways can a fire department ensure high productivity?
5. Identify the management responsibilities that would be involved in each item in the following list of managerial tasks:
   (a) Procuring a new pumper.
   (b) Replacing an existing fire station.
   (c) Retiring a fire officer.
   (d) Forming a budget.
   (e) Ensuring adequate water supplies.
   (f) Training a member of the department.

6. What are the roles of chief officers? Of chiefs' aides? Of company officers?

7. Using examples of your own, describe how a department chief could include the entire department in setting goals.

8. (a) How is the Linking Elements concept used in the chief's goal-setting process for long-range goals?
    (b) How can intermediate-level officers and company officers provide satisfaction for some of the linking elements?

9. You are the chief of a fire department in a rapidly expanding community. The growth of your community has necessitated that your department increase its personnel and facilities. Using what you have learned about areas of management responsibility, briefly outline what you would do to ensure a high level of efficiency as each of the following changes is made in your department.
    (a) Adding ten new members to your department.
    (b) Needing two new pieces of fire fighting apparatus.
    (c) Needing a revised budget that would include new members and new expenses.

REFERENCES

[1]Cote, A. E., ed., *Fire Protection Handbook*, 16th edition, National Fire Protection Association, Quincy, MA, 1986, p. 15-3.

[2]Cote, A. E., ed., *Fire Protection Handbook*, 16th edition, National Fire Protection Association, Quincy, MA, 1986, p. 15-11.

[3]Cote, A. E., ed., *Fire Protection Handbook*, 16th edition, National Fire Protection Association, Quincy, MA, 1986, p. 15-18.

[4]*Uniform Fire Incident Reporting System*, National Fire Protection Association, Quincy, MA, 1977.

[5]NFPA 1201, *Recommendations for the Organization for Fire Services*, National Fire Protection Association, Quincy, MA, 1984, p. 1201-15.

[6]NFPA 1201, *Recommendations for the Organization for Fire Services*, National Fire Protection Association, Quincy, MA, 1984, p. 1201-16.

[7]NFPA 1201, *Recommendations for the Organization for Fire Services*, National Fire Protection Association, Quincy, MA, 1984, p. 1201-17.

[8]NFPA 1201, *Recommendations for the Organization for Fire Services*, National Fire Protection Association, Quincy, MA, 1984, pp. 1201-45, 1201-46.

[9]NFPA 1201, *Recommendations for the Organization for Fire Services*, National Fire Protection Association, Quincy, MA, 1984, p. 1201-46.

7

Fire Prevention Activities — Codes, Operational Tasks, and Inspections

The major part of a fire department's resources — including personnel, equipment, facilities, and support services — is committed to fire suppression efforts. There are, however, additional tasks performed by fire suppression personnel that are not tactical operations, but are equally important. These tasks include fire prevention activities, prefire planning, and training. This chapter addresses the application of management techniques to fire prevention activities, as well as fire prevention efforts through enforcement of codes, inspections, and involvement in related operational tasks.

OBJECTIVES OF FIRE PREVENTION

The *Fire Protection Handbook* describes fire prevention as follows:[1]

> Fire prevention includes all fire service activity that decreases the incidence of uncontrolled fire. Usually, fire prevention methods utilized by the fire service focus on inspection, which includes engineering and code enforcement, public firesafety education, and fire investigation.
>
> Inspection, including enforcement, is the legal means of discovering and correcting deficiencies that pose a threat to life and property from fire. Enforcement is implemented when other methods fail. Education informs and instructs the general public about the dangers of fire and about firesafe behavior. Fire investigation aids fire prevention efforts by indicating problem areas that may require corrective educational efforts or legislation.

Good engineering practices — another fire prevention method — can provide built-in safeguards that help prevent fires from starting and limit the spread of fire should it occur.

The participation of fire suppression personnel in fire prevention activities is as necessary as their participation in tactical operations. Because the majority of the fire department's resources are committed to suppression activities and are systematically distributed throughout the protected area, it is important that these resources also be allocated to fire prevention efforts.

Good fire department objectives can provide the proper approach for involvement in fire prevention activities. Fire suppression personnel can perform routine inspections on a regular basis within their first-due response area, and some of the fire prevention personnel can perform follow-up inspections, enforcement, and special technical inspections. The total involvement of all personnel, particularly those assigned to suppression activities, should not only decrease the incidence of fire, but should also demonstrate maximum utilization of personnel and competent management.

Fire department management is responsible for maintaining highly trained and effective operational units to perform tasks involving both fire suppression and fire prevention. The degree of competency achieved by a department in these areas reflects well upon the abilities of a department's management.

History of Fire Prevention: A Brief Overview

One of the first tasks of the early settlers in the Boston area was to build shelter against the harsh New England winters. Using local materials, they constructed wood houses with thatched roofs similar to the ones they were accustomed to in Europe. The chimneys were made from wood frames covered with mud or clay. Exposure to the elements dried the thatch and washed or blew away the mud or clay that protected the wood frames of the chimney stacks. Such structures invited catastrophe from fire; burning embers, drawn up the chimneys, ignited the roofs and set the houses ablaze.

Early Fire Laws

Recognizing these construction hazards, the town fathers of the Bay Colony outlawed thatched roofs and wood chimneys. A fine of ten shillings (a large sum in those days) was levied on any homeowner who had a chimney fire. This encouraged people to keep their chimneys free from soot and creosote. In effect, the first fire law was thus established and enforced.

As the town of Boston grew in prosperity and size, the need grew for new laws to protect it from the ravages of fire. The laws outlined the joint responsibilities of the homeowner and the authorities for fire protection. These new laws required every homeowner to have a ladder long enough to reach the ridgepole of the roof. They also required that homeowners have in their possession poles with swabs on the ends of them. When soaked in water, these poles were used to help extinguish roof fires.

The modern fire department was most likely started when Boston provided centrally located equipment and supplies to help residents extinguish fires. Attached to the outside of the town meeting house were several ladders and a pole with a hook on it. The purpose of the hook-ended pole was to tear away neighboring structures and thus stop a fire from spreading. The need for a readily available water supply was recognized by the establishment of a cistern, and night patrols were formed to sound alarms.

The town of Boston enacted laws to punish those people who exposed themselves and others to fire risk. No person was allowed to build a fire within "three rods" (49.5 ft) of any building, or in ships tied up at the docks. It was illegal to carry "burning brands" for lighting fires, except in covered containers (there were no matches in those days). The penalty for arson was death.

Thus, several of the important elements of organized fire prevention and control existed in these early days: codes and enforcement for fire prevention, quick alarm, water supply, and readily available implements for control of fire. Despite such precautions, in Boston and other municipalities, conflagrations were commonplace, and it was necessary to enact more laws to govern the construction of buildings and to make provisions for public fire protection. The result was a growing body of rules and regulations concerning fire prevention and control.

The Beginnings of Fire Insurance

In early United States cities, buildings usually were constructed in close proximity to one another, due to inadequate building codes. The year before the great Chicago fire of 1871, Lloyd's, a London insurance company, stopped writing policies in that city because Lloyd's officials were horrified at the haphazard way construction was proceeding. Other insurance companies, too, had difficulty selling policies at the high premiums they had to charge because of the poor construction. Even with these high rates they often suffered great losses when fires spread out of control. As often happens, even today, many of the early fire laws and insurance policies were written as the result of tragedies.

The National Board of Fire Underwriters* realized that the adjustment and standardization of rates was a paper solution to an essentially technical problem. It began to emphasize safe building construction, control of fire hazards, and improvements in both water supplies and fire departments. New, tall buildings constructed of steel and concrete adhered to controlled specifications that helped to limit the risk of fire. These were called Class A buildings.

---

*In 1965, the National Board of Fire Underwriters (organized in 1866) merged with the Association of Casualty and Surety Companies (organized in 1926) and the former American Insurance Association (founded in 1953) to become the American Insurance Association. The basic objectives of the Association are to promote the economic, legislative, and public standing of its participating insurance companies.

Although there were some new Class A steel and concrete structures in the downtown section of San Francisco in 1906, much of the city was still composed of flimsily built fire-prone wood shanties. The National Board of Fire Underwriters was so alarmed by these hazardous conditions that it predicted major disaster ("San Francisco has violated all underwriting traditions and precedents by not burning up"). That same year, because of a devastating earthquake, the city of San Francisco did indeed burn up.

Although the contents of the new buildings were destroyed, the steel and concrete walls, frames, and floors remained intact and could be renovated. After analysis of the fire damage, fire protection engineers realized that further improvements were necessary. For example, glass must be reinforced to prevent shattering and deformation under the intense heat of fire, and auxiliary water towers on roofs would be needed to supplement the regular local water supplies. Furthermore, it was concluded that vertical spaces—especially stairways and elevator shafts in tall buildings—would have to be enclosed in order to stop the vertical spread of fire.

Increasing awareness of the importance of fire prevention brought additional knowledge about the subject. Engineers began to accumulate information about fire hazards in building construction and in manufacturing processes, developing a new science to meet newly perceived needs.

Principles of Fire Prevention

From its studies of the San Francisco disaster and other major fires, the National Board of Fire Underwriters became convinced of the need for more detailed, comprehensive standards and codes relating to the construction, design, and maintenance of buildings. Regulations based on such codes could undoubtedly prevent most fires and reduce losses in the ones that did occur.

Obviously, codes alone are only guidelines. If they are to be meaningful and fulfill the purpose for which they were created, regulations covering their enforcement must be enacted. Thus, it is the responsibility of the fire department and the local authority to identify and order the correction of potential fire hazards. The local government has the power to do this through the enforcement of state regulations in support of codes where they exist and through the enactment of its own ordinances. The fire department, for its part, must see to the enforcement of these regulations and ordinances. If there have been changes within the district that make present codes inadequate, such as the development of mobile or trailer parks, it is the fire department's responsibility to voice the need for modification and to help develop new codes and regulations where they are needed. To be effective, regulations must be supported with inspections. This means that buildings in which large numbers of people work, live, or meet must be inspected to ensure that they are free from any known hazards and that they do indeed conform to the standards and codes specified in the regulations and ordinances.

Identification alone, however, does not always bring compliance. The owner of a building can refuse to remove the fire hazards or to renovate a building so that it conforms to the standards. To eliminate these possibilities, firesafety ordinances—regulations built around a model fire code—must not only outline inspection procedures, but they must also be capable of enforcement and carry penalties for violators. Violators can be fined, certificates of occupancy can be withheld, or permits for specific businesses or manufacturing processes withheld until compliance with the codes is obtained.

In the United States the full value of fire prevention was not realized until fire departments and agencies began to compile meaningful information concerning the causes and circumstances of fires. Such information caused the more progressive departments to initiate more effective fire prevention efforts in addition to maintaining their fire fighting forces. The results of such efforts are being more clearly defined every year. In 1973, fire prevention received its greatest endorsement when the National Commission of Fire Prevention and Control reported on the fire problem in America. Throughout the report, top priority was given to the necessity for increased fire prevention activities in reducing fire loss.

Organization for Fire Prevention

In Canada there are provincial fire commissioners for the various provinces and a Dominion Fire Commission. In the United States, although certain branches of the federal government conduct research and gather data concerning fire problems, no national governmental agency has been created to maintain a fire fighting or fire prevention force. Most states have offices at the state level to oversee certain phases of fire prevention. The chief administrator at the state level usually is called the state fire marshal.

State Fire Marshal

The makeup of state fire marshal offices differs from state to state. Most receive their authority from the state legislature and are answerable to the governor, a high state officer, or a commission created for that purpose. In some states the fire marshal's office is a division of the state insurance department, state police, state building department, state commerce division, or some other state agency. Few are organized as separate agencies.

State or provincial agencies normally function in those areas that go beyond the scope of the municipal, county, or fire district organizations. Local fire protection organizations sometimes are granted the authority to act as agents for the state in stipulated areas of inspection, enforcement, and investigation.

Chief of Fire Prevention or Local Fire Marshal

Various local, state, and fire district regulations delegate the responsibility and authority of fire prevention to the fire chief or fire department head. Provision is then made for that person to delegate this authority to an individual or division, depending on the size of the department. The individual or head of the division should be a high-ranking chief officer and should also function as a staff officer to the fire chief. This division of the fire service usually is called the fire prevention bureau, and its top officer is chief of fire prevention or local fire marshal. Where size permits, a bureau is divided into subdepartments of inspections, investigations, and public education. These subdepartments are then headed by subordinate chiefs.

Fire Inspector or Fire Prevention Officer

The positions of fire inspector and fire prevention officer usually have different meanings in different departments. Sometimes the two titles are the same and denote the position responsible for conducting fire inspections assigned to the fire prevention bureau. In bureaus not large enough for multiple subdepartments, the fire inspector is also responsible for conducting fire investigations and performing public education duties. Consult NFPA 1031[2] for complete details about fire inspector qualifications.

Fire Protection Engineer

The complexity and magnitude of fire protection problems make the services of fire protection engineers very desirable. Although most of their work is done on a consulting basis, some public fire protection agencies have recognized the need for full-time staff engineers.

Delegating Responsibilities

How does a department organize itself to carry out all of its fire prevention tasks and concerns? In a fire department in a large city these functions might be separated and assigned to two or more distinct sections, with, for example, responsibilities for fire prevention and education in one and inspection, enforcement, and investigations in the other. Medium-sized departments might concentrate all of the fire prevention duties into one centralized bureau.

In small departments the chief might conduct inspections with the assistance of fire fighters who are specially interested in this facet of fire department work. Generally, fire prevention personnel do not work in shifts. However, in every department, whatever its size, there should always be at least one person on call to carry out immediate investigations of specified fires that might have resulted in high loss of life or severe property damage, or that are considered suspicious in origin.

A fire fighter who has assumed fire prevention duties might receive compensation for the extra training. The fire fighter's additional responsibilities lead to greater competence and understanding of fire department activities. In addition, this broader perspective enhances the likelihood of promotion when opportunities arise.

Alternative Organizational Patterns

Instead of keeping fire prevention solely as a staff function, some departments have modified their organizational framework by assigning fire prevention inspectors to shifts. Following are some of the advantages to this method:

1. Someone with special knowledge about specific buildings and their hazards is always on hand to provide additional information to fire fighters.
2. An immediate investigation into the cause of a fire can proceed. However, a major disadvantage to shift assignments is that very few technical inspections can be conducted at night. The result of this disadvantage is, of course, lower productivity.

Volunteer Departments

Volunteer departments can organize themselves to carry out fire prevention activities in various ways. Following are a few possibilities:

1. Offer special training for those fire fighters who wish to assume fire prevention duties.
2. Hire paid staff on a full- or part-time basis. Sometimes retired fire department personnel can be hired for these positions.
3. The chief or deputy chief can assume fire prevention duties, sometimes in rotation.

National Standards and Codes

Fire prevention programs and activities are designed to prevent fires and loss of life, and to minimize damage to property by ensuring compliance with fire codes. Fire department management is directly involved in the supervision of these programs and activities.

Regulations relating to firesafety are determined and subsequently enforced by the different levels of government. Although some of these functions overlap, federal and state laws generally govern those areas that cannot be regulated at the local level.

Role of the Federal Government

Under the United States Constitution, the legal authority of the federal government in fire matters is limited to those of an interstate or international character. Thus, principal items covered by federal law are mainly related to transportation. These items include the control of the shipment of hazardous substances by road or rail across state lines, and the enactment and enforcement of fire protection regulations aboard planes and ships. National parks and forests are under the jurisdiction of the Fire Service Division of the U.S. Department of Agriculture, which oversees the maintenance and utilization of fire prevention programs.

The federal government also makes a contribution to research on fire prevention and protection through its various agencies. A wide range of fire research is conducted by the Center for Fire Research of the National Bureau of Standards, which is under the Department of Commerce. The United States Fire Administration of the Federal Emergency Management Agency (FEMA) conducts programs in such areas as public fire education, arson, and fire data analysis. Also under the FEMA umbrella is the National Fire Academy, located in Emmitsburg, Maryland, where a wide range of resident and field programs is available to members of the fire service.

However, it is the nongovernmental organizations that have the greatest influence on the development of knowledge and standards relating to fire prevention. The most influential organization in the United States is the National Fire Protection Association.

National Fire Protection Association (NFPA)

The National Fire Protection Association, which is based in Quincy, Massachusetts, was organized in 1896 "to promote the science and improve the methods of fire protection and prevention, to obtain and circulate information on these subjects, and to secure the cooperation of its members in establishing proper safeguards against loss of life and property by fire." The NFPA was originally organized by 18 men drawn primarily from the insurance industry. Now the majority of members come from commerce, industry, and the fire service.

One of NFPA's most important functions concerns the development of basic firesafety standards for processes, materials, and operations that involve a degree of fire hazard. Although these standards often are adopted and incorporated into state and local ordinances, the NFPA considers its status to be solely advisory. The standards and codes are published in reference volumes, and cover a wide range of subjects—including flammable liquids and gases, electricity, building construction, and the installation of sprinkler systems. Two of the better-known codes are the *National Electrical Code®* and the *Life Safety Code®*. The codes are revised periodically to encompass updated construction techniques, processes, materials, and uses.

Preparation of NFPA Standards: NFPA technical committees are charged with providing reasonable standards for firesafety without prohibitive expense, interference with established processes and methods, or undue inconvenience. Each committee is a balanced working group made up of all the interests concerned with a particular standard. In general, committees include appropriate manufacturers, users, installers and maintainers, labor and insurance representatives, researchers and testers, enforcing authorities, consumers, and special experts.

Adoption of NFPA Standards: The Association makes every effort to give consideration to all individuals or groups interested in any standard, and such individuals or groups are given opportunities to present their views to the appropriate committee. Public interests always receive first consideration by all of the committees.

When a committee has compiled a proposed standard or a revision to an existing standard, such recommendations are distributed to interested members of the Association, affected industries, and the technical press at annual meetings of the Association. The committee's report is then officially acted on at the next annual meeting of the Association. If approved at the annual meeting, the proposed or revised standard is adopted. Annual meetings are open to the general public and afford additional opportunities for individuals to present their views.

American Insurance Association (AIA)

A series of studies conducted by the American Insurance Association isolated the factors that contributed to the major fires in United States cities in the late 1800s and early 1900s. The AIA used this information and the early NFPA standards to establish levels of adequacy for fire prevention in cities. AIA activities have brought about the development of the *National Building Code*, a model code that has been adopted by many municipalities across the United States. The AIA has also suggested a fire prevention code for cities. Both the *National Building Code* and the *AIA Fire Prevention Code* are based largely on NFPA standards as well as on recommendations relating to various problems encountered by industries in their manufacturing processes.

Underwriters Laboratories

At one time the AIA also sponsored Underwriters Laboratories (UL), a testing laboratory originally organized to investigate electrical hazards. UL is now a separate organization supported by fees from manufacturers who want their products tested and approved in follow-up inspections. The official UL label, which certifies compliance with nationally recognized safety standards, can be issued only after these second-stage follow-up inspections are made.

UL's current corporate membership is drawn from the following categories: consumer interest groups, public safety bodies or agencies (responsible primarily for enforcement in the field of public safety), governmental bodies or agencies, the insurance industry, safety experts, standardization experts, public utilities, educators, and corporations (usually at the officer level). UL is managed by a Board of Trustees drawn from the aforementioned categories, plus an additional "at large" position. Only one officer of the corporation is included on its Board of Trustees.

Factory Mutual Research Corporation

The Engineering Division of the Factory Mutual Research Corporation (FM) also maintains laboratories for testing building materials and fire equipment and, like UL, issues labels to indicate that certain products have passed its tests. The FM research staff includes standards, research, and approvals groups.

The standards group is made up of engineers in many fields who develop information and recommendations based on research and loss experience, and also are available to offer advice to Factory Mutual members on specific loss prevention matters.

The research group consists of two groups of scientists: one group is a basic research group whose objective is to secure information pertaining to the initial phases of fire, its detection, and growth patterns. The theories that they develop are expected to lead to new methods of loss prevention and control. The other group, an applied research group, is concerned with improvement in effectiveness of fire protection systems, fire modeling studies, rack storage and plastics storage fire tests, new suppression agents and systems, ignition and flammability of materials, and design and cost evaluation of effective fire protection systems.

The approvals group subjects equipment and materials to stringent tests to determine that devices submitted by manufacturers will operate dependably, and that materials have an acceptable low flammability rating when subjected to fire tests. An approval guide is issued annually.

Other Groups

There are also a number of other technical groups that prepare standards for specific manufacturing processes or for potential fire risks. Just as the AIA uses the NFPA standards to prepare its own codes and grading schedules, these groups, which represent various occupancies or industries with fire protection interests, prepare even more stringent codes, using NFPA and other standards as a base. Their purpose is to obtain lower insurance rates for those industries that comply with stricter requirements and allow regular inspections by the group's inspectors.

State Regulatory Offices

The principal instrument for implementing regulatory authority for fire laws at the state level is often the state fire marshal's office. Almost all states have a state fire marshal's office, and in most states enabling legislation gives the fire marshal the authority to make regulations covering various hazards and, in many cases, such regulations have the effect of law. The state fire marshal's authority extends to the following general areas:

1. Prevention of fires.
2. Storage, sale, and use of combustibles and explosives.
3. Installation and maintenance of automatic alarms and sprinkler systems.

4. Construction, maintenance, and regulation of fire escapes.

5. Means and adequacy of exits in case of fire in public places or buildings where many people live, work, or congregate (such as schools, hospitals, and large industrial complexes).

6. Suppression of arson and the investigation of the cause, origin, and circumstances of fire incidents.

In most states the fire marshal has the legal power to draw up rules and regulations covering various fire hazards. In many cases these rules and regulations have the force of law. The precise responsibilities and organization of the fire marshal's office vary from state to state. The fire marshal's office is concerned with the maintenance of fire records, the investigation of suspected arson, and all matters related to fire. The office is sometimes associated with the state insurance department. In those states that do not have a fire marshal's office, responsibilities are divided among other state agencies, such as the Attorney General's office and the State Police.

Although the state fire marshal's office has legal authority for fire prevention, much of this power is delegated to the local fire departments and local government. Fire departments are responsible for inspecting private properties to determine if there are fire hazards or code violations, and local authorities are given the power through enabling acts to adopt their own regulations related to fire prevention.

Local Codes and Ordinances

Local codes and ordinances are of greatest interest for fire fighters and officers because many of the standards and codes set up by state and private organizations also are incorporated in the local codes and ordinances. Some states have adopted uniform codes in areas such as building construction, and such uniform codes might supersede any existing local ordinance.

Laws for local firesafety generally fall into two categories: 1) those related to buildings, and 2) those related to hazardous materials, processes, and machinery that might be used in buildings.

Local planners frequently disagree as to what should go into a building code and what should go into a fire code. In general, requirements relating to construction go into the building code and are enforced by the building inspector and the building inspector's department. The requirements relating to hazardous materials, hazardous processes, and the safe operation of machinery or equipment are the responsibility of the fire department and thus are covered by the fire code. Following is a general outline of what is usually covered under the building code, and what is covered under the fire prevention code:[3]

Most municipal building codes cover, in general, the following items: (1) administration, which spells out the powers and duties of the building official; (2) classification of buildings by occupancy; (3) establishment of fire limits or fire zones; (4) establishment of height and area limits; (5) establishment of restrictions as to type of construction and as to use of buildings; (6) special occupancy provisions which stipulate special construction requirements for various occupancies such as theaters, piers and wharves, garages, etc.; (7) requirements for light and ventilation; (8) exit requirements; (9) materials, loads, and stresses; (10) construction requirements; (11) precautions during building construction; (12) requirements for fire resistance, including materials, protection of structural members, fire walls, partitions, enclosure of stairs and and shafts, roof structures, and roof coverings; (13) chimneys and heating appliances; (14) elevators; (15) plumbing; (16) electrical installations; (17) gas piping and appliances; (18) signs and billboards; [and] (19) fire extinguishing equipment.

The principal provisions usually found in two national fire prevention codes cover the following: (1) administration, which includes the organization of the bureau of fire prevention and defines its powers and duties; (2) explosives, ammunition, and blasting agents; (3) flammable and combustible liquids; (4) liquefied petroleum gases and compressed gases; (5) lumberyards and woodworking plants; (6) dry cleaning establishments; (7) garages; (8) application of flammable finishes; (9) cellulose nitrate plastics (pryoxylin); (10) cellulose nitrate motion picture film; (11) combustible metals; (12) fireworks; (13) fumigation and thermal insecticidal fogging; (14) fruit-ripening processes; (15) combustible fibers; (16) hazardous chemicals; (17) hazardous occupancies; (18) maintenance of fire equipment; (19) maintenance of exit ways; (20) oil burning equipment; (21) welding and cutting; (22) dust explosion prevention; (23) bowling establishments; (24) automobile tire rebuilding plants; (25) automobile wrecking yards, junk yards, and waste material handling plants; (26) manufacture of organic coatings; (27) ovens and furnaces; (28) tents; and (29) general precautions against fire.

Although there might seem to be some overlap in the administration of these requirements, close scrutiny will show that the inclusion of the original fire prevention item (for example, duct, vent, exit, or sprinkler system) should be supervised by the building department, but the determination of its continuing adequacy should be the responsibility of the fire department.

The NFPA provides standards for both the building code and the fire prevention code. In spite of the establishment of these standards, confusion and rivalry sometimes exist between the departments of building and fire prevention as to who is responsible for inspecting and enforcing which safety provisions. An article from the periodical *Fire Command!* points to this controversy:[4]

> Building code hearings find little or no effective input from fire officials, yet when a major fire occurs, the same fire officials are found on the front page of the local newspaper condemning the building officials. All too often, the fire department leaves code writing and enforcement (plan review, construction inspections, etc.) to a building official who does not have the background to evaluate and correct any fire code deficiencies. The fire experts are found sitting in the station waiting for the code deficiencies to provide their work load. The initial questions for each fire official are:

1. Are you aware of the intent of your local code?
2. Did a fire official provide input when the code was written?
3. Is your code compatible with local needs?

One might add to this: What can be done to change or modify an inadequate code?

Code Modification

In an effort to lessen some of the confusion about enforcement of fire codes, some states depend on model building codes, such as: 1) the *Basic Building Code* of the Building Officials and Code Administrators International, Inc. (BOCA); 2) the *Uniform Building Code* of the International Conference of Building Officials; and 3) the *Standard Building Code* of the Southern Building Code Congress. Each of these model building codes has an accompanying fire prevention code. The states that have adopted one of the model building codes might recommend that local governments also adopt its companion fire prevention code to provide a uniform functional separation of the building and fire departments. Because the codes are to be adopted in their entirety, the duties of each department are clarified in relation to the other.

Wherever problems exist, they usually can be lessened by a frank approach and open communication. When high-level officials from both departments meet on a continuing basis to discuss their responsibilities and mutual concerns, problems about conflicting jurisdiction can be reduced.

In some European countries this problem has already been eliminated. In Germany, for example, the question of overlap has been resolved by making fire department officials responsible for both building and fire codes. Some local governments in the United States have also elected to assign fire fighters to the job of inspecting for building and fire code violations at the same time.

Operational Tasks and Concerns of Fire Prevention

Some of the operational tasks and concerns directly related to effective fire prevention are: 1) plans review and prefire plans, 2) inspections, 3) public education, 4) seasonal activities, 5) special-interest groups, 6) fire prevention codes, 7) public information, 8) consultation, 9) records and reports, 10) photography, 11) fire ignition sequence investigation, 12) legal aspects, and 13) water supply. The following briefly introduces these operational tasks and concerns as they relate to the fire service. Chapter 9 presents more detailed information on their applicability in loss prevention programs.

Plans Review and Prefire Plans

The review of construction plans for various classes of buildings is now legally mandatory in many localities. It provides the fire service with the best opportunity to see that fire protection standards are met before construction begins. Plans review must be followed up with on-site inspections to ensure that the fire protection provided for in the plan is not overlooked or compromised in construction.

Prefire plans include detailed layouts of properties (except for one- and two-family dwellings) in the fire district showing entrances, exits, stairs, fire walls, standpipes, areas covered by sprinkler systems, and the information pertinent to a fire attack. Sometimes outlines for attack preparation, such as the positioning of apparatus and initial hose layouts, are also shown. Prefire plans are drawn up by fire fighters and their company officers. After they have been approved by the department, the prefire plans usually are carried on the apparatus so that they can be referred to on the way to a fire. Prefire plans can also serve as a basis for simulation in fire company training drills. Prefire plans and inspections overlap in two areas: 1) they familiarize personnel with buildings where other than routine fires could occur, and 2) prefire plan surveys can sometimes uncover code violations, thus helping to support inspection work. Prefire planning is covered in detail in Chapter 9.

Inspections

Local fire codes call for the inspection of several categories of hazards within the district served by a fire department. The frequency of inspections generally depends on the type of occupancy, which are listed below.

1. One- and two-family dwellings (usually are not inspected except on request of owner/occupant).
2. Three- or more family dwellings.
3. Commercial office buildings.
4. Industrial (high, moderate, and low hazard).
5. Mercantile (high, moderate, and low hazard).
6. Public assembly complexes.
7. Institutions.

Institutions, places of public assembly, and high-hazard mercantile and industrial plants frequently are designated as "target properties" for inspections. See "Objectives of Inspections" later in this chapter for further information.

There are two kinds of inspections: 1) company (regular) and 2) technical. Fire fighters perform company inspections (or field inspections as they sometimes are called). These are routine inspections that check for compliance with the general regulations concerning access to standpipes and sprinkler valves, adequacy of fire extinguishers, lack of obstructions to emergency evacuation exits, and for the more obvious safety problems such as multiple connections from electrical outlets (circuit overloads). Records of each building are maintained. Where code violations are found, violation notices are issued and follow-up visits are made to ensure that deficiencies are corrected.

Because the complexities of many modern industrial processes and operations are beyond the scope of standard fire department training, a cadre of specially trained fire prevention inspectors is needed to perform technical inspections. Detailed inspections ensure that hazardous materials and processes are subject to definite safety procedures and regulations. Businesses and industries using such materials are required to obtain permits from the fire department and cannot start hazardous activities (or continue them) without such permits. The technical inspections are carried out before a permit is issued or renewed.

Public Education

Educational programs help to obtain the cooperation of the citizens served by the fire department. These programs can include media publicity, flyers, and special informational programs such as slide shows at special group activities and at schools.

Public education is a vital tool in fire prevention. If people are to take the initiative in helping to solve the fire problem, they must be made aware of it. If the fire service fails to provide adequate information and motivation, lack of public concern could result. The intrinsic purpose of the fire service logically makes it the best organization for helping to educate the general public in fire prevention. However, individual organizations also can provide effective campaigns that help to draw attention to particular problems.

Public fire education must be continually updated and upgraded in order to maintain public interest and support. Failure of the educator to be up to date in fire prevention methods can result in the loss of excellent opportunities for communicating vital information to special-interest groups as well as to the general public.

Seasonal Activities

The four seasons of the year present a natural timetable that often is used as the basis for informative public education programs. Two examples of public education programs are Fire Prevention Week (conducted annually in October) and Operation EDITH (Exit Drills in the Home).

The NFPA provides many materials that are used in public education programs. Since the introduction of NFPA's *Learn Not to Burn*® *Curriculum*, in 1979, more than 43,000 U.S. elementary school classrooms have used it. The National Education Association recommends it to elementary schools as another way to protect young people from the ravages of fire.

Special-Interest Groups

In some communities, groups spring up spontaneously or are organized by the Fire Prevention Bureau to provide channels of communication between various segments of the community and the fire department. Special interest groups have information needs similar to those of the general public, but different enough to require individual programs. These groups include educational, industrial, institutional, residential, high-rise dwellers, civic, service, professional, and commercial interests. There are many ways to reach such groups, including public service columns in print media, public service announcements on radio or television, speakers bureaus, or gifts of fire prevention materials to local schools.

Fire Prevention Codes

A fire prevention code that has been adopted into law is essential for any successful fire prevention program. The major objective of any successful code is to provide a reasonable degree of safety to life and property from fire, and, accordingly most well-developed fire prevention recommendations receive unquestioning public acceptance and compliance.

As mentioned earlier, several of the organizations that write model building codes have developed companion fire prevention codes for use in conjunction with the building codes. For example, the National Fire Protection Association has developed NFPA 1, *Fire Prevention Code*,[5] which covers all of the basic information. Some states and local governments have adopted the complete set of NFPA codes, the *National Fire Codes*®. These fire codes often are considered to be the most authoritative fire codes in the United States.

Public Information

At times there is certain information that the general public needs to know immediately, and time does not permit its dissemination by means of regular public education channels. The information could be recognition of a particular fire problem (such as hazardous toys or garments) or a particular need of the fire service, or about a large fire that is in progress and of concern to the public. Some departments have officers on their staffs who serve as public information officers; in the absence of such officers, such information is usually handled by the Fire Prevention Bureau.

Consultation

The general public looks to the public fire service for answers to its fire problems. Because fire prevention covers such a broad area and reaches so many people, consultation services are necessary. Fire prevention officers must be capable of explaining the fine points of fire codes to professionals, such as architects and engineers, who might be dealing with fire codes for the first time when they file their fire plans for review, as well as be able to explain the dangers of playing with matches to children.

Records and Reports

Records are essential for effective fire prevention. They also form the basis for studying trends to develop new programs. The development of the National Fire Incident Reporting System (NFIRS) by the U.S. Fire Administration, in concert with the NFPA, has improved data-gathering capabilities. This system can form the basis of any reporting system. Other records that could be maintained include:

1. Copies of violations, inspections, and follow-ups.
2. Prefire plans — maps and attack practices.
3. Statistical information organized into maps, charts, etc., for use in fire prevention planning.
4. Recommendations dealing with specific problems in certain occupancies or areas, or for decisions about future needs.

Records and reports of fire prevention activities should be clear and concise. Every time an inspector or fire prevention officer visits a site, information about that location should be included in a report. The occupancy file of each building visited should include: a complete history of the building site; building plans; specifications (when possible); permits issued for the use, storage, and handling of various hazardous materials; inspection reports; and fire incidents.

Photography

The inclusion of photographs in records and reports is invaluable. A properly taken and correctly identified photograph is one of the best ways to fully illustrate conditions to a city attorney, an owner of the building, a chief officer, a judge, or members of a jury. Photographs and detailed reports can help eliminate much argument about actual conditions at the time of fire exposure. Photography also is useful for educational purposes, such as training programs. Many fire departments have full-time photographers with complete camera and laboratory facilities.

Fire Ignition Sequence Investigation

Fire departments endeavor to investigate all fires to determine the first ignition sequence. In cases where arson is suspected, appropriate investigative assistance is summoned if it is not available at the local level. Such assistance can come from local, county, or state agencies. Data compiled from investigations are useful in determining future fire prevention strategies.

Most fire departments were organized to provide for the immediate task of fighting fires. Few departments were set up to develop and compile comprehensive, in-depth information on the number of fires occurring by location and occupancy, the fire ignition sequence or causative factors, the time of day or week of occurrence, the room or floor in which the fire occurred, and similar information that is basic to any effective evaluation of a fire incident.

Obviously, fire prevention is one of the major concerns of all fire department personnel. However, a point that has not been as well recognized is that comprehensive investigation of fires, and all the factors influencing or contributing to their ignition sequence or communication, is the very foundation on which fire prevention is built. Without the extensive and detailed information obtained from these factors, it is impossible to develop the most effective regulatory codes, standards, inspection and suppression procedures, and similar actions designed to prevent or control fire.

Legal Aspects

In most instances, each state or province delegates to local officials its police power to regulate persons and properties for the safety of the public. The courts rule on any conflicts that might develop in the interpretation of these regulations.

Accurate determination and reporting of a fire ignition sequence is in the public interest. This public interest is addressed by the broad powers given most fire marshals in rights of entry for fire inspection and investigation, fire marshal's hearings, rights of subpoena of any records or persons who might have information about the fire ignition sequence, etc. These powers have been upheld by most courts of law. Such powers are invaluable in establishing and corroborating ignition sequence of fire, and such authority should be honored when utilized by members of the fire service performing their duties.

Such broad powers generally are not applicable, however, to criminal investigations. For example, because arson is a felony, these rights do not apply to fire investigation after the fire ignition sequence has been established as arson. These powers also can become diffused when a recognized police agency conducts fire ignition sequence investigations in cases where the ignition sequence is not established immediately. For this reason, it is usually advantageous to maintain some distinction between civil actions involving fire ignition sequence and criminal investigations of arson.

Water Supply

The fire department usually is responsible for making recommendations to the local government about the adequacy of water supplies for fire fighting, especially when plans are considered for the development of new industrial, commercial, or residential areas in the community.

Usually, a Fire Prevention Bureau works with a local authority and water company to make surveys that ensure there is sufficient water supply to extinguish fires in the district. In such a review, the size of water mains is examined in relation to the size and population density of buildings, as well as in relation to sprinkler systems and water towers (where they exist). The number, location, and maintenance of hydrants are also checked.

Personnel Assignment and Fire Prevention Priorities

To a certain extent, the personnel assigned to fire prevention duties reflects not only the size of the department, but also the department's financial resources and the degree of priority assigned to fire prevention by the fire chief, local government officials, and taxpayers.

The 1973 report of the National Commission on Fire Prevention and Control recommended that local governments make fire prevention at least equal to suppression in the planning of fire department priorities. However, few departments, if any so far, have committed 50 percent of their resources to this function: It is very difficult to give fire prevention that kind of attention because massive changes would be required in the way fire departments were organized. Many of the jobs that currently are done during the day, such as inspections, checking apparatus, and housekeeping chores would have to be performed at night to free personnel for additional daytime fire prevention activities. Special features would have to be provided to accommodate such changes, and everyone, from the taxpayer to the fire fighter, would have to be willing to accept such an arrangement. Because society generally is unaware of the need to emphasize fire prevention, it is unlikely that such a change will occur in the near future. Currently, several factors hamper the expansion of fire prevention activities.

Barriers to Expansion of Fire Prevention Activities

Inspections make up the bulk of fire prevention activities. If the greater proportion of available personnel was assigned to carry out more inspections during daytime shifts, a fire department might find its night shifts so depleted that it could not respond effectively to some major emergencies. To offset this disadvantage, daytime personnel might be placed in rotating on-call shifts to respond in the case of a serious fire.

In most departments there are not sufficient inspectors assigned to cope effectively with the present workload. Fire fighters conduct company inspections not only to familiarize themselves with the district, but also to enable the department to carry out the required number of inspections per occupancy. The hiring and training of additional personnel would necessitate additional resources at the time when local authorities are looking for ways to trim their budgets. Portions of existing funds would have to be reallocated from fire fighting activities to fire prevention—a highly unlikely step.

Ways to Expand Fire Prevention Activities

Although it might be too difficult to commit a greater percentage of available working hours to fire prevention, some departments could take advantage of the following suggestions:

1. Inspect some restaurants, bars, schools, etc., in the evening
2. Overcome some of the obstacles involved in inspections to produce greater efficiency (discussed in detail later in this chapter).
3. Conduct public education programs to reduce the incidence of fire and the need for any expansion of fire fighting capabilities. Such programs also can help change the attitudes of public and government officials regarding current financial allocations for fire prevention.

Role of the Company Officer in Fire Prevention

Fire prevention activities could, if allowed, take up as much time as all other fire fighting activities combined. This, however, is seldom the case. One important reason that fire prevention activities receive less attention is that many officers and fire fighters find these activities less than satisfying functions in the overall role of fire fighting.

From the viewpoint of the company officer, fire prevention can provide an opportunity to put meaning and greater job satisfaction into an important segment of a company's work — especially for those companies that, unlike most metropolitan companies, are not called upon to fight fires very frequently. Fire prevention activities can also present an opportunity for officers to stimulate a kind of job enthusiasm that can spread to other activities as well. To do this is not easy. Such enthusiasm can, however, be instilled through creative leadership. For example, company officers should consider the following suggestions:

1. Use prefire plans to simulate fires at various locations.
2. Rotate command of the simulations among the fire fighters.
3. Discuss processes being used at various locations, the fire hazards they contain, and the implications for fire fighting after inspections are conducted.
4. Make training sessions more interesting and realistic so that fire fighters will better appreciate the sessions conducted on codes, inspection procedures, and fire investigation.

A few sample goals for a company officer might be as follows:

Overall:

- Establish inspection schedule to be accomplished next month by the 20th of this month.
- Develop jointly with the training officer training programs on inspection procedures and other inspection-related knowledge/skills by (date).
- By (date) establish the schedule of prefire plans to be drawn during the next quarter.
- Begin to use prefire plans for simulations in training sessions by (date).

Goals for the Chief

As with other types of fire fighting activities, good management approaches to fire prevention functions start with good goals. A few sample goals for a chief in fire prevention functions might be as follows:

Overall:

- Obtain budget and establish a fire prevention bureau by (date).
- Obtain budget and establish fire prevention capabilities for each shift by (date).
- By (date) establish a program that will provide for use of prefire plans and inspection results in training sessions.

Within Each District or Individual Company:

- Establish jointly with the commanding officer in each district the number of inspections to be conducted by each company during each month.
- Establish jointly with each district commander the number of prefire plans to be prepared or reviewed by each company during each month.
- Develop jointly with the district commanders a public education program by (date).
- Establish by (date) a citizen's committee to help with fire prevention.
- Ensure that all district commanders have Fire Prevention Week plans ready by September 1.

Inspections

Inspections are necessary for enforcement of the fire code. Fire department inspections fall into four general categories. Occupancies to be inspected in the first three inspection categories include places of public assembly, educational, institutional, residential (exterior), mercantile, business, industrial, manufacturing, and storage. Private dwellings make up the fourth category. The four general categories follow:

1. **Inspections required by law**: These inspections include all buildings and premises with the exception of the interiors of private dwellings, and are usually conducted by members of the Fire Prevention Bureau. Inspections are made to identify those conditions that violate the fire code and that are liable to cause fire or endanger life and property. Emphasis is also placed on conditions of interest to fire officers for prefire planning and training purposes (see Figure 7.1).

2. **Inspections conducted by fire company personnel that supplement inspections of the Fire Prevention Bureau**: Before performing inspection work, fire fighters should receive proper training and be granted the

FIGURE 7.1 Inspection reveals fire department connection with access blocked by fence. (Courtesy of Michael W. Magee)

authority to conduct inspections as fire prevention officers. These inspections normally are conducted in the fire company's first due area. The fire prevention bureau provides assistance where needed in obtaining compliance to company recommendations.

3. **Inspections made by fire company personnel for prefire planning and training purposes:** Emphasis is also placed on conditions that violate the fire code, and that are liable to cause fire or endanger life. Conditions that require more than on-the-spot correction usually are referred to the Fire Prevention Bureau.

4. **Inspections conducted by fire company personnel in private homes:** Fire fighters can inspect private homes when requested by the owner or occupants. Recommendations made are not mandatory; however, if definite code violations are found (see Figure 7.2), an effort should be made to have the hazard corrected through proper department channels of authority.

In June 1967 the United States Supreme Court made a landmark decision affecting inspections and right of entry. The decision points out that in those rare cases where the owner of a business might insist on a warrant before the business can be inspected, it is best to obtain the warrant (see "Legal Aspects" in Chapter 9). This decision, while important to remember, has not affected fire inspectors of public or private commercial establishments very often.

FIGURE 7.2 *Inspection of the house in the foreground revealed unsafe fire escape stairs. Most of the wood in this fire escape is rotted, and the handrails have collapsed. (*Courtesy of Amy E. Dean)

Objectives of Inspections

The functions that are performed during an inspection, and the compilation of the report resulting from the inspection, are covered in detail in the *NFPA Inspection Manual.*[6] Major inspection objectives consist of the following:

1. Uncovering code violations and potential fire hazards.
2. Acquainting fire fighters with fire codes, SARA (Superfund Amendments and Reauthorization Act) Title III, and OSHA (Occupational Safety and Health Act) building and safety codes. A knowledge of these codes often will help in actual fire fighting operations.
3. Familiarizing fire fighters with contents and construction hazards, thus making fire fighting operationally more efficient. For example, fire fighters gain an understanding of how a fire can spread through vertical openings (such as elevator shafts, stairwells, and the stairways of buildings), or they gain an awareness of where the primary potential sources of fire hazard are located.
4. Using personnel more efficiently for assigned fire prevention duties. Most fire departments try to inspect target properties at least four times a year, depending on the model fire code being used by the department. Moderate- and low-hazard occupancies should be inspected at least twice a year. This objective sometimes is accomplished by combining technical inspections with company inspections.

Inspectors from the Fire Prevention Bureau might inspect target properties twice a year, especially when permits are due or when changes of occupancy or process require a more detailed inspection. If the Fire Prevention Bureau conducts these inspections, only two inspections must then be completed by the fire department.

The Inspection Process

Whether inspections are carried out by fire fighters or by Fire Prevention Bureau personnel, the basic process is as follows:

1. Before conducting an inspection, review all records related to the prescribed area, premises, or occupancy. An inspector needs to know which violations have been found previously, the owner's attitude toward correcting them, and the causes of any fire that might have occurred in the building.

2. Take a comprehensive list of items to look for in each occupancy inspected. Although some large fire departments might produce lists for each type of occupancy, fire fighters must sometimes compile their own. Figure 7.3 is a sample fire inspection report for fire prevention inspectors. Sample lists for the fourteen occupancies identified in the *Life Safety Code* can be found in *Conducting Fire Inspections: A Guidebook for Field Use.*[7]

3. Before entering the building examine the property to see where apparatus might be stationed, check the location of fire escapes and their condition, and survey for obstructions of standpipes or emergency exits.

4. Upon entering the building, inform the person in charge that an inspection is about to be made (see Figure 7.4).

5. The actual inspection is often begun at the roof where exposures and adjacent rooftops and parapets can be seen. Wherever started, the inspection should proceed in a systematic fashion (e.g., from attic to basement, from floor to floor). Each item or measurement should be checked off or recorded on the inspector's reporting form.
   Certain specific points must be checked. For example, the panic hardware on exit doors could have been inadvertently removed and replaced with regular fixtures. The door itself could be jammed or blocked. No-smoking signs might be unreadable or blocked. There might be a need to designate a smoking-permitted area. All exit signs must be visible from all approaches.

6. During a company inspection, special attention should be given to the way in which the building could be ventilated, to fire protection equipment, stairways and corridors, doorways and exits, heating and exhaust ducts, insulation and wiring, storage areas, facilities for disposal of refuse, and general maintenance procedures.

A number of fire departments have fully computerized their fire inspection operations. Inspectors can also use hand-held computers to record the inspection data. When the inspectors return to the department at the end of the day,

FIRE INSPECTION REPORT FOR			DISTRICT	
Street			Number	
Owner/Agent/Superintendent				
Address of above				
Class Construction	Roof		Stories	
Occupancy			Fl.	No. of Tenants
			DATES OF INSPECTIONS	
FIRE HAZARDS				
Heating System				
Clearances				
Heat Deflectors				
Condition of Flue				
Flue Pipe Fit				
Burner Controls				
Storage of Explosives				
Storage of Flammables				
CONDITION OF				
Fuses/Breakers				
Electrical Wiring				
Electrical Appliances				
Chimneys				
Vent Ducts				
Rubbish				
Storage of Ashes				
Air Conditioning				
Gas Appliances				
Miscellaneous				
FIRE PROTECTION				
Sprinklers	Wet	Dry		
Standpipes				
Second Egress				
Extinguishers				
Fire Doors				
Fire Escapes	W	M		
Aisles				
Halls				
Chutes				
STRUCTURAL DEFECTS				
Roofs				
Walls				
Floors				
Foundations				
Stairs				
Elevators				
Enclosures				
Stairway Enclosures				
LOCATION OF CUT OFFS				
Sprinkler				
Standpipe				
Gas				
Electricity				
Water				
LOCATION OF SIAMESE CONNECTIONS				
Sprinkler			Standpipe	
Inspector's Initials				
Violation Notice Issued				
Date Corrected				
REMARKS				

FIGURE 7.3 *Sample fire inspection report* (Courtesy of Plainfield Fire Department, Plainfield, New Jersey.)

FIGURE 7.4 *The fire inspector should always make contact with building management before beginning an inspection.* (Courtesy of Harry Carter)

the data from the hand-held device are transferred into the department's computer system and automatically added to the ongoing database.

All conditions that are not in compliance with regulations should be included in a report. Violation notices should be issued for more important violations to the regulations. Minor violations should be recorded for checking during a follow-up inspection (see Figure 7.5). The owner or person in charge should be given a copy of the inspection report, in addition to any notice of violation.

A well-groomed appearance—clean and pressed uniforms—will help promote a positive and professional image for the department. As the inspection proceeds, the inspector (whether a fire fighter or a technical inspector from the Fire Prevention Bureau) has the opportunity to emphasize the preventive aspects of the inspection work. The inspector who explains the implications of violations to the owner or employee of the premises being inspected helps to enhance the image of the department while also educating the public.

Private Dwelling Inspections: Inspections of residential areas should be carried out in much the same manner as other inspections. However, the inspection of private dwellings is not required by regulation. Private dwellings are inspected only on request of the owner or occupant. These inspections should only be made as long as personnel are available. When inspecting private dwellings, inspectors should point out possible escape routes in the event of fire and provide information about fire detection equipment and portable fire extinguishers.

FIGURE 7.5 *A lightly supported television antenna is too close to power lines and should be noted in an inspection report.*

Reasons for Code Violations: People sometimes violate codes because it costs money to comply; it costs money to have sufficient fire extinguishers, to put in additional electrical circuits, or to add extra storage space. Sometimes people simply forget to be careful about fire hazards. They sometimes forget to check whether the fire escape is still in good condition and whether the sprinklers work. If there is not enough storage space for all the boxes, it is easy and convenient to pile them in a corridor for a few days — just until more room for storage is found. The required space often will not be found unless a fire inspection calls attention to the fact that obstructions in corridors and doorways are fire code violations. Most inspections produce some code violations. When code violations are discovered, they should be corrected within a prescribed period of time.

Correction of Violations: Where corrections of code violations involve a substantial amount of money, a discussion of how the owner might best rectify the situation can be helpful. If necessary, special technical advice could be sought from the Fire Prevention Bureau.

A grace period is allowed for correcting violations. It is up to the technical inspector or company officer to determine how much time to allow. This usually depends on whether the violation is a simple one like removing obstructions in doorways, or whether it is a comparatively difficult one like installing a fire escape.

In the case of industrial inspections, follow-up visits are needed to determine whether violations have been corrected. In the case of voluntary inspections of private dwellings, follow-up visits usually are not made, unless requested by the owner or occupant.

Role of the Company Officer in Inspections

It is the responsibility of the company officer to integrate all aspects of company inspections into the general purpose and goals of fire prevention. This task is not easy because many fire fighters have negative feelings about conducting inspections. There are many reasons for this.

Fire Fighter Attitudes Toward Inspections: Fire fighters sometimes feel negative about conducting inspections, due to the perceived inherent nature of the work of a fire fighter. This is a difficult situation to correct (see items 1 through 4 below). Other situations, however, are much easier to correct if the company officer understands what can be done and how to do it (see items 5 through 10 below).

1. Most fire fighters join the fire service because they want to fight fires, not because they want to prevent fires from occurring.
2. Some fire fighters do not have outgoing personalities, thus making it difficult for them to relate easily to the people they must deal with when doing inspection work.
3. To carry out inspections, fire fighters must wear clean, pressed uniforms, which either costs the fire fighter extra money or necessitates extra effort.
4. Inspections often occur at inconvenient times for a building owner, e.g., when an owner is busy or the premises to be inspected is in full use. This can cause a fire fighter to feel uncomfortable.
5. Fire fighters often find it difficult to understand how inspections relate to their primary job of fire fighting.
6. When asked why they are conducting an inspection, fire fighters who have not been trained properly might have no response other than to say that they were told to do it.
7. To many fire fighters, it is frustrating to impose on people and to carry out some safety procedures that are not understood very well by the public.

8. When asked questions, some fire fighters might feel insecure about the accuracy of their responses and might become frustrated when confronted with a questioner who assumes that all fire fighters know all there is to know about fire prevention.

9. The attitudes and reactions of the people whose premises are being inspected often make fire fighters feel uncomfortable.

10. Inspections often result in a longer work day.

There are several ways in which a company officer might begin to modify attitudes about inspection work so that fire fighters obtain greater satisfaction from this part of their work. Included are: 1) careful planning and scheduling, 2) better training, and 3) appropriate supervision.

Planning and Scheduling: A company officer is responsible for planning company inspections so that the entire area assigned to that officer's jurisdiction is covered within a prescribed period of time. To do this, the company officer must estimate how long it will take the available number of assigned fire fighters to conduct each inspection, as well as the number of hours needed to cover the entire area undergoing inspection.

Because inspections often result in a longer-than-average workday, the officer who wants to reduce any unfavorable impact must carefully plan and schedule inspections so that they can be finished within the allotted time. The company officer should ensure that all of the materials needed to carry out inspections are available, such as reporting sheets, checklists, records, maps, flashlights, tape measures, pencils, and special equipment, such as hard hats. A book of codes and regulations can help provide easy reference when questions arise. Other good references include the *NFPA Inspection Manual*[6] and *Conducting Fire Inspections: A Guidebook for Field Use*.[7]

Training in the Understanding of Codes: Fire fighters better understand the importance of inspections and how they relate to their primary job of fire fighting and fire prevention if they understand codes and the purposes of inspections. Once such an awareness is gained, fire fighters are better able to impart some of this knowledge to the people whose premises they will inspect. This helps promote a more comfortable atmosphere for both parties involved. To a great extent, most people dislike being questioned in areas where they might not be able to provide an adequate response. Thus, fire fighters feel more confident if they are able to accurately answer many of the questions they are asked during inspections. To be able to do this requires training in the appropriate codes and in answering the more common questions.

Training in the Application of Codes: It is not sufficient for fire fighters merely to be aware of and understand codes and the purpose of inspections. It is also necessary that fire fighters be trained to apply this knowledge in order to distinguish code violations as distinct from a normal, safe environment. Skill is needed in analyzing the present conditions in a building and in determining how a fire might begin and spread. Competent fire fighters also must be able to determine whether escape routes are adequate enough to ensure quick evacuation in case of fire or other emergencies. This type of skill involves more than simply knowing that electrical circuits cannot be overloaded or that flammables must be stored in approved, self-closing containers, although these precautions are important parts of the codes (see Figure 7.6).

Fire fighters also must be able to take the knowledge of firesafety accumulated over the years and embodied in the codes and apply this knowledge to the present situation. For example, if a floor or space is of substantial height, a fire fighter usually knows that there should be fire curtains so that when heat from fire rises it does not spread, but is contained. It is important that fire fighters either know, or can quickly find out, the answers to questions like: How should fire doors be hung, and when do they meet specifications? When are the windows an approved design? What is required to put a fire escape in compliance with the codes?

Training in Public Relations: The company officer must help fire fighters understand the importance of good public relations in order to gain cooperation from the community. For example, although regulations generally give an inspector the right of entry, it is often advisable to provide advance notification of an inspection or, in certain situations, it is preferable to make an appointment

FIGURE 7.6 *Fire fighter applies training in fire prevention codes by inspecting the power generator in a community barn for possible electrical hazards.* (Courtesy of L. Franklin Heald)

or obtain a warrant. Upon arrival at the inspection site, an inspector should seek out the person in charge and request that person's permission to make the inspection. In addition, the inspector should suggest that the owner, the manager, or a representative accompany the fire fighter during the inspection.

Providing Adequate Supervision: During fire prevention inspections, the company officer should provide close guidance for, and maintain frequent contact with, the members of the inspection team. Follow-up procedures enable a company officer to evaluate the performance of fire fighters; they can provide information such as how knowledgable fire fighters are in specific areas and how seriously they take their work. They also give the company officer a chance to observe areas in which additional training might be needed. Often opportunities present themselves for commending a fire fighter in the presence of others, thus adding to positive experiences in field inspections.

ACTIVITIES

1. Describe the meaning of fire prevention. Then list the three areas that are part of fire prevention, and explain what role each plays in preventing fires.

2. How have past fires influenced the formation of fire prevention codes and laws that exist today? How have past fires brought about the formation of fire protection agencies?

3. Describe how each of the following fire protection agencies was formed and the purpose of each organization.
   (a) National Board of Fire Underwriters.
   (b) National Fire Protection Association.
   (c) American Insurance Association.
   (d) Underwriters Laboratories.
   (e) Factory Mutual Research Corporation.

4. Explain the role of the following entities in formulating national standards and codes.
   (a) Federal government.
   (b) National Fire Protection Association.
   (c) American Insurance Association.
   (d) Underwriters Laboratories.
   (e) Factory Mutual Research Corporation.

5. Explain the effect of a fire department's input concerning the formation of codes and regulations. How does a fire department enforce fire prevention codes?

6. What is the role of each of the following officials in fire prevention?
   (a) State fire marshal.
   (b) Chief of fire prevention or local fire marshal.

(c) Fire inspector or fire prevention officer.

(d) Fire protection engineer.

7. Why is it important that fire department personnel participate in fire prevention activities as well as in fire suppression operations?

8. As the chief of fire prevention in your municipality, you have been called upon to discuss the inspection process during a local fire department training seminar. Prepare an outline of the inspection process. Include in your outline a brief summary of the four types of inspections.

9. If you were the company officer of a fire department that was experiencing a negative attitude toward fire inspections, how might you go about eliminating some of the negative feelings?

10. With a group from your class, discuss the tasks and concerns related to effective fire prevention. Next, compile your answers into a list. Then divide the items on the list equally among the group. Each group member should write a summary of the assigned tasks and concerns, including:

(a) The importance of each task and concern in the overall program of fire prevention.

(b) The duties that must be performed in each task.

(c) The role of fire department members in each task.

REFERENCES

[1]Cote, A. E., ed., *Fire Protection Handbook*, 16th edition, National Fire Protection Association, Quincy, MA, 1986, p. 15-37.

[2]NFPA 1031, *Standard for Professional Qualifications for Fire Inspector*, National Fire Protection Association, Quincy, MA, 1987.

[3]Tryon, G. H., ed., *Fire Protection Handbook*, 13th edition, National Fire Protection Association, Quincy, MA, 1969, pp. 3-7, 3-8.

[4]"What's Your Apartment Problem?," *Fire Command!*, Vol. 42, No. 11, Nov. 1975, p. 16.

[5]NFPA 1, *Fire Prevention Code*, National Fire Protection Association, Quincy, MA, 1987.

[6]*NFPA Inspection Manual*, 6th edition, National Fire Protection Association, Quincy, MA, 1989, 450 pp.

[7]*Conducting Fire Inspections: A Guidebook for Field Use*, 2nd edition, National Fire Protection Association, Quincy, MA, 1989, 460 pp.

Firesafety Education

Firesafety education is designed to develop or change the attitudes and behaviors of men, women, and children toward fire. It encompasses a wide spectrum of programs and activities directed toward such diverse audiences as school children, senior citizens, homeowners, preschoolers, apartment dwellers, handicapped people, employees, hospital and nursing home staffs, and church, service, and civic organizations. The main objective of firesafety education is to increase awareness of human actions that could lead to fires and to develop skills and knowledge to prevent fires or to minimize exposures in the case of fire.

EDUCATION PROGRAMS FOR FIRESAFETY

Historically, the primary exposure of the general public to fire-related subjects came only during Fire Prevention Week in October. Once a year the fire service visited schools, placed announcements in the newspapers, and, in general, made the people think about fire. Occasionally, a spectacular fire would bring to peoples' attention the high toll of fire on human life and property damage. Temporarily, the huge cost of the fire would bring some gains in fire consciousness and firesafety.

Gradually, an increasing number of fire departments began to provide firesafety education in their communities. Progress has been slow. Even in the late 1980s, there are fire departments that have not yet adopted a proactive approach to the delivery of such knowledge.

Gus Welter of the National Volunteer Fire Council summed up the problem by asking, "Why is there always time to put out fires but not to teach fire prevention?"[1] Why indeed? It has been well known, at least since the 1973 report of the National Commission on Fire Prevention and Control that "among the many measures that can be taken to reduce fire losses, perhaps none is more important than educating people about fire."[1]

There are three basic phases a fire department can use to implement firesafety education within a community: 1) initial planning phase, 2) design and implementation phase; and 3) evaluation phase.[2]

Initial Planning Stage

The initial planning stage involves four steps:

1. Establishing responsibility and support.
2. Forming a planning team.
3. Identifying local fire problems.
4. Defining goals and objectives.

Establishing Responsibility and Support

Generally, it is the chief fire executive in a community who is legally charged with the delivery of fire protection services. During the planning phase, this executive must decide who will be involved with providing the services.

The firesafety education program can be delegated in both career or voluntary departments in various ways. For example, personnel can be assigned from the fire prevention division or the community relations division, a separate division can be formed to deliver the public education message, public education can be assigned as an additional duty for shift personnel, or a specialist can be hired to develop and deliver these educational programs. In smaller suburban departments, a specialist is sometimes a part-time public educator who works on an as-needed basis. Some excellent existing programs started on a part-time basis and grew into full-time operations.

During the planning phase, consideration has to be given to all personnel who will be a part of the public education effort. How are they to be trained to understand and deliver an effective firesafety message? These people should take a course in firesafety education at the National Fire Academy or at a state or local school where courses are taught by fire service professionals.

Forming a Planning Team

Once the staff members have been identified, a planning team can be created to develop an implementation strategy. This group should be responsible for the initial planning of community firesafety education efforts and can later serve in an advisory capacity.[3]

A wide range of disciplines from inside and outside the fire service should be represented on a planning committee to ensure a successful program. These people should include fire service personnel, educators, community leaders, and representatives from the medical community. Depending on the unique needs of the community, others might be included, such as representatives from the media, the building industry, civic associations, arson investigators, and social workers. The ideal size for this group is ten people, but if a larger group is needed to include everyone, smaller sub-groups or committees can be formed to expedite work.

Identifying Local Fire Problems

Before the development of a program to address local firesafety needs can begin, it is important to obtain an in-depth understanding of the fire-related problems in the community. What types of fires have occurred and how frequently? What were the causes? Is there a specific pattern that can be identified? Answers to these and similar questions should be obtained before developing a program.

Answers to many of these questions can be found in fire department records as well as the records from hospitals, insurance agencies, and state agencies. Data from the United States Fire Administration, which maintains the National Fire Incident Reporting System (NFIRS), and the National Fire Protection Association are excellent sources of supplementary information. For procedural questions, the *Firesafety Educator's Handbook*[4] is a useful reference.

Defining Goals and Objectives

After the fire situation in a community has been identified and understood by the planning committee, these data can become the basis of a workable set of goals and objectives. Table 8.1 can be used to help a community planning committee separate the various tasks that must be accomplished in order to implement an effective firesafety education program.

Note that the NFPA definitions of goals and objectives are essentially the same as those used in Chapters 4 and 5. Only the words used are different. NFPA uses *goals* to mean strategic goals/objectives and *objectives* to mean operational goals/objectives.[3]

> Goals are achieved through completion of specific objectives, and objectives are completed through individual steps in an action plan. Goals are what should be ultimately achieved; objectives are the programs needed to achieve your goal. Action plans are the detailed steps to be completed to accomplish the objectives. Some objectives consist of on-going programs, while others are one-time efforts. Goals, objectives, and action plans form a pyramid with development beginning at the top and completion [achievement] beginning at the bottom. [See Figure 8.1]

An example of an overall goal might be to reduce the number of fires and the resulting deaths, injuries, and property damage by educating the public. The various objectives should be designed to move toward this goal at all times. The

TABLE 8.1 Differentiating among goals, objectives, and action plans. (Source: *Fire Protection Handbook*[3])

	Goal	Objective	Action plan
	Ultimate end	Interim end	Means to the end
Time frame	Future	1–2 years	Less than 1 year
Responsibility for completion	Entire department's organization	Program manager, regional leader	Individual staff
Emphasis	Ultimate benefits to community. Future direction of the department.	Your program's measurable results that constitute progress toward your goal.	Your resources— how you will allocate time, money, and staff to achieve your objectives.
Specifics	Not specific; does not include target completion dates and measurement of success.	Specific results, including target completion dates and measurement of success.	Specific results, including responsibility for carrying out the plan.

action plan also must be structured to work toward this goal in a responsible, timely fashion. Examples of two specific objectives follow.[5]

Objective—Reduce House Fire Deaths, Especially of Children

To provide firesafety lessons during October/November and April/May for all children enrolled in local preschools and daycare centers.

To provide four firesafety lessons to all fifth grade students (approximately 2000) in public schools beginning in September and ending in June.

To provide annual firesafety assembly programs for grades K-4 in the 22 public elementary schools during January, February, and March.

To include firesafety messages for children in on-going programs conducted by the Parks and Recreation Department and the public libraries.

Objective—Reduce Nursing Home Fires

To conduct three lessons in fire prevention and fire survival for all three shifts at the four local nursing homes within the next month.

Design and Implementation Phase

After the groundwork has been established by the planning committee, the design of specific firesafety programs can begin. To gain public interest and cooperation, each program should be designed to be "functional (reducing the fire problem) as well as appealing and motivational to the public."[5] The design and implementation stage involves six steps: 1) conducting audience/market research, 2) developing program strategies, 3) developing action plans for

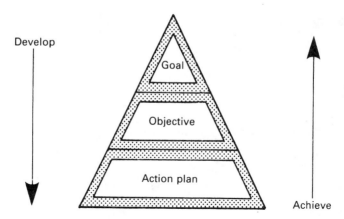

FIGURE 8.1 Development pyramid. (Source: Fire Protection Handbook[5])

program objectives, 4) making a program proposal, 5) preparing teaching aids and training instructors, and 6) conducting pilot tests.

Conducting Audience/Market Research

To find out what will make programs more effective, sometimes it is useful to follow the example of entertainers. Good comedians, for instance, study audiences and other comedians to see what is currently perceived as funny and how that humor is delivered most successfully. Firesafety educators must research their target audiences and the programs of other fire departments for ideas about how to develop programs that have strong popular appeal. Many well-intentioned public educators have spent time and talent developing programs that were not successful because the message and the medium were not appropriate.

Effective public educators know the target audience, address it with an appropriate tone and language, and literally provide reasons for listening (see Figure 8.2). These educators have a product to sell (firesafety), and they develop a way to reach their customers (the public). Useful research provides information on the learning capabilities, attitudes and behaviors, accessibility, and current knowledge of the target audience. Because the size of a group for the program can have a direct impact on the effectiveness with which the message is delivered, research also should provide estimates of potential group size.

Developing Program Strategies

Program strategies concern decisions about where, when, and how often an audience will be reached. These decisions are crucial to effectively delivering firesafety messages.

There is often a communication network of some kind already in use by the target audience. There are places where the audience meets or publications

FIGURE 8.2 *This captain of the Toronto Fire Department was awarded a certificate from children who had learned about firesafety from him.* (Source: Toronto Sun, Toronto, Ontario, Canada)

from which it already obtains information.[6] Tying into any such identifiable, existing networks will help achieve greatest practical impact. The best example of this comes from the integration of NFPA's *Learn Not to Burn® Curriculum*[7] into a wide range of United States schools. The schools are already there, and they are already in the business of education. With a little thought, one additional use of the schools now assists the public in learning firesafe behaviors.

Competent fire education officers are creative and seek new audiences in their communities or even sponsor affairs on fire prevention in parks or at fairs. Timing is as important as location and source of audience. A firesafety educational message is best received when it is the most prominent event on the agenda and when it is made appropriate for the audience. It should not, for example, be delivered to a senior citizen audience on the same evening as an annual senior club banquet, and a lecture on the chemistry of fire would be far less appropriate for a first grade class than a discussion of the behaviors from the *Learn Not to Burn® Curriculum*. Other points of contact with the public might include industrial safety committees, scouting organizations, church groups, or similar citizens' groups.

Developing Action Plans for Program Objectives

The deadlines and responsibilities for the various tasks that must be accomplished are of particular importance in any action plan. A sample action plan, which was written with the objective of providing four firesafety lessons to every fifth grade student in the local public schools (September–June), is shown in Table 8.2.

TABLE 8.2 Sample action plan. *(Source: Fire Protection Handbook[8])*

Steps	Target date	Responsible person
Revise program format.	7/01	Bob and Nancy
Develop and order handout materials.	11/15	Bill, Bob, and Nancy
Schedule schools.	6/01	Bill
Provide the schedule to the school board for approval and distribution.	7/15	Bill
Contract each principal to verify the schedule four weeks prior to program.	As stated	Bob and Nancy
Present the assembly program.	Per schedule	Bob and Nancy
Ask the nearest fire company to arrange for a fire fighter to assist with the program.	Two weeks prior to the program	Bob and Nancy
Develop an evaluation tool for this program.	11/04	Bill

Making a Program Proposal

Before scheduling a firesafety education session, many groups will require that a proposal be given to the decision-making committee or person. Such a proposal should be written to make the value of the program stand out over other proposals competing for limited time or resources. To be effective, a proposal should include the following five sections: 1) statement of needs, 2) behavioral objectives, 3) format description, 4) cost estimates of the program for any fees requested from the audience, and 5) description of evaluation tools.

The format description should specifically cover: 1) the number and length of lessons, 2) the topics to be covered, and 3) the audiovisual materials to be used. Sample handouts should be included with the proposal.

Preparing Teaching Aids and Training Instructors

Once approval for a program has been obtained, the available teaching aids should be reviewed to ensure that they are appropriate for the plan of the program. If new materials are needed, it is necessary to decide whether to purchase professionally developed items or to make them, using fire department personnel. If pilot-testing is contemplated, preliminary materials should be used whenever possible, so that they can be revised after the results of the testing have been compiled.

Instructors for the program do not have to be certified teachers, but it is essential that they have demonstrated competence in teaching classes for the expected audience (see Figure 8.3). There is nothing more important to the success of educational efforts than the selection of competent and dedicated instructors. Two ways to ensure such staffing are to provide training for the instructors and to give them the necessary support to implement a quality program.

Initial training can be obtained from the National Fire Academy in Emmitsburg, Maryland, where a residential course in public fire education is offered. Printed materials, such as the *Firesafety Educator's Handbook*,[4] are available from NFPA to assist with training instructors. The International Fire Service Training Organization (IFSTA) publishes a manual, *Public Fire Education*,[9] which is used by many fire departments for this type of training.

Conducting Pilot Tests

Pilot tests are useful and desirable to validate the elements and teaching aids of a program before full implementation takes place. This ensures the effectiveness, accuracy, and appeal of the program before large amounts of time and resources are committed to the project.[10]

There is no set length for pilot tests. They can range from a few deliveries to a small number of groups, to a city-wide program with several months of presentations and alterations to fine-tune a large-scale program. Audience reaction must be monitored carefully to ensure that the material is readable,

FIGURE 8.3 *This fire officer is beginning a lesson on firesafety for grade school children.* (Courtesy of Harry Carter)

understandable, appealing, and relevant to their actual and perceived needs. Pilot programs also provide opportunities for instructors to practice delivery skills and enhance their knowledge of the subject. When everything is ready, the program can be delivered to the target audience on a wider scale. It can also serve as a foundation for programs directed at other audiences.

Evaluation Phase

The evaluation phase provides feedback on the effectiveness of the program and leads to improved programs in the future. This phase includes three steps: 1) providing for program documentation, 2) determining effectiveness, and 3) revising action plans and objectives.

Providing for Program Documentation

To ensure that the program fully serves its intended purpose, the results must be compared with the objectives. If the objective was to lower the number of cooking-related fire incidents, the effectiveness of the program can be evaluated by the extent to which such incidents have declined after the program started. The research compiled when local fire problems were identified can be used as baseline data to evaluate the effectiveness of the firesafety education program. The number of programs conducted, people attending, and personnel participating should be compiled. Also needed is information from any pre- or post-testing, or any surveys or questionnaires completed by the target audience.[11]

Determining Effectiveness

To show the effect, a report should be prepared that outlines a baseline of data, documentation of firesafety educational programs delivered, and the improved firesafety after a given period of time. Not every program will result in a lower incidence of fires, but documenting the benefits that were attained will ensure continued acceptance and support for firesafety programs.

If a firesafety educator can demonstrate that a change in behavior has occurred, there is a high degree of probability that fires will be reduced or lives saved in the future. That is the goal. The NFPA's *Learn Not to Burn® Curriculum*[7] provides an excellent example of this. From 1975 to 1988, NFPA records show that more than 250 lives have been saved by use of the behaviors taught in this curriculum.

Revising Action Plans and Objectives

Action plans and program objectives provide the basis for well-organized and effective programs. Once revised and approved, the plans and objectives should be used as management tools.[11] Although these plans and objectives are to be used as tools, remember that they must never become static, but must evolve to meet the changing needs of a community.

Educating the Public About Inspections

Generally, inspections make the community more aware of the importance of loss prevention by pointing out the existence of fire hazards in the home, plant, or office. When carried out in a competent and professional manner, inspections can make the public more receptive to further information about firesafety. For example, a good public image and a well thought-out plan for publicity and public education programs can encourage homeowners to call up the Fire Prevention Bureau or local fire department and ask to have their homes inspected.

Howard Boyd, retired Fire Marshal of Metropolitan Nashville and Davidson County, Tennessee, pointed out that Fire Prevention Bureau education programs need to concentrate on one- and two-family dwellings—the area in which 50 percent of deaths due to fire occur.[12]

> Unfortunately, I'm afraid that most fire departments are spending very little time on one- and two-family dwellings. This is because "a man's home is his castle," and once he gets there he thinks he is safe. Actually, he's in the most dangerous place in America, the home. We need a long program of public education—I see no other way by which we can reach the homeowner in his 'castle.'

Inspections can show a person what is unsafe in their home. Often, the fact that an inspection is coming can stimulate people to discard debris and tidy up their surroundings.

Public Education Through Publicity

Publicity through the media and printed brochures, flyers, and handouts are needed to generate interest in inspections of private dwellings. A good publicity program can help the public understand the diverse functions of a fire prevention bureau and thus help support the other educational objectives of the department. Such a program can also emphasize the importance of public participation in loss prevention. To be most effective, a publicity program should adhere to the following principles:

1. Information should be disseminated in a steady and continual flow over a period of time. (Isolated messages are not as likely to be remembered.)

2. Publicity should be geared to events and seasons. This can be accomplished by emphasizing the current seasonal hazards, Fire Prevention Week, delivery of new apparatus, plans to build a new fire station, and so on.

3. Sometimes news items can be used to pave the way for more specific educational information. For example, an article describing how the fire department helped bring a specific house fire under control, with minimal damage and no loss of life, could mention that the occupants had recently installed a smoke detector. A follow-up article discussing smoke detection equipment could then be arranged.

FIGURE 8.4 *Example of an NFPA poster emphasizing public participation in fire prevention.*

Using the Media: Gaining the attention of the public through the media is more easily accomplished if the department's personnel are organized to deal with the media. Many departments have officers on their staffs who serve as public information officers. In the absence of such officers, publicity is usually handled by the Fire Prevention Bureau.

It is advantageous for the chief or designated officer to set up a meeting with the editor of a local paper and/or manager of a local radio station to plan an entire publicity program. A member of the department then can be assigned to work directly with the newspaper or TV station staff in the development of the program. This type of planning can help bring higher priority at times when the media might not normally consider items on fire prevention to be of foremost importance.

Television or radio interviews and prepared articles for the newspapers (especially during Fire Prevention Week in October) draw attention to particular hazards and the importance of fire codes. Some departments look for volunteers to write general-interest articles dealing with specific problems. Examples of such articles include how to deal with grease fires in the kitchen, how to plan escape routes, and what to do in case of a fire.

The opportunity to publicize the importance of fire prevention comes with every large fire — especially when loss of life is involved. At such times, the press and public are more receptive to ways in which the risk of fire can be reduced. People are then more likely to take steps to protect themselves.

NFPA Posters, Flyers: The NFPA and other organizations having fire protection interests publish many posters (see Figure 8.4), flyers, and other handout materials that can be left with local businesses and in public places. When private dwellings are inspected, flyers with information about specific hazards can be left with the homeowners. School systems often distribute fire prevention flyers and posters to students to take home to their parents.

The bulk of any fire department's public educational work is done by specially trained and assigned personnel. Whether they are in a fire prevention bureau, community relations division, or some similar special segment of the department, their job is the same: They teach the people in the community to live in a firesafe manner.

This function represents many opportunities for fire fighters and officers to perform interesting tasks, such as public speaking, visiting schools, or writing, all of which can have a positive impact on the community.

ACTIVITIES

1. Discuss the main purpose of firesafety education.
2. List and explain the three basic phases used in implementing a community firesafety education program.
3. List the four steps in the initial planning stage for a firesafety education program, and explain the importance of each.
4. Develop a series of goals and objectives for implementing a community firesafety program in 1) a small local fire department, and 2) a large metropolitan fire department.
5. Explain what a program strategy is and develop a suitable example for your own fire department.
6. Why is a program proposal required before scheduling a firesafety education session? What should it cover?
7. Discuss the importance of pilot testing a community firesafety education program.
8. List and explain the three steps in the evaluation phase of a firesafety education program.
9. Discuss with your class the methods a fire department can use for public education in fire prevention. Then, based on your discussion, answer the following questions.
   (a) Does your community's fire department use any of the methods you have listed? If so, describe them.

(b) What methods of public education are not used by your community's fire department?

(c) With your group, choose one method that is not being used. Then discuss how this method could be used in your community.

REFERENCES

[1]Schaenman, Phillip, et al., *Overcoming Barriers to Public Fire Education*, TriData Corporation, Arlington, VA, 1987, p. 1.

[2]Cote, A. E., ed., *Fire Protection Handbook*, 16th edition, National Fire Protection Association, Quincy, MA, 1986, p. 3-2.

[3]Cote, A. E., ed., *Fire Protection Handbook*, 16th edition, National Fire Protection Association, Quincy, MA, 1986, p. 3-3.

[4]Adams, R. C., ed., *Firesafety Educator's Handbook: A Comprehensive Guide to Planning, Designing and Implementing Firesafety Programs*, National Fire Protection Association, Quincy, MA, 1983, 180 pp.

[5]Cote, A. E., ed., *Fire Protection Handbook*, 16th edition, National Fire Protection Association, Quincy, MA, 1986, p. 3-4.

[6]Cote, A. E., ed., *Fire Protection Handbook*, 16th edition, National Fire Protection Association, Quincy, MA, 1986, p. 3-5.

[7]*Learn Not to Burn Curriculum*, 3rd edition, National Fire Protection Association, Quincy, MA, 1987.

[8]Cote, A. E., ed., *Fire Protection Handbook*, 16th edition, National Fire Protection Association, Quincy, MA, 1986, p. 3-6.

[9]Osterhout, Connie, ed., *Public Fire Education*, IFSTA No. 606, International Fire Service Training Association, Stillwater, OK, 1979.

[10]Cote, A. E., ed., *Fire Protection Handbook*, 16th edition, National Fire Protection Association, Quincy, MA, 1986, p. 3-7.

[11]Cote, A. E., ed., *Fire Protection Handbook*, 16th edition, National Fire Protection Association, Quincy, MA, 1986, p. 3-8.

[12]"*Interview*" Fire Command!, Vol. 42, No. 9, Sept. 1975, p. 27.

CHAPTER

9

Loss Prevention Activities — Prefire Planning and Related Functions

Loss prevention activities are critical to fire protection needs because they not only prevent some fires, but ensure that damage from fire is limited. Fire department procedures and fire codes are often modified because data compiled from fire incidents leads to suggestions of methods that will prevent or reduce future incidents or severe consequences from fire.

LOSS PREVENTION ACTIVITIES

Loss prevention activities include: 1) prefire plans, 2) fire ignition sequence investigations, 3) water supplies and systems, and 4) loss prevention information management systems. The legal aspects of conducting some of these procedures are also covered.

Prefire Plans

A prefire plan is a survey of a potential fire hazard and a plan for fighting a fire that might strike a particular occupancy. The plan includes the key matters that influence a fire attack. The purpose of prefire plans is to enable attack preparations and fire fighting operations to be carried out at the scene of a fire as efficiently and effectively as possible. At the fireground operation, attack preparations can begin more quickly if details about the fire site are known before fire fighters arrive and if advantageous positions of apparatus and hose layouts have been predetermined. When effective prefire plans have been made, much less time is spent on making decisions concerning the fire site during and after the size-up process.

Size-Up Process

The size-up process is one of the most important tactical operations that takes place before any physical activity at the scene of a fire. Size-up is a continuous mental evaluation of the situation and all related factors that can determine the success or failure of the fireground operation. This mental evaluation should begin as soon as companies are alerted and should be continuous throughout the incident. Size-up should not be limited to the fireground commander; it should be practiced by each fire fighter and officer involved with the incident.

Prefire Planning Process

Prefire planning should involve all fire suppression personnel on a continual basis. It is a course of action against a potential fire that is based on the collective experiences of those involved in the planning process, on known or existing conditions, on the relationship of cause and effect, and on reasonable expectancy. The prefire planning process involves four steps: 1) information gathering, 2) information analysis, 3) information dissemination, and 4) review and drill.

Information Gathering: This involves collecting pertinent information at the selected site that might affect fire fighting operations, such as building construction features, occupancy, exposures, utility disconnects, fire hydrant locations, water-main sizes, and anything else that would affect fire fighting operations if a fire should occur.

Information Analysis: The information gathered must be analyzed in terms of what is pertinent and vital to fire suppression operations. Then, an operable prefire plan must be formulated and organized into a format that is usable on the fireground.

Information Dissemination: All companies that might respond to each prefire plan location should receive copies of the plan so that they become familiar with both the plan and the pertinent factors relating to it.

Review and Drill: Each company that might be involved at the pre-planned location should review the plan on a regular schedule. Periodic drills with all companies involved should be scheduled at the property.

Prefire plans are necessary for all target hazards and special risks, but need not be developed for single-family dwellings or other small occupancies because a standard operating procedure should be sufficient for these occupancies. Prefire planning is a necessary adjunct to tactical operations and, if used, should increase operational efficiency, reduce fire losses, and help provide an optimal level of fire protection.

Description of a Prefire Plan

Prefire plans usually consist of two parts: 1) data sheets (see Figures 9.1 through 9.3) and 2) a building layout (see Figure 9.4). Together, data sheets and layout should contain the following information:

1. The exact location of the building and the best response routes at various times of the day and for different weather conditions (see Figure 9.1). Such information helps eliminate delays on steep hills, or delays caused by heavy traffic or flooding.

2. A building layout (see Figure 9.4) showing access routes, dimensions, construction materials, location of stairs, windows, exits, sprinklers and their valves, standpipes, hydrants, and all other fire protection equipment and utilities, as well as any other pertinent information about building construction. Supplementary water supplies from other mains might also be indicated for companies other than those making the first response.

3. Details about the type of occupancy, special volatile materials, hours that the building would normally be occupied, and construction of any adjacent buildings.

4. The best positions to station apparatus in relation to water supply, space, grade, and traffic conditions. Figure 9.1 details a sample of a fire bureau's company assignments, positions, and prefire plan for an apartment complex.

In order to be most useful, a prefire plan should contain only the most valuable information that is not likely to change. Secondary information or items that might become outdated should be noted in pencil. The inclusion of too much information, however, can make a prefire plan too complicated and less effective for the user.

The symbols that are usually used on prefire plans are an important shorthand method for providing information as quickly and simply as possible. Because they are used to save time and space, symbols should be understood more easily and more rapidly than words. The use of symbols is defeated if they are complicated. Different fire departments and organizations use different symbols. In cases where the use of a symbol does not describe the situation sufficiently, it is also necessary to label that point on the plan—often using abbreviations.

The symbols and plans presented in this text will enable any inspector or fire fighter to develop an acceptable plan in accordance with convention. However, it should be realized that there are many organizations using slightly different sets of symbols and layouts. When taking information from a plan developed by another source, it is necessary to refer to the legend of symbols used by that organization to accurately interpret the information.

A thorough understanding of the features depicted on a complete plan is necessary. The features of any property can be placed in one of four categories: Construction (C), Occupancy (O), Protection (P), or Exposure (E), otherwise known as COPE. These major classifications of important features are composed of many elements. Some of the standard plan symbols that can be used to represent the general location and type of COPE features found in a facility are shown in Figure 9.5.

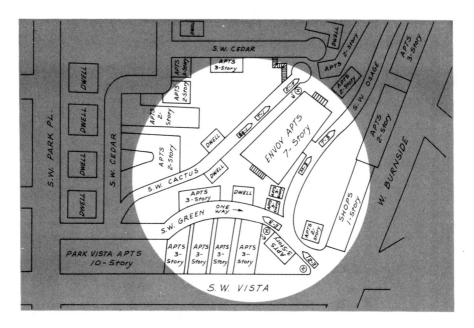

ASSIGNMENTS

E-3	E-15	E-21	T-3	T-1	Sq.-1
C-2		102			

COMPANY POSITIONS

1. Engine 3 connect to hydrant on Green @ junction of Green and Osage, Manifold 3 lay lines from Engine to main entrance.

2. Truck 3 take a position on Osage.

3. Engine 15 spot on hydrant on Cactus Drive.

4. Truck 1 spot behind Engine 15 on Cactus Drive.

5. Engine 21 spot on hydrant at Burnside & Osage. Work off Manifold 3.

6. Squad 1 spot on Cactus Drive behind Truck 1.

NOTES ON ENVOY PLAN:

The building is well constructed of reinforced concrete with slab floors. The only standpipe is a wet-pipe interior one supplied by city pressure. There is no sprinkler system. There are adequate hydrants. The mains are well gridded.

Because of the narrow streets (Cactus and Cedar are dead end) it will not be practicable to change positions once the rigs are committed.

Company officers should give thought to best deployment for other fires in this area.

FIGURE *9.1 Description and drawing of the prefire plan for an apartment complex showing company assignments and positions. Note the access routes and water supplies used by each apparatus. (*Source: Portland Fire Bureau, Portland, Oregon)

Refer to Table 9.1 for commonly used standard abbreviations. "Abbreviations for Use on Drawings and in Text," prepared by the American National

T.I.P.S. PHASE 1 INFORMATION FORM

BF-35 (1/72)

1. ADDRESS   (Include all if more than one)

UNIT	BATT.	DIV.	DATE

558 Main St.
ALSO REAR 94–96 Lake St.

2. T.I.P.S. HAZARD (S)   Briefly note major item(s) or hazard(s) that made building a T.I.P.S. Bldg. Info to be repeated below in more detail.

LARGE AREA ON ALL FLOORS
HEAVILY STOCKED (CARDBOARD, COTTON ETC.)
BUILDING RUNS FROM 94–96 Lake St. to 558 Main St.

3. BUILDING CONSTRUCTION INFORMATION

CLASS	HEIGHT	WIDTH	DEPTH	SHAPE IF IRREGULAR
	2	25 & 50	200	L

4. EXPOSURES   List rear exposure. Include others only if not visible from street.

END OF PHASE 1   Further information concerning structural data and chiefs operational tips available upon request.

T.I.P.S. PHASE 2 STRUCTURAL DATA INFORMATION

5. LIFE HAZARD (Civilian)

6. STAIRWAYS & EGRESSES   (To upper floors, horizontal, etc., locate each)

TYPE	LOCATION, FRONT/REAR	EXPOSURE SIDE	FLOOR START/STOP	...R START/STOP
ENCLOSED STAIRS	FRONT	ADJ #2	CELLAR/1ST	...AR/2ND FL
ENCLOSED STAIRS	REAR	ADJ #2 & 3	CELLAR/1ST	...ND FL
OPEN INTERIOR STAIR	CENTER	ADJ #4	CELLAR/MEZZANINE	...AR/STREET
FIRE ESCAPE	REAR	#4	/2ND FL	
ENCLOSED STAIRS	FRONT	ADJ #1 & 2	STREET/2ND FL	
ENCLOSED STAIRS	REAR	ADJ #2 & 3	STREET/2ND FL	

IRON STAIRWAY. LADDER TO SCUTTLE IN ROOF

8. OCCUPANCY   (Include only if unusual or not visible from street)

9. FIRE PROTECTION

THERMOSTATIC ALARM   CELLAR

10. OTHER   (Include any special condition or hazard)

LARGE OPEN AREA ON ALL FLOORS. HEAVILY STOCKED WITH FAST BURNING & SMOKE PRO-
DUCING STOCK (CARDBOARD, COTTONS ETC.) MEZZANINE ON LAKE ST. ADDS ANOTHER
2500 SQ. FT. OF FLOORING & STORAGE TO 1ST FLOOR.

11. BELOW GRADE INFORMATION   (If this area pertains to T.I.P.S. Hazard #2 above include access, ventilation, life, etc.)

ACCESS TO CELLAR ONLY FROM INTERIOR OF BUILDING FRONT AND REAR AND AT EXP
#4 CENTER OF BLDG. THE STAIR AT EXP #4 IS OPEN. STAIRS AT REAR AND FRONT OF BLDG.
ARE ENCLOSED STAIR.
CHUTE   REAR OF BLDG. 3' X 4' TO CELLAR.
LARGE   CELLAR AREA.

END OF STRUCTURAL PHASE 2: CHIEFS OPERATIONAL INFORMATION AVAILABLE UPON
REQUEST

FIGURE 9.2 *Data sheets for a prefire plan.* (Source: New York City Fire Department, New York, New York)

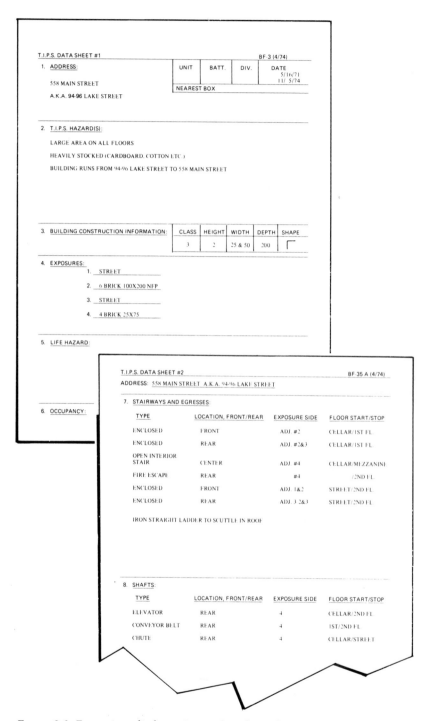

FIGURE 9.3 Expansion of information on data sheets shown in Figure 9.2. (Source: New York City Fire Department, New York, New York)

T.I.P.S. DATA SHEET #3   BF-35 B (4/74)

ADDRESS: 558 MAIN STREET A.K.A. 94-96 LAKE STREET

9. BELOW GRADE INFORMATION:

    ACCESS TO CELLAR ONLY FROM INTERIOR OF BUILDING FRONT AND REAR AT

    EXPOSURE 4 CENTER OF BUILDING.

    THE STAIR AT EXPOSURE 4 IS OPEN.

    STAIRS AT REAR AND FRONT OF BUILDING ARE ENCLOSED

    CHUTE REAR OF BUILDING 3' X 4' TO CELLAR

    LARGE CELLAR AREA

10. FIRE PROTECTION:

    THERMOSTATIC ALARM IN CELLAR

11. OTHER:

    LARGE OPEN AREA ON ALL FLOORS. HEAVILY STOCKED WITH FAST BURNING AND SMOKE

    PRODUCING STOCK. (CARDBOARD, COTTONS ETC.) MEZZANINE ON LAKE STREET ADDS

    ANOTHER 2500 SQUARE FEET OF FLOORING AND STORAGE TO 1ST. FLOOR.

T.I.P.S. DATA SHEET #4   OPERATIONAL   BF-35 C (4/74)

ADDRESS: 558 MAIN ST. A.K.A. 94-96 LAKE ST.

    FIRE FIGHTING TIPS

    VERTICAL EXTENSION: VIA OPEN STAIRS   A. CELLAR TO 1ST FLOOR
                                                  B. 1ST FLOOR TO MEZZANINE
                                 VIA CONVEYOR CHUTE 1ST FLOOR TO 2ND FLOOR

    HORIZONTAL EXTENSION: VERY LARGE OPEN AREAS ON ALL FLOORS.
                                 HEAVILY STOCKED WITH FAST BURNING AND SMOKE
                                 PRODUCING STOCK (CARDBOARD, COTTONS ETC.)
                                 200 FOOT DEPTH AND 25' FRONT ON MAIN ST.; 50' FRONT
                                 ON LAKE ST.
                                 MEZZANINE ON LAKE STREET SIDE ADDS ANOTHER
                                 2500 SQUARE FEET OF FLOORING AND STORAGE TO
                                 1ST FLOOR.

    CELLAR FIRE: STRETCH ADDITIONAL LINES AT REAR (LAKE ST.)
                                 1. TO COVER CONVEYOR OPENING
                                 2. TO ADVANCE TO OPEN STAIR ON S/S 1ST. FLOOR
                                    TO PREVENT FIRE FROM COMING OUT OPEN STAIR
                                    AND ALSO TO PROTECT MEZZANINE OVERHEAD

FIGURE 9.3 (Continued).

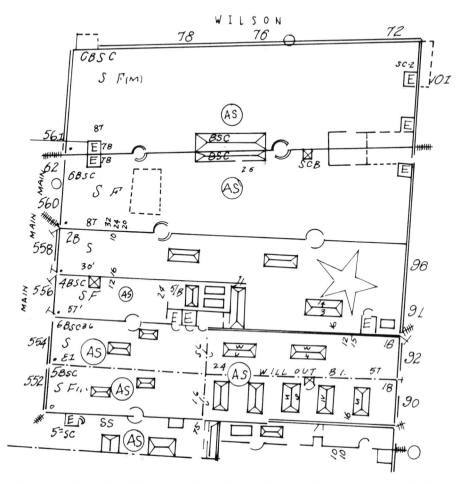

FIGURE 9.4 *Typical building layout sketch for a prefire plan. This sketch includes the data sheets from Figures 9.2 and 9.3.* (Source: New York City Fire Department, New York, New York)

Standards Institute (ANSI), provides a list of additional, less common abbreviations.[1] Figure 9.6 shows a prefire plan building layout with symbols.

Relationship Between Prefire Planning and Inspections

Prefire planning and inspections overlap in a number of ways. Like inspections, prefire plan surveys often uncover code violations. Reports of violations might be sent to the Fire Prevention Bureau or to the departmental officer responsible for enforcement of codes. Prefire plan surveys and inspections reinforce each other by familiarizing fire fighters with the buildings in their districts and by offering opportunities for good public relations.

SYMBOLS FOR SITE FEATURES

Buildings.

(a) The exterior walls of buildings are outlined in single thickness lines if other than masonry and double thickness lines if masonry.

(b) The perimeter of canopies, loading docks, and other open walled structures are shown by broken lines.

Railroad Tracks. Railroad tracks are shown by parallel lines.

Streets. Streets are shown, usually at property lines.

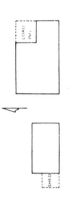

DOWNING STREET

Bodies of Water. Rivers, lakes, etc., are outlined.

POND

CREEK

Fences.

Fences are shown by lines with "x's" every inch (25mm).

Gates are shown.

Property Lines.

Fire Department Access.

F.D.

SYMBOLS FOR BUILDING CONSTRUCTION

Types of Building Construction. Types of construction are shown narratively.

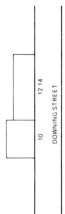

FIRE-RESISTIVE CONST (TYPE II)

WOOD FRAME CONST (TYPE V)

Height. Height is shown to indicate number of stories above ground, number of stories below ground, and height from grade to eaves.

Roof, Floor Assemblies.

Fire-resistive Floor or Roof

Wood Joisted Floor or Roof

Other Floors or Roofs

(Stl deck on stl joists)

#

Floor/Ceiling or Roof/Ceiling Assembly

Details indicated, as necessary.

Floor on Ground

Truss Roof

FIGURE 9.5 *Standard plan symbols representing general location and type of COPE features. (Source: Fire Protection Handbook[2])*

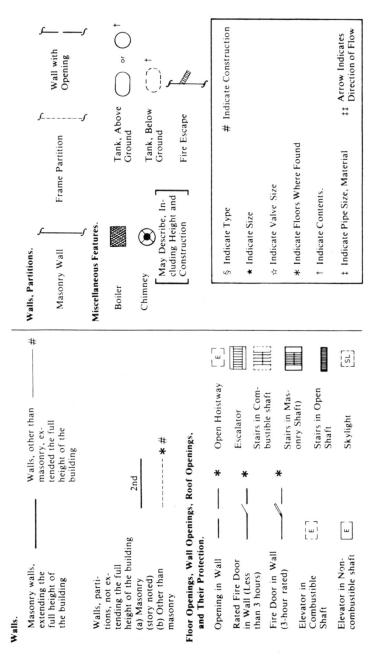

FIGURE 9.5 (*Continued*).

SYMBOLS FOR WATER SUPPLY AND DISTRIBUTION

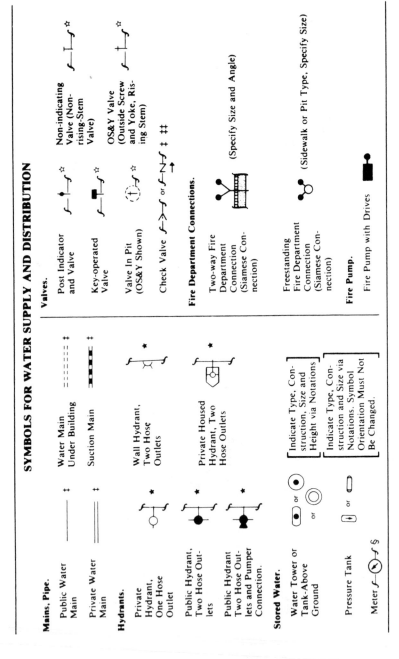

FIGURE 9.5 (Continued).

SYMBOLS FOR SPRINKLER SYSTEMS[1]

Piping, Valves, Control Devices.

Sprinkler Riser

Check Valve, General

Alarm Check Valve

Dry Pipe Valve

Dry Pipe Valve with Quick Opening Device (Accelerator or Exhauster)

Deluge Valve

Alarm/Supervisory Devices.

Flow Detector/ Switch (Flow Alarm)

Pressure Detector/Switch

§ (Specify Type—Water, Low Air, Hi Air, etc.)

Water Motor Alarm (Water Motor Gong)

(Shield Optional)

Electric Alarm Bell (Electric Alarm Gong)

SYMBOLS FOR EXTINGUISHING SYSTEMS

Wet (Charged) System.

(a) Automatically Actuated   or

(b) Manually Actuated

Dry System.

(a) Automatically Actuated   or

(b) Manually Actuated

Foam System.

(a) Automatically Actuated

(b) Manually Actuated

For Liquid—, Gas—, and Electrical-type Fires.

(b) Automatically Actuated

For Fires of All Types, Except Metals.

(a) Automatically Actuated

(b) Manually Actuated

Carbon Dioxide System.

(a) Automatically Actuated

(b) Manually Actuated

Halon System.

(a) Automatically Actuated

(b) Manually Actuated

Supplementary Symbols

Nonsprinklered Space

Partially Sprinklered Space

[1] These symbols are intended for use in identifying the type of installed system protecting an area within a building.

FIGURE 9.5 (Continued).

Table 9.1 Legend of common abbreviations. Some words that have a common abbreviation, e.g., "ST" for "street," are spelled out fully to avoid confusion with similar abbreviations used herein for other terms. (Source: *Fire Protection Handbook*[3])

Above	ABV	Liquid	LIQ
Accelerator	ACC	Liquid oxygen	LOX
Acetylene	ACET	Manufacture	MFR
Aluminum	AL	Manufacturing	MFG
Asbestos	ASB	Maximum capacity	MAX CAP
Asphalt protected metal	APM	Mean sea leves	MSL
Attic	A	Metal	MT
Automatic	AUTO	Mezzanine	MEZZ
Automatic fire alarm	AFA	Mill use	MU
Automatic sprinklers	AS	Normally closed	NC
Avenue	AVE	Normally open	NO
Basement	B	North	N
Beam	BM	Number	No
Board on joist	BDOJ	Open sprinklers	OS
Brick	BR	Outside screw & yoke valve	OS & Y
Building	BLDG	Partition (label composition)	PTN (i.e., WD PTN)
Cast iron	CI		
Cement	CEM	Plaster	PLAS
Centrifugal fire pump	CFP	Plaster board	PLAS BD
Cinder block	CB	Platform	PLATF
Composition roof	COMPR	Pound (unit of force)	LB
Concrete	CONC	Pressure	PRESS
Construction	CONST	Unit of pressure (pounds per square in.)	PSI
Corrugated iron	COR IR	Protected steel	PROT ST
Corrugated steel	COR ST	Private	PRIVATE
Diameter	DIA	Public	PUB
Diesel engine	D ENG	Railroad	RR
Domestic	DOM	Reinforced concrete	RC
Double hydrant	DH	Reinforcing steel	RST
Dry pipe valve	DPV	Reservoir	RES
East	E	Revolutions per minute	RPM
Electric motor driven	EMD	Roof	RF
Elevator	ELEV	Room	RM
Engine	ENG	Slate shingle roof	SSR
Exhauster	EXH	Space	SP
Feet	FT	South	S
Fiber board	FBR BD	Stainless steel	SST
Fire escape	FE	Steam fire pump	SFP
Fire department pumper connection	FDPC	Steel	ST
Fire detection units	FDU	Steel deck	ST DK
Products of combustion	POC	Stone	STONE
Rate of heat rise	RHR	Story	STO
Fixed temperature	FTEP	Street	STREET
Fire Pump	FP	Stucco	STUC
Floor	FL	Suspended acoustical plaster ceiling	SAPL
Frame	FR	Suspended acoustical tile ceiling	SATL
Fuel oil (label with grade number)	FO #___	Suspended plaster ceiling	SPC
Gallon	GAL	Suspended sprayed acoustical ceiling	SSAL
Gallons per day	GPD	Tank (label capacity in gallons)	TK
Gallons per minute	GPM	Tenant	TEN
Galvanized iron	GALVI	Tile block	TB
Galvanized steel	GALVS	Timber	TMBR
Gas, natural	GAS	Tin clad	TIN CL
Gasoline	GASOLINE	Triple hydrant	TH
Gasoline engine driven	GED	Truss	TR
Generator	GEN	Under	UND
Glass	GL	Vault	VLT
Glass block	GLB	Veneer	VEN
Gypsum	GYM	Volts (indicate number of)	450 v
Gypsum board	GYM BD	Wall board	WLBD
High voltage	HV	Wall hydrant	WLH
Hollow tile	HT	Water pipe	WP
Hose connection	HC	West	W
Hydrant	HYD	Wire glass	WGL
Inch, inches	IN	Wire net	WN
Iron	IR	Wood	WD
Iron clad	IR CL	Wood frame	WD FR
Iron pipe	IP	Yard	YD
Joist, joisted	J		

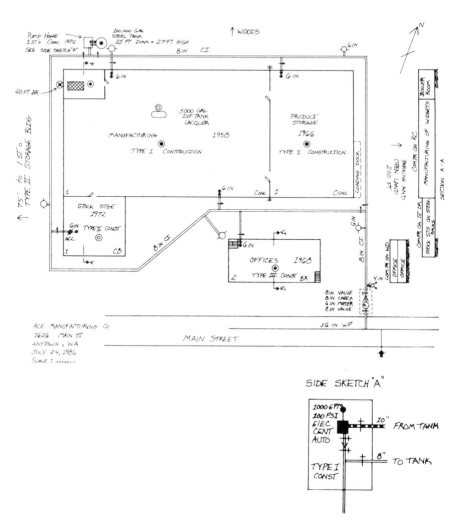

FIGURE 9.6 *A typical site sketch (top), with section detail, and side sketch (bottom) showing fire protection facilities and equipment. (Source: Fire Protection Handbook[4])*

People recognize the advantages of advance planning, especially for emergencies, and usually are impressed by prefire plans. Before an inspection, a company officer should review the prefire plan. Then, if an inspection indicates that certain features of the plan have changed (e.g., if an opening has been filled in, or the location of hazardous material storage has been changed), such information can be incorporated into the prefire plan. Although direct contact with people is limited to the initial visit and follow-ups, newspaper articles about prefire plans also can help make the general public more aware of the competence of a fire department.

Drafting Prefire Plans

Generally, a fire department cannot efficiently cover an entire district as frequently as it would prefer in the limited time available. Therefore, priority is given to certain areas or occupancies of high value or those with a great potential for loss of life or property. Outlined below are procedures for conducting a prefire plan.

The Survey: The entire company actively participates in the survey process, which is very similar to an inspection. The department usually supplies checklists and reporting forms that provide guidance in making the information-collecting process more efficient. These checklists should be marked as each category of information is obtained. Fire fighters can gather data in teams or separately; at times, the company officer might need to collect or verify certain pieces of information alone. When the building has been surveyed thoroughly (the amount of time will vary depending on the size of the building) and the entire company is satisfied that the survey information is correct, a final map of the building and a data sheet showing the specific hazard(s) in the building should be prepared. The best response route and initial attack positions can also be indicated at this stage.

The Drafting Process: A fire department that is formulating a program of prefire planning might use a procedure similar to the following:

1. Determine order of priority for buildings to be surveyed.
2. Plan a schedule for surveys.
3. Notify owners or managers of properties about the prefire plan program, and request permission to make a survey. As with inspections, this request is legally unnecessary, but it is made to help maintain good community relations.
4. Decide which units will carry out the survey.
5. After the survey data is gathered, incorporate it into the prefire plan.
6. Modify prefire plans whenever there are changes in occupancies or buildings, and incorporate all changes into the plan as soon as possible. Also, changing traffic patterns, improvements in apparatus and equipment, and new concepts in fire fighting operations require updating of plans.

Use and Application of Prefire Plans

Prefire plans often are carried on apparatus so company officers and fire fighters can refresh their memories about the details of a building. Many prefire plans are now available on a computer. A dispatcher then can print out the plan when needed or the plan can be displayed on remote terminals in fire department vehicles.

Additional benefit can be derived from prefire plans by using them as a basis for simulation drills. Strategy and tactics for fighting possible fires can be discussed during these drills. The use of prefire plans for training purposes helps to enhance the attractiveness of simulation drills, increases fire fighter interest in departmental procedures, and, most importantly, helps increase company awareness of hazards in the district. Further information on the use of prefire plans for training purposes can be found in Chapter 14. It should be kept in mind that drills using prefire plans can become dull and monotonous if the only objective is to become aware about an emergency that might never happen. Be sure to rotate the target hazard structures in the drill.

The Future of Prefire Planning

The development of prefire planning strategies for the most important and/or likely hazards can be a complex and time-consuming task, especially for those fire departments that have many industrial complexes, institutions, and commercial occupancies in their district.

In the past, barriers to extensive prefire planning included the inability to gather, sort, and store the data generated by a comprehensive prefire planning program. These barriers were further compounded by the difficulties in quickly recovering the information for use during an emergency.

Rapid advances in microcomputer technology have provided the fire service with the necessary hardware and software to maintain the data generated by a community-wide prefire planning system. However, the gathering of the data is still highly labor intensive, and many fire departments are unwilling or unable to devote the time and energy to such a task. This is true despite the fact that the dividends — in terms of operating efficiency, fire fighter safety, and level of protection for the community — are extensive.

Role of the Company Officer in Prefire Planning

The company officer has the responsibility for managing the process of developing and maintaining up-to-date prefire plans. The officer can also use the plans to increase interest in fire prevention and details about the hazards in the district.

The initial survey of a building generally is regarded as interesting, probably because it usually is more inspiring to do something for the first time. The officer must continue to emphasize the importance of prefire planning and its relevance to improving fire fighting operations, or subsequent visits for updating information might be treated less enthusiastically. This is especially true if the same personnel have frequently inspected the same building for violations.

The Linking Elements concept (see Chapter 4) can be a useful tool for company officers who are attempting to create greater interest in prefire planning. To create such interest requires the following:

1. Setting goals for developing and updating prefire plans, keeping in mind the eight problem areas that often arise in MBO programs: extent,

quality, involvement, frequency, accountability, participation, performance appraisal/evaluation, and operational/development issues (see Figure 5.3).

2. Ensuring that planning and scheduling for development of prefire plans are thorough and realistic.

3. Making work assignments that place equal demands on all fire fighters, considering their respective skills and talents.

4. Providing the necessary training to eliminate any knowledge/skill deficiencies that might create apprehension or feelings of inadequacy in a fire fighter. The company officer should ensure that all fire fighters know how to use a prefire plan, can draw maps that show building dimensions, understand how to use symbols, and are able to decide which details about a building are important enough to record.

5. Making frequent use of prefire plans in training for interesting simulations or joint planning sessions.

6. Using prefire planning for providing recognition to individuals.

7. Assigning to individual fire fighters those tasks that provide greatest satisfaction to them and rotating the tasks that are widely desired or that present opportunities for increasing competence.

Fire Ignition Sequence Investigation

Investigations into fires that are not considered to be of suspicious origin are conducted by department officers or fire prevention inspectors. They provide the basis for learning about the causes of fires, the reasons for their spread, and the performance of whatever fire prevention equipment had been installed in the building. Much can be learned from the causes for these fires and their effect on the buildings where they occurred. There are four basic reasons for investigating fires:

1. To develop new fire prevention methodology for addressing special causes identified by the investigation. This permits strategies to be fine-tuned for similar situations in the future.

2. To determine whether fires are due to arson in order to notify appropriate authorities.

3. To determine compliance with codes.

4. To provide documentation for insurance company inquiries.

In those cases where arson is suspected, a higher degree of sophistication is required from the people conducting the investigation. Additional information must be gathered, from investigations and interrogations, that will strengthen a criminal case.

Arson Investigations

The authority for investigating fires of a suspicious nature rests primarily with the state fire marshal's office or, in the absence of this position, with the state police. However, in practice, many states delegate this power to local fire department officials who cooperate fully with the police.

Some large departments have arson squads whose special task is the investigation of suspicious fires (see Figure 9.7). Within these squads there are officers, trained by the police department, who might have the power of arrest and the responsibility for preparing cases for prosecution. Others are composed of officers from both fire and police departments. Depending on local ordinances, fire prevention officers might also have such police powers.

The special training needed for fire investigation might not be available in smaller fire departments. In such instances, when arson is suspected, the work often is turned over to the local police department or to the police department in the nearest large community.

The investigation of a suspicious fire usually begins with a search for evidence of the way the fire might have started (see Figure 9.8). The fire scene is searched for clues, and statements are obtained from witnesses and others who can contribute ideas and information. Sometimes the officer in charge of the investigation will call on the fire fighters for their assistance. Care should be taken to ensure that all possible evidence is collected and that pictures are taken

FIGURE 9.7 *Fire investigators examining debris in a nursing home fire.* (Source: Desert News, Salt Lake City, Utah)

of all significant places. As part of the investigation procedure, departmental records are searched for relevant information. The insurance companies are contacted for additional information.

Because arson is a felony in every state, the ignition sequence must be investigated further after arson has been determined as the cause. At the arson investigation phase police authorities normally have primary responsibility, much the same as for other felonies occurring within their jurisdiction. However, in many areas of the United States, particularly at the state level or in larger cities, state and municipal laws give fire authorities the power to perform the police function of arson investigation.

If a suspect is apprehended and charged, it is the primary responsibility of the fire service to prove that the fire was willfully and maliciously caused. When developing an arson case, three elements must be established:

1. That there was an actual charring or destruction by fire.
2. That the ignition sequence of the fire was the result of willful and malicious design or intent.
3. That the suspect or an agent of the suspect had the opportunity to cause the fire.

An established motive is of great value in an arson case, although motive is not, from a legal standpoint, considered an essential element of arson. Many

FIGURE 9.8 This carpet clearly shows evidence of an arson fire. After the carpet was dried and swept clean, flammable liquid stains established conclusively the malicious ignition of the fire. (Source: Portland Fire Bureau, Portland, Oregon)

incendiary fires were set with no known motive. When presenting an arson case, each of the three preceding elements must be established to the satisfaction of the court in the order listed.

Fire Loss Reporting

A fire protection duty of equal importance to comprehensive investigation is the accurate reporting of such investigations. This duty has seldom been recognized as an essential part of fire protection. Fire departments and fire protection interests have, in the past, often had to depend on unreliable or incomplete projections and reports in order to put forth a case for corrective action of potential fire problems.

NFPA 901, *Uniform Coding for Fire Protection*,[5] establishes uniform language, methods, and procedures for fire loss reporting and coding. This system is designed so that all information can be coded for electronic or manual data processing. The use of computerized data processing is essential if meaningful and readily retrievable fire loss data is to be collected.

Computers provide an almost unlimited capability for storing, organizing, and retrieving the great volume of reports generated by a large jurisdiction, as well as the many details related to ignition sequence or communication of fire. Through the use of database programs, fire departments are able to gather, analyze, and utilize great quantitites of information and statistics. Spread-sheet analyses can be used to identify fire hazard trends, which help authorities pinpoint problems, suggest answers, and assist in eliminating any misdirection of fire protection dollars, thereby having a major effect on fire suppression procedures and the enforcement of fire prevention codes.

Computers have become essential to even the smallest fire department. Many small departments now use personal computers to maintain their records and reports. Some field inspectors use hand-held units to record information at an inspection site. When the inspector returns to the office, the information on the portable unit is transferred to the department's main database. By eliminating several steps of paperwork, each inspector can be more productive.

Role of Company Officer in Fire Ignition Sequence Investigations

It is the responsibility of the company officer to try to determine the origin of any fire immediately upon arrival at the scene and to continue the investigation, if necessary, after the fire has been brought under control. If an inspector from the Fire Prevention Bureau is available, that inspector should assist with, or in some departments take charge of, the investigation.

Arson can be suspected by conditions such as an absence of evidence that the fire was due to accident, a smell of gasoline or kerosine, simultaneous start of the fire in several different parts of the building, and so on. In such instances the officer should call the arson squad, the Fire Prevention Bureau, or the chief immediately so that a more detailed investigation can be made. As long as there are fire fighters at the scene, the fire department retains control of the property and can prevent members of the public, including the owner, from entering and possibly disturbing any evidence. Thus, fire fighters and other officials conducting investigations can search the premises and collect necessary evidence without obtaining legal sanction.

To help with investigations, company officers must schedule training in fire investigation so that fire fighters can help with finding clues to the causes of fires. Such training would also ensure that pieces of evidence are not disturbed in the clean-up process after a fire.

Water Supplies and Systems

Water is, and has long been, the most common extinguishing agent. An adequate and reliable water supply is necessary for preventing the spread of fires and extinguishing them. Traditionally, the Insurance Services Office (ISO) grading schedule has placed emphasis on the capability of a given municipality to deliver sufficient water for the control of fires.

A thorough knowledge of water supplies and systems is necessary for fire service managers. The following is a brief history of water supplies for fire defense and a synopsis of the importance of water supplies and systems to the fire service. For more detailed information on water supplies for fire protection, consult the *Fire Protection Handbook*.[6]

History of Water Supplies for Fire Defenses

Although the importance of providing adequate domestic water supplies was recorded as early as the time of the Roman Empire, water supplies for fire fighting were neglected until the late 18th century. At that time, engineers began developing plans for building waterworks in cities. Much of their emphasis was on systems that could provide water for fire fighting purposes as well as for other uses, such as drinking and sanitation. Many of these engineers based their calculations on the number of fire streams needed to protect a given population. This led to research into the cost of a waterworks system that could provide water for fire fighting purposes as well as for other uses. Several renowned engineers affiliated with individual waterworks examined the problem, and their findings were discussed in technical papers presented at engineering society meetings. Consult papers by J. Herbert Shedd (1889),[7] J. T. Fanning (1892),[8] and Emil Kuichling (1897)[9] for details about the discussions from which standards were developed.

Much of the basic data now employed in hydraulic work in fire protection was developed in a series of extensive investigations conducted in 1888 and 1889 by one of the first fire protection engineers, John R. Freeman.[10] In 1892 Freeman noted a relationship pertinent to fire fighting that was beyond a simple proportion between population and fire flow.[11] He reported that sometimes ten or more streams might be needed for a "compact group of large valuable buildings, irrespective of a small population." Fire fighting operations, he noted, required a concentration of water, while domestic needs were a matter of distribution. He drew attention to the need for large main pipes, and to hydrant distribution according to the nature of the buildings to be protected.

Elements of Water Supply

The modern water supply system, whether publicly or privately owned, should be adequate and reliable. Water systems designed today for municipal use have dual functions: they supply potable water for domestic consumption and they supply water for fire protection. Domestic water consumption includes water used for human consumption, sanitation purposes, industrial processes, gardening purposes, such as irrigating and lawn sprinkling, and air conditioning and similar water-consuming processes. Industrial sites often provide separate systems for supplying process water and water for fire protection. Any dual-purpose system should be able to supply enough water for fire protection and at the same time meet the maximum anticipated consumption for other purposes. A good working relationship between the fire department management and the water company management will ensure that the available supply of water is used most efficiently.

Adequacy and Reliability of Water Supply[6]

The adequacy of any given water supply system can be determined by engineering estimates. The source, including storage facilities in the distribution system, must be sufficient to furnish all the water that combined fire and domestic needs might require at any one time. Poor arrangement of the supply works and details of the pumping facilities could limit the adequacy of the supply or affect its reliability.

In a pumping system, a common arrangement is to have one set of pumps that takes suction from wells or from a river, lake, or other body of water. If the water does not have to be filtered, the pumps can discharge directly into the distribution system. Where filtration or other treatment is necessary, pumps take suction from the primary or raw water source and discharge to sedimentation basins or other facilities and then to filter beds. After processing, the water flows to clear-water reservoirs where a second set of pumps takes suction and discharges the water directly into the supply system. Unfortunately, failure of any part of the equipment can affect the entire system. This problem usually is handled by duplication of units and by arrangement of the plant to facilitate repairs.

When assessing the reliability of the supply works, features that should be evaluated are: minimum yield; frequency and duration of droughts; condition of intakes; possibility of earthquakes, floods, and forest fires; ice formations and silting up or shifting of river channels; and absence of guards or lookouts where needed to protect the facility from physical injury. Reservoirs out of service for cleaning and the interdependence of parts of waterworks also affect reliability. The condition, arrangement, and dependability of individual units of plant equipment, such as pumps, engines, generators, electric motors, fuel supply, electric transmission facilities, and similar items, are also factors. Pumping stations of combustible construction are subject to destruction by fire unless protected by automatic sprinkler systems.

Duplication of pumping units and storage facilities, and arrangement of mains and distributors so that water can be supplied to them from more than one direction, are measures that can ensure continuous operation. The importance of duplicate facilities is shown by the frequency of their use.

Standpipes and Automatic Sprinkler Systems: Standpipes and automatic sprinkler systems are sometimes referred to as the first line of defense against the spread of fire. Standpipe and hose systems provide a means for the manual application of water to fires in buildings. Although standpipes are required in buildings of large area and height, they do not take the place of automatic sprinkler systems. Fire losses have been reduced considerably by sprinkler systems, a fact considered by insurance companies in establishing rates.[12] Sometimes the savings in annual premiums is sufficient within a few years to pay for the installation of a sprinkler system.

In his book on *Automatic Sprinkler & Standpipe Systems*, John L. Bryan comments on the efficiency of automatic sprinkler systems:[13]

> In those fires in which automatic sprinkler systems were unsuccessful, the principal reasons were: (1) closed water control valves, (2) obstructions to sprinkler distribution, and (3) only partial protection of occupancies by sprinkler systems. Primarily, the major cause of unsatisfactory performance of automatic sprinkler systems has been the result of human action: such action involves the closing of water supply control valves before the fire occurs, or before the fire is completely extinguished. Fire department, security, and industrial personnel have all been involved in the premature closing of water control valves.

The overall effectiveness of a sprinkler system usually depends on the adequacy and reliability of the public water supply system. This can be the case even if a water tower on top of, or adjacent to, the building is available. Such supplies often are limited in quantity, and alone might not be adequate for a large fire. When a sprinkler system exists, the probability is, of course, very small that any fire can spread.

Areas of Overlapping Responsibility Between Water Company and Fire Department: There are several areas in the maintenance of an adequate and reliable water supply in which the water company and fire department cooperate, and in which responsibilities somewhat overlap.

1. When extensive new construction in any community is considered, both the water company and the fire department are involved in determining if a water supply system could provide the required fire flow for the type of development planned.

2. The fire department often has maps of the complete water system. Hydrant checks of the entire district usually are carried out on a rotating basis so that every hydrant is checked at least once a year (more frequently in high-value areas) to determine whether the hydrant is in operating condition and whether it can deliver the required fire flow. The water company usually is responsible for promptly correcting any problems that are found.

3. When changes of occupancy occur before permits are issued, inspectors should consider the adequacy of water supplies relative to the hazards of the new occupancy.

4. Where the relationship with the water utility is good, all problems affecting the water supply should be communicated immediately to the fire department. Conversely, when there is a major fire, the water utility should be so informed so that it can increase pressure, if necessary, or begin the operation of emergency valves.

Auxiliary Water Supplies—A Fire Department Responsibility: It is the responsibility of the fire department to arrange for auxiliary water supplies. Where these are located on private property, the cooperation of the property owner is needed. Where the water supplies are under the jurisdiction of a public authority, agreements for the use of the water supplies must be established before the need arises.

Some rural and suburban departments maintain large-capacity tank trucks and tanker shuttles for the transportation of water where no hydrants exist. Other departments have apparatus specially designed to draw water by suction from natural bodies of water. A department must, of course, arrange for access to water supply for every possible fire in the district; sometimes this means considerable planning and negotiations with those who control the supplies.

Changes in the ISO grading schedule have made it more performance oriented. It is now easier to meet the minimum flow requirements via alternative means, if that is all that is available.

Department Organization to Ensure Adequate Water Supplies: Of major concern to fire department management is departmental organization to ensure adequate water supplies. For example, a large fire department might appoint a special committee to work with the water company to ensure adequate water supplies for fire protection. This committee could include a water liaison officer from the fire department, a water supply company representative, and representatives from governmental agencies affected by the decisions. Smaller departments usually do not need to organize committees for such functions, and generally delegate these responsibilities to specific personnel within the department.

Regardless of the way the water supply planning is handled, fire companies must know how to obtain the supply they need at every point in the district. At least one person in each first-due company should know the water supply system well.

This person should know the general range of pressures in the water mains and the size of the mains available for fire fighting. The distribution of hydrants and mains should be studied so that pumpers can be located without unnecessarily long hose lays. Prefire planning for all large buildings or plants should emphasize water supply.

Role of the Company Officer: Water Systems and Supplies

It is the responsibility of the company officer to become familiar with the water supply system maps and the location, flow capabilities, and operation of hydrants in the district. The company officer should see that scheduled inspections of hydrants in the district are done, and should ensure that a reasonable priority is given to inspecting all water supply system components in the department's district.

A fire department connection is mandatory on all standpipe systems, and is recommended on sprinkler systems. The connection provides the only means of supplying water to the dry standpipe system. The fire department connection should always be inspected by fire companies when in-service inspections are conducted. A regular inspection and testing program relative to fire department connections for both standpipe and sprinkler systems, and the complete testing of both, is a necessity for every fire department. It is the company officer's responsibility for seeing that tests, inspections, and evaluations for all standpipes and sprinkler systems in the department's district are carried out in accordance with accepted procedures (see Figure 9.9).

Automatic sprinkler systems, one of the greatest aids to fire departments, can only function effectively if there is sufficient water pressure. As stated previously, the major cause of unsatisfactory performance of automatic sprinkler systems is, primarily, the result of human action. Such action involves the closing of water supply control valves before the fire occurs or before the fire is completely extinguished. Therefore, upon arrival at a sprinklered building, one of the first responsibilities of the officer in command should be to station someone at the operating sprinkler system water supply control valve to prevent the water from being turned off until the fire is effectively controlled. Another responsibility upon arrival is to supplement the sprinkler system's water supply with hose lines from adequate public water mains or natural sources to the fire department connection on the sprinkler system. These essential and simultaneous procedures will depend, in part, on information obtained during fire department prefire planning. In *Fire Attack: Command Decisions and Company Operations*, Warren Kimball states:[14]

> In any event, the primary responsibility of the fire department on responding to fires in sprinklered buildings is to see that the sprinklers have ample water supply and pressure, and that small hose teams are provided for mop-up. The fire department will also provide ventilation, overhaul, and salvage service.

FIGURE 9.9 *A fire department officer checks the condition of the discharge valve from a standpipe system.* (Courtesy of Stephen C. Leahy, College Park Volunteer Fire Department, College Park, Maryland.)

Details on the testing, maintenance, and periodic inspection of standpipe systems are contained in NFPA 14, *Standard for the Installation of Standpipe and Hose Systems.*[15] Details on acceptance tests and water supplies for sprinkler systems can be found in NFPA 13, *Standard for the Installation of Sprinkler Systems,*[16] and details on inspections and prefire planning for both automatic sprinkler and standpipe systems are contained in NFPA 13E, *Recommendations for Fire Department Operations in Properties Protected by Sprinkler and Standpipe Systems.*[17]

Loss Prevention Information Management Systems

In loss prevention, as in other aspects of fire department operations, the development of an effective information management system is crucial. Although the system should be as thorough as possible, it should also provide a simple and easy-to-use procedure for gathering and retrieving information necessary to manage the loss prevention program.

To assist in future efforts, justify past actions, and assist outside agencies, the system must be able to record, retrieve, and rapidly utilize data that are gathered on a continual basis. To manage the large volume of data in a loss prevention information system, most fire departments use computers.

When a fire occurs, information about that incident is recorded along with all pertinent data on the structure or occupancy in question. Some of the uses for this information, which are many and varied, include:

1. Providing updates for existing prefire plans and helping develop new plans. This can reduce the amount of time needed to complete a survey and produce the document.
2. Developing a history of code compliance for specific properties. This information assists with scheduling inspections and designating problem occupancy classes (types) for special inspection efforts.
3. Adding to the database on continuing compliance with inspection results and providing the information for re-inspection procedures or follow-up.
4. Assisting insurance companies and ISO grading personnel in determining rates and ratings.
5. Serving as the basis for statistical analyses to show what changes in practices and regulations might be desirable to strengthen fire prevention activities or to reduce the probability of fires through structural changes.

Rather than listing a series of standard reports, it is suggested that a fire department determine what is needed and set up a system for gathering and using the information. The best systems are designed to meet a specific department's needs, which do not contain unnecessary and duplicate facts. If a department already has an information system, it should be screened for extraneous data. If setting up a new one, the department should organize a committee to study the needs and design a system to meet the precise needs identified for the community served.

Legal Aspects

The importance placed on fire prevention activities in the United States is indicated by the wide range of powers given most fire marshals in rights of entry for fire inspection and investigation, fire marshal's hearings, rights of subpoena of any records or persons who might have information concerning fire ignition sequence, and so on. Such powers have been upheld by most courts of law, and should be honored when being used by members of the fire service in the performance of their duties.

Ordinances and Inspections

Ordinances define the procedures to be carried out for each hazard in the various occupancy categories, and recommend the number of inspections that should be made to ensure compliance. The ordinances and regulations also specify the penalties for violation of any code.

Balancing Individual Rights with Those of the Public for Protection from Fire Hazards: Ordinances and regulations also confer the authority for inspection of premises on fire department officials, subject to certain safeguards. These safeguards protect the rights of the individual against unreasonable search and seizure as guaranteed by the U.S. Constitution.

When a conflict arises between the rights of the individual and the fire department's police powers, the issue is subject to rulings by the courts. Two sample cases—*Camara* v. *Municipal Court of the City and County of San Francisco*, and *See* v. *Seattle*[18]—involved the right of individuals to refuse admission to the fire department to inspect commercial occupancies, as provided for in fire code safety regulations. In both cases, the courts maintained that a person cannot be prosecuted for resisting inspection unless a search warrant has been issued by a legally appointed judicial officer.

In the case of Camara, the U.S. Supreme Court ruled in favor of the appellant where the right of entry without a warrant involved a housing code inspector. In the See case (which involved a warehouse), the fire department wanted to inspect under authority of a City of Seattle ordinance granting the fire chief the right "to enter all buildings and premises except the interior of dwellings as may often be necessary." The owner refused to permit an inspection on the grounds that the ordinance was invalid. He said the fire chief had no search warrant, nor any probable cause to believe that a violation of any law existed on the premises. In upholding the constitutionality of the ordinance, the Washington Supreme Court (later overruled by the United States Supreme Court) said:[18]

> The purpose of the fire code inspection is to correct conditions hazardous to life and property. The problem of keeping cities and their inhabitants free from explosions and fires is a serious task facing all fire departments. It is obvious that routine inspections are necessary to ensure the safeguarding of life and property.
>
> The need to conduct routine inspections of commercial premises, in regard to which probable cause for the issuance of a warrant could not ordinarily be established, outweighs the interest in privacy with respect to such premises. The purpose of the inspection contemplated by the code is not unreasonable.

The U.S. Supreme Court reversed the conviction of the warehouse owner on the ground that the Seattle ordinance, authorizing a warrantless inspection of his warehouse, was an unconstitutional violation of his rights under the Fourth and Fourteenth Amendments.

The Court cited its decision in *Camara* v. *San Francisco* and declared that, "The businessman, like the occupant of a residence, has the constitutional right to go about his business free from unreasonable entries upon his private commercial property."[18]

The Court felt that its decisions restricting administrative agencies in their attempts to subpoena corporate books and records supported their view that any agency's particular demand for access should be measured in terms of probable cause to issue a warrant, against a flexible standard of reasonableness that takes into account the public need for effective enforcement of the particular regulation involved. "But the decision to enter and inspect will not be the product of unreviewed discretion of the enforcement officer in the field." The Court concluded as follows:[18]

> We therefore conclude that administrative entry, without consent, upon the portions of commercial premises which are not open to the public may only be compelled through prosecution or physical force within the framework of a warrant procedure. We do not in any way imply that business premises may not reasonably be inspected in many more situations than private homes, nor do we question such accepted regulatory techniques as licensing programs which require inspections prior to operating a business or marketing a product. Any constitutional challenge to such programs can only be resolved, as many have been in the past, on a case-by-case basis under the general Fourth Amendment standard of reasonableness. We hold only that the basic component of a reasonable search under the Fourth Amendment—that it not be enforced without a suitable warrant procedure—is applicable in this context, as in others, to business as well as to residential premises. Therefore, appellant may not be prosecuted for exercising his constitutional right to insist that the fire inspector obtain a warrant authorizing entry upon appellant's locked warehouse.

However, while in theory the courts might ultimately decide that certain inspections constitute an invasion of privacy, in practice a search warrant is often not needed because property owners are aware that the fire department can usually obtain one. When a fire department does face a problem with an owner and seeks a warrant, it must show that probable cause exists, based on the length of time since the last inspection, the nature of the occupancy, and the condition of the entire area—but not necessarily based on specific knowledge of a violation.

Fire Codes Retroactive Where Life Safety Is Involved: The courts have attempted to maintain a balance between an individual's right to privacy and the need to protect against potential fire hazards. However, they have consistently recognized the need to protect life through upholding the right of the fire department to enforce regulations retroactively where life safety is involved.

For this reason, a local government might sometimes add items to the firesafety code regulations such as the installation of sprinkler systems in nursing homes and high-rise apartment buildings. Owners would then have to install sprinkler systems in all buildings in both occupancy categories, whether the structure is already in existence, in the process of being built, or planned for the future.

Role of the Company Officer in Legal Matters

Company officers must know their legal responsibilities as specified in the fire codes and interpreted by the courts. In the performance of duty, the company officer must keep in mind the following:

1. One- and two-family units usually can be inspected only upon request of the owner or occupant. An officer should be aware, however, whether local regulations require or permit an inspection. If a citizen complains about another person's violation of the safety ordinances, the department has the responsibility to investigate and inspect the premises.

2. Officers and inspectors must be aware that they have to inform an owner or person in charge of noncompliance with fire codes before a hazard can be considered a violation.

3. A reasonable period of time must be allowed for correction of code violations. Although unreasonableness in itself is not illegal, an officer must be aware that it would probably invalidate a department's police power to enforce compliance. Judges tend to dismiss cases brought by the department for failure to comply with ordinances unless a reasonable amount of time for correction has been allowed. Furthermore, harsh interpretation of codes and ordinances could eventually lead to poor public relations.

4. An inspector is legally responsible for recording all violations, and nothing can be disregarded intentionally.

5. An officer or inspector cannot recommend a specific company or individual as contractor for correction of deficiencies; only procedures to be carried out can be suggested.

ACTIVITIES

1. Describe the purpose of prefire planning. Then explain the four steps used in the prefire planning process.

2. Your department's existing prefire plan must be expanded to include a recently constructed chemicals storage facility. This building is located at the top of a steep hill in the outskirts of your community. What other information would be needed for the preparation of a prefire plan for this building?

3. (a) Explain why symbols and abbreviations are used in prefire plans. Do you think these symbols and abbreviations should be universal? Why or why not?

   (b) What effect would the following description of a building have in your prefire plan: CEM LOX plant, no FDU?

4. (a) Why should prefire plans be updated continually?
    (b) What methods are used to help fire fighters remember prefire plans before or during a fire in a given occupancy?
5. (a) In what specific ways are prefire plans and inspections similar?
    (b) What is the role of the company officer in ensuring that all fire fighters are familiar with prefire planning?
6. Outline the purposes of a fire ignition sequence investigation.
7. (a) Who is usually responsible for arson investigations within a large fire department?
    (b) How is a suspicious fire investigated, and how is an arson case developed?
8. Discuss and list with your class the requirements that determine adequacy and reliability of water supplies and systems for a fire department.
    (a) Describe the water supplies and systems that are available to your community's fire department.
    (b) What is the fire department's role in ensuring adequate water supplies and systems for fire fighting?
9. Based on the legal matters involved in inspections, determine which of the following statements are false and explain why.
    (a) An inspector with a search warrant can be refused entry into a commercial occupancy.
    (b) A local government can force a high-rise building owner to install a sprinkler system.
    (c) If an inspector feels that a building might contain a violation, a search warrant can be obtained without stating the nature or probability of the violation.
    (d) If a citizen complains about a neighbor's firesafety violations, the responsibility to investigate rests with the police department.
    (e) Inspectors must inform a building owner of a violation before a hazard can be considered a violation.
    (f) Violations noted on a property inspected by a fire department officer must be corrected within five hours after the premises have been inspected.

REFERENCES

[1] "Abbreviations for Use on Drawings and in Text," ANSI Y1.1–1972, American National Standards Institute, New York, NY, 1972.

[2] Cote, A. E., ed., *Fire Protection Handbook*, 16th edition, National Fire Protection Association, Quincy, MA, 1986, pp. 22-5, 22-6.

[3]Cote, A. E., ed., *Fire Protection Handbook*, 16th edition, National Fire Protection Association, Quincy, MA, 1986, pp. 22-7.

[4]Cote, A. E., ed., *Fire Protection Handbook*, 16th edition, National Fire Protection Association, Quincy, MA, 1986, pp. 22-8.

[5]NFPA 901, *Uniform Coding for Fire Protection*, National Fire Protection Association, Quincy, MA, 1986.

[6]Cote, A. E., ed., *Fire Protection Handbook*, 16th edition, National Fire Protection Association, Quincy, MA, 1986, pp. 17-36, 17-37.

[7]Shedd, J. Herbert, discussion on a paper by Sherman, William B., "Ratio of Pumping Capacity to Maximum Consumption," *Journal of New England Water Works Association*, Vol. 3, 1889, p. 113.

[8]Fanning, J. T., "Distribution Mains and the Fire Service," *Proceedings of the American Water Works Association*, Vol. 12, 1892, p. 61.

[9]Kuichling, E., "The Financial Management of Water Works," *Transactions of the American Society of Civil Engineers*, Vol. 38, 1897, p. 16.

[10]Freeman, J. R., *Transactions of the American Society of Civil Engineers*, Vols. 12 and 14.

[11]Freeman, J. R., "The Arrangement of Hydrants and Water Pipes for the Protection of a City Against Fire," *Journal of New England Water Works Association*, Vol. 7, 1892, p. 49.

[12]Bryan, J. L., "Economic Variables of Automatic Sprinkler Systems," *Automatic Sprinkler & Standpipe Systems*, 1st edition, National Fire Protection Association, Quincy, MA, 1976, pp. 64–76.

[13]Bryan, J. L., "Fire Department Procedures for Automatic Sprinkler and Standpipe Systems," *Automatic Sprinkler & Standpipe Systems*, 1st edition, National Fire Protection Association, Quincy, MA, 1976, p. 30.

[14]Kimball, W. Y., *Fire Attack: Command Decisions and Company Operations*, National Fire Protection Association, Quincy, MA, 1966, p. 134.

[15]NFPA 14, *Standard for the Installation of Standpipe and Hose Systems*, National Fire Protection Association, Quincy, MA, 1986.

[16]NFPA 13, *Standard for the Installation of Sprinkler Systems*, National Fire Protection Association, Quincy, MA, 1987.

[17]NFPA 13E, *Recommendations for Fire Department Operations in Properties Protected by Sprinkler and Standpipe Systems*, National Fire Protection Association, Quincy, MA, 1984.

[18]United States Supreme Court decisions: Camara v. Municipal Court of the City and County of San Francisco, 387 U.S. 523, 87 S. Ct. 1727 (1967); See v. City of Seattle, 387 U.S. 541, 87 S. Ct. 1737 (1967).

10

Fireground Command Management Functions

In fire fighting operations, a fire department's fire suppression effectiveness is put to the ultimate test. All of the activities used by a fire department must come together at the fireground. It is here that the results of planning and preparation for emergency operations come into play, forming the basis for strategy and tactics at the fire scene.

FIREGROUND OPERATIONS[1]

Fire suppression operations involve utilizing a fire department's resources to combat a fire. The success of a fire fighting operation depends on the ability of a fire department to use the available resources effectively and efficiently to protect lives and property. The fireground commander is responsible for managing the available personnel and equipment to achieve maximum results.

A fireground commander is responsible for the direction and control of operations in every incident. From the arrival of the first unit at the fire scene there should be one identified person in command, with the responsibility and authority to direct all phases of the operation. The officer in charge of the first arriving company assumes the role of fireground commander until relieved by a higher-ranking officer. In complex situations, command can be transferred one or more times as higher-ranking chief officers arrive and assume command.

The fireground commander is responsible for strategic decision making and the translation of strategic goals into tactical objectives and task assignments. Intermediate levels of command are responsible to the fireground commander for geographical portions of the operation (sectors) or for the supervision of particular functions. These sector officers coordinate the operations of a group of companies under the overall command of the fireground commander (see Figure 10.1).

A major incident might require a fairly complex command staff with a number of sector officers reporting to the fireground commander. Several officers might be assigned to support the fireground commander at a command post, providing additional information, or further subdividing the span of control into manageable units.

Standard operating procedures are an important aspect of fireground command. Every fire department should have a set of procedures that outlines the basic operating principles to be employed for any situation, from the most simple to the most complex. The procedures should be flexible enough to allow fire fighters to react to different situations and incremental to permit adjustment to the scale of the incident.

The fireground commander must utilize *strategy*—the development of a basic plan—to deal effectively with a situation and *tactics*—the methods to implement strategic plans—in the management of any fire suppression effort.

Preparation

Adequate preparation is necessary for effective fire fighting, for ensuring adequate water supplies to extinguish fires, and for reducing the extent of fire spread in order to minimize loss. In addition to all of the fire prevention activities, each of the following goals are important aspects of adequate preparation:

1. Efficient distribution of apparatus and personnel to make the best use of available equipment, while at the same time providing sufficient coverage for contingencies in each situation.

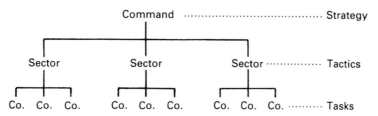

FIGURE 10.1 *A common type of fireground organization. The fireground commander (FGC) develops a strategic plan. The sector officers use tactical operations to achieve the goals of the plan and to assign specific tasks to individual fire companies within each sector. (Source: Fire Protection Handbook[2])*

2. Ability of available personnel and apparatus to extinguish any potential fire. This ability results from drills, training, prefire planning, and the availability of adequate supplies of extinguishing agents (mainly water).

3. Provision for applying the greatest possible tactical power with the first alarm units. If these companies do not succeed in confining the fire, the response of additional personnel and equipment might not be rapid enough to prevent loss of life or serious damage.

Achieving these goals depends on the extent of prefire planning, which helps to give a first-alarm company a head start in attack preparations, and the extent of prior training and drills, which helps to ensure that each unit makes efficient use of time and effort during actual fire fighting operations.

Fire Attack

At the fire scene two major factors contribute to the effectiveness with which a fire is attacked and controlled.

Strategy: A basic plan must be developed to deal effectively with various situations. The plan must identify major goals and prioritize objectives for the tactical elements. Strategic decisions are based on an evaluation of the situation, the risk potential, and the capabilities of the available resources.

Tactics: The fireground commander must select various methods to implement the strategic plan. The tactical objectives define specific functions that are assigned to groups of companies operating under sector officers (see Figure 10.2). The achievement of these objectives contributes to the strategic goals and must be compatible with the overall strategic plan.

Fireground Strategy[2]

Strategy is the foundation for all actions necessary to achieve fire fighting objectives. The strategic plan must identify major goals and prioritize objectives for the tactical elements. Strategic decisions are based on an evaluation of the situation, the risk potential, and the capabilities of the available resources.

The strategic options available to the fireground commander involve some very important, but basic, decisions. The most fundamental decision is the choice between offensive and defensive modes of operation, based on the capability of available resources and the risk to personnel. For offensive operations, companies extend hose lines into the interior of an involved fire area and extinguish the fire where they find it. In defensive operations, heavy streams are applied from the exterior to confine or control a fire, conceding the loss of the involved area. Offensive and defensive modes of operation must not be mixed in the same place at the same time. The fireground commander must make a conscious decision to identify what can be saved without undue risk to personnel.

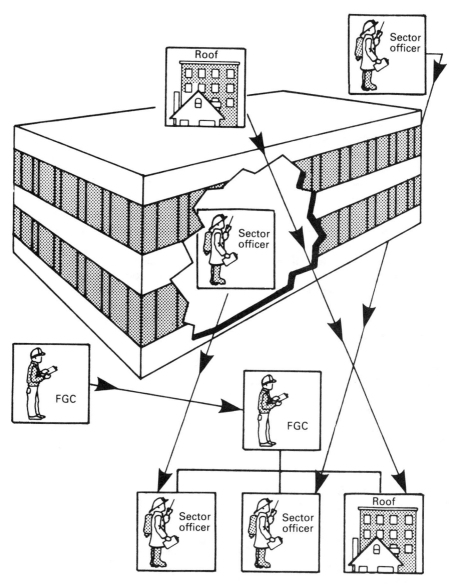

FIGURE 10.2 *Geographical sectors are responsible for all general fire fighting activities in an assigned area.* (Modified from Figure 3.5.5 of *Fire Command*,[3] p. 91, copyright © 1985 by Don Sellers, AMI.)

Chief Engineer Raymond Hill of the Los Angeles Fire Department described it this way:[4]

> In fire combat, the ultimate objective is the extinguishment of the fire. Each mission and task must contribute to the ultimate objective. The

ultimate objective may not be immediately obtainable and intermediate objectives must be selected. Each intermediate objective must be such that its attainment will quickly and economically contribute to the ultimate objective. The selection of intermediate objectives must be based upon a consideration of the fire itself, the operational environment, and the resources available at the fireground.

Hill believed that planning is not static, but is a progressive and continuing process; that strategy might need to be modified as changes in the fire situation or the arrival of additional resources dictates; that planning must take all foreseeable contingencies into account; and that careful planning is useful in small fires as well as in the larger ones. Hill also pointed out that:[4]

> The great majority of fires are small and their control and extinguishment becomes routine in nature. In fact, their handling becomes so routine that they are fought without making plans. This is a dangerous trap to fall into because when the large or critical fire comes along there is a tendency to fight this one too without a plan. So—develop the habit of *planning* for every fire, no matter how routine it may seem.

In order to make the best strategy decisions, the officer in charge must follow the basic decision-making process, which involves defining the problem, obtaining the data, identifying the alternative courses of action, selecting the alternative that is best for a given situation, continually evaluating the decision, and making adjustments when necessary. At the fire scene, the definition of the problem and the data come from the following separate and distinct analyses:

1. **Analysis of the fire situation (What's there?).** This includes facts and probabilities pertaining to: 1) threats to life, 2) the involved structures, 3) the fire itself, 4) the exposures, 5) the weather and time, and 6) fire fighting resources available. This analysis provides part of the definition of the problem and supplies some of the data.
2. **Needs assessment (What does the situation need?).** What is needed for the existing situation and the various probabilities that deserve consideration, including: 1) rescue, 2) exposure protection, 3) confinement, and 4) extinguishment. This analysis supplies additional definition of the problem and more data.
3. **Available resources at the fireground (What have I got?).** These must be viewed in terms of currently available and expected resources: 1) apparatus, 2) personnel, 3) equipment, 4) water and other extinguishing agents, and 5) hose. This analysis provides further information for thoroughly defining the problem and the rest of the necessary data.

Once these three analyses have been completed, the strategy for attacking the emergency can be built. Although this is a highly complex process, thorough preparation, practice, and experience allow the competent officer to compare the available resources with the needs of the situation, to review quickly several alternative courses of action, and to select the one course of action that seems to be the best. However, before any discussion of choosing alternatives can be meaningful, these three analyses require more detailed exploration.

Analysis of the Fire Situation

Obtaining the Information: Some information needed to analyze the fire situation should be known in advance, or obtained on the way to the fire. This includes:

1. Specific information about the fire scene and necessary details about fire science that pertain to the situation.
2. Data about the specific features (the terrain and the building) from maps, prefire surveys, or prefire plans. This data would either be carried on the apparatus or relayed by the dispatcher.
3. Factors that might influence decisions on the fireground such as weather and traffic conditions, the degree to which open hydrants might reduce water pressure in the summer, or the effect of dry weather.

The remainder of the information related to the fire situation — the facts and the probabilities — would be acquired at the fireground itself during the initial size-up process.

Threat to Life: Although all fires, if not confined, are a potential threat to life, some obviously represent a more immediate danger than others. Responding units might be partially aware of the seriousness of a fire situation from prior data and from on-site reports being relayed by courier or computer. Still, the officer who arrives first must obtain a complete picture by sizing up the situation and by questioning knowledgable individuals regarding any people who might be inside a structure.

In addition to the direct danger to people in a burning structure or vehicle, a fire can indirectly threaten the lives of other people in adjacent buildings. If the fire is spreading rapidly, occupants in adjoining structures must be made aware of the emergency and helped to evacuate if necessary. Bystanders who gather to watch a fire can also be endangered by explosions, debris, or falling parts of structures. The potential risk of injury to fire fighters must also be considered when deciding the method of rescue or attack.

The Involved Structure or Fireground: During the size-up process, the officer must make a rapid assessment of the problems presented by the involved structure, vehicle, or materials. While doing this, the officer must consider several important factors:

1. Construction features and materials that might contribute to fire spread or intensity.
2. Height.
3. Layout (separation and compartments, access routes, ventilation options, etc.).
4. Protective devices (sprinklers, fire curtains, fire doors, etc.).

5. Routes by which a fire could travel and spread, even in sprinklered premises (raised floors, suspended ceilings, cable ducts, air ducts, open stairwells, or elevator shafts).

6. Contents and the special problems that they might present (highly combustible materials, flammable liquids, and poisonous gases and smoke).

7. Location (terrain features that might influence decisions).

8. Special problems of outdoor fires (dry brush or timber, unknown contents in trash, storage areas, trucks, etc.).

9. Water sources.

Fire: The fire itself must be considered in relation to:

1. Location.
2. Spread potential.
3. Type of combustible.
4. Intensity.

Exposures: Exposures that need immediate attention to prevent the spread of fire include all the problems presented by adjacent exposures. These fall into the same categories as the involved structures themselves.

Weather and Time of Day: These considerations include:

1. Wind direction and intensity.
2. Temperature.
3. Precipitation (rain, snow, or the effect of dry conditions).
4. Time of day (traffic volume, number of people to be evacuated, or other related problems).

Fire Fighting Resources That Are Part of the Fire Location: Prefire plans or data about the location provide the responding officer with information about resources (fire flow from hydrants, external and internal fire protection equipment, and other automatic fire extinguishing systems and extinguishing agents).

Probabilities: The probabilities define the likelihood that various events will occur that will affect the course of the fire and the kind of resources and strategies needed to bring it under control. Probabilities change during the course of fireground operations. They are influenced by weather, time, features of the involved structure, and by the actions of the fire fighters.

A set of complex decisions faces the officer in charge of the size-up process. This officer must be able to look at the facts and select from the large amount of supporting data those issues that are the most relevant to the particular situation. Then, based on these issues, the officer must forecast various possibilities about the future course of the fire. For example, in assigning probabilities to a fire on the top floor of a seven-story building, an experienced officer would assess the likelihood of fire spreading to the undivided attic area and estimate the dangers associated with that possibility. The officer would consider the chances of extension throughout the top floor and give some thought to the probability of the fire involving adjacent structures. At the same time, the officer might regard the chance of fire spreading to lower floors as unlikely, but that contingency must be weighed. In preparing to make strategic decisions (that is, the allocation of resources), an officer must assess numerous probabilities, including:

1. Danger to life.
2. Danger to property.
3. Changing conditions.

In addition to the probabilities that are part of the environment of the changing fire scene, the officer must evaluate the effects of various fire fighting steps. For example, the possibility that resources might be reduced through fatigue or injury should be taken into account.

Analysis of Facts and Probabilities: Once the facts and probabilities are known, a total picture of the fire situation emerges. This total picture then becomes one of the foundations on which decisions are based. It provides part of the definition of the problem and a large segment of the data. Another foundation for decision-making comes from analyzing what is needed to cope with the situations and the probabilities presented.

Needs Assessment

The resources needed to deal with the emergency will fluctuate, depending on changing circumstances. The officer must again think and evaluate in terms of the probable needs of likely events.

Rescue: Life-saving operations require:

1. Rapid containment of the fire.
2. Ladders for evacuation (aerial, elevated, and extension ladders).
3. Equipment to gain access to trapped people.
4. Medical capabilities.
5. Adequate number of skilled personnel.

Exposures, Confinement, and Extinguishment: Attack on a fire requires:

1. Adequate amounts of extinguishing agents.
2. Equipment for applying extinguishing agents in adequate quantities.
3. An aggressive attack by an adequate number of skilled personnel.
4. Proper ventilation techniques.
5. Special equipment such as lights, cutting tools, etc.
6. Protective equipment for fire fighters.
7. Communications equipment.
8. Support services for maintenance, medical aid, utilities, information, traffic, and spectator control.

An analysis of these actual and probable future requirements provides additional information about the problem and more data on which the strategy decisions and the allocation of resources must be based. Because these needs can change, the officer in charge must take into account the need for reserves or personnel to relieve those in action, or the possibility that the emergency will diminish sufficiently to allow some of the personnel and/or units to return to headquarters.

Available Resources at the Fireground

An assessment must be made about the resources available at the fireground.

Apparatus: How many pumpers, ladder and rescue trucks, and specialized vehicles are available?

Personnel: How many skilled personnel are available?

Equipment: What type and how much was carried on apparatus as standard equipment? What was brought along in addition for rescue, ventilation, suppression, salvage, and overhaul?

Water: What supplies of water are available? Were supplies of other extinguishing agents brought to the fireground?

Hose: Which size and how much hose is carried by apparatus? What are the type and number of nozzles carried? What supplementary equipment, such as suction basins, is available?

Decisions about Resources

At this point in the size-up process, the officer is ready to make decisions about alternative courses of action to meet the emergency. The problem has been defined and the necessary data has been obtained. The final two steps in the decision-making process—defining and evaluating the alternatives to determine the best ones for the particular situation—must be taken.

In developing a strategy, a whole series of decisions has to be made. One of the first ones involves comparing needs with available resources to determine the number and types of reinforcements required, if any.

Guidelines for Decisions about Reinforcements: It is often difficult to decide if, when, and how much help is needed. In his book *Fire Attack 1: Command Decisions and Company Operations*, Warren Kimball offered the following guidelines:[5]

> Fire experience has shown that in a relatively high percentage of cases where only one or two additional companies have been called, second or third alarm has been required subsequently. In general, recommended practice is to promptly sound a second alarm in all cases where the first alarm response is not adequate. Calling companies piecemeal frequently has permitted further extension of a fire.
>
> There are seven main purposes for which multiple alarms are commonly ordered by officers in charge of fires:

1. To obtain extra personnel and equipment to aid in rescue operations.

2. To obtain additional personnel and equipment to run and man additional 2½-in. hand lines (this may involve covering additional positions).

3. To obtain additional personnel and equipment needed to place heavy streams in service.

4. To set up and help staff a command post or field headquarters at major fires.

5. To obtain additional help principally for truck duty such as forcible entry, ventilation, and salvage.

6. To provide relief personnel in situations where the fire fighting is unusually exhausting.

7. To cover exposures downwind from the fire where the main body of fire presents a possible flying brand hazard.

One or more of these situations may be involved in any decision to sound a multiple alarm, and the officer in charge must anticipate the need for extra help and not allow the situation to get ahead of the resources at hand.

Standard operating procedures for the local department and mutual aid companies determine which and how many companies respond to each alarm. Knowledge of local practices would, therefore, allow an officer to decide how many alarms should be called and whether specific items would be required that are not automatically available through a standard response. Thus, two questions must be answered: 1) How many alarms are needed? and 2) What special equipment and/or extinguishing agents might be needed? Both questions are difficult to answer in those borderline cases when it appears that the resources on the scene might be sufficient to control the situation. When there is doubt, the additional resources should be summoned.

Even though it is costly to bring additional resources to the scene, it is usually wiser to have too many rather than too few pieces of apparatus. This is true because the decision to bring reinforcements is reversible. Additional units can be turned back or released if subsequent developments show they will not be required. However, a decision not to call for reinforcements is essentially irreversible because additional fire damage will have been done if they are not at the fire scene when they are needed. Whether or not additional resources or reinforcements have been called, the officer in charge has to decide what to do with the available resources.

Very often, one of the resources is in limited supply. When this happens, the officer in charge has to rearrange the resources in order to make best possible use of the limited one. For example, in some situations, it will be possible to conserve personnel by using a heavier flow of extra water from deluge nozzles. However, if water or extinguishing agents are the resource in limited supply, the decisions are more difficult. Various options can be considered in this case, such as calling for tank trucks and running a relay operation to the fire. It might also be necessary to adopt a more defensive strategy such as taking a stand at a defensible wall, or segments of the fireground, instead of attacking the fire directly and depleting reserve supplies of extinguishing agents. When water supply is known to be limited, decisions about how best to use available supplies can be made in advance and integrated into prefire plans, thus avoiding the possibility of indecision at the fire scene.

Evaluating these alternatives is, of course, difficult. Good practice in decision-making skills can make the process easier and faster, and can give an officer confidence that the best possible decisions are being made.

Selecting the Best Strategy: Strategy must be decided first, before any tactical decisions are made, because strategy concerns the allocation of resources. The officer who begins to make tactical decisions before the resources have been allocated could find that inadequate resources are available for the tactical decisions, thus causing inefficient changes to be made in the field.

Decisions based on the allocation of resources should focus initially on the following: rescue, exposure protection to reduce life hazard, exposure protection (confinement) to reduce property damage, and fire attack (extinguishment). The officer in charge must consider each of these fireground operations and decide what proportions of the resources should be allocated to each. Sometimes concentrating on extinguishing the fire will take care of rescue and exposure protection simultaneously.

Different Kinds of Strategy: Basically, there are two major strategy groups: offensive and defensive. A primarily offensive strategy might be called for if a fire emergency is routine and first alarm companies are sufficient for quick extinguishment of the fire. However, if resources are inadequate, a more defensive approach is necessary. When possible, direct and immediate offense is

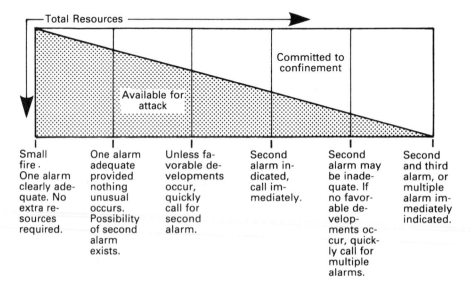

FIGURE 10.3 Options available to an officer during the size-up process.

highly desirable because damage will be minimized when exposures can be protected at the same time that a vigorous attack is being launched on the fire.

Figure 10.3 shows that when more resources are committed to confinement, fewer are available for attack. At the left side of Figure 10.3, the officer arrives on the scene and sees that no exposures need to be protected, and therefore all available resources can be used for direct attack on the fire. At the other extreme, at the right side of the diagram, the structures are so involved that all available resources on the first alarm might be inadequate for confinement, leaving none for direct attack. In that situation an immediate call for several additional alarms is indicated. Figure 10.4 shows what happens when additional resources have been called.

There are many possible variations of defensive strategies. Following is an outline of some of the alternatives a command officer would consider. They are listed in increasing degrees of fire fighter involvement.

1. Allowing the fire to burn itself out. In some cases it is not a question of whether resources are sufficient for an attack, but whether an attack is worthwhile. If the involved structure or vehicle is no longer salvageable, and if attempts to put the fire out would be potentially dangerous, then it might be better to let the fire burn itself out. A small detachment of fire fighters should stand by to make sure there is no extension of fire.

2. Taking a stand at a fire wall and allowing everything on the other side to burn. This might be the option chosen when forces on the scene are inadequate for direct attack (see far left side of Figure 10.3) and adequate forces cannot be obtained in time.

3. Holding the perimeter of the fire while encroachments are made gradually. These encroachments could include cooling a specific area to

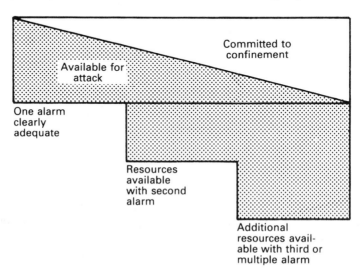

FIGURE 10.4 *Options available to an officer during the size-up process, with respect to reinforcements.*

prevent an explosion or partial collapse of a structural element, or preventing extension in a predictable direction, or allowing rescue operations to take place at the expense of protecting other extensions. This strategic option might be chosen when resources are somewhere left of center in Figure 10.3.

4. Protecting exposures and attacking the fire in the most crucial areas or gradually from all sides. This strategic option would be possible if the availability of resources is close to the center of Figure 10.3.

The officer in charge must select the strategic combination (outlined in Figure 10.3) that is most likely to have the least risk for people and involve the least amount of property damage. Selecting a strategy should not only focus on the attack alternatives that would hold fire damage to a minimum, but also on those that would cause the least damage from the fire fighting operations themselves. For instance, a very poorly trained company might apply such an excessive amount of water to a weak structure that the weight of the water added to the existing load might collapse the building. Less extreme are actual cases where excessive water caused damage to contents (e.g., furnishings, carpets), thus creating more damage than would have been caused by smoke and fire if a less aggressive attack plan had been followed.

All of these potential and actual consequences influence the degree of offensive attack. In certain circumstances it might be more desirable to allow a fire to burn a little longer if less water can be used. This decision influences both strategy and tactics, e.g., type and volume of streams. Frequently, greater awareness on the part of fire fighters of preventing potential damage by nondirect actions, such as turning off sprinkler valves as soon as a fire is sufficiently under control, will alleviate this problem.

Overall Strategic Plan

In fire fighting, protection of life is the first priority for assigning resources, no matter what the personnel limitations might be.

Protection of Life: In formulating strategies to protect life, the officer in charge needs to consider the degree of danger to which occupants are exposed and the resources available for effecting rescue. In so doing, the following questions should be considered:

- What risk would there be to the safety of the fire fighters involved in a rescue mission? What is the threat of injury and possible loss of life?
- Are resources sufficient for all rescue operations? If not, what rescue efforts can be undertaken? Inadequate personnel might make it impossible to proceed with all desirable rescue operations at the same time and have all of them succeed.
- Which rescue operations should receive priority? The officer in charge must decide which people are in most imminent danger, either from the fire itself or from other hazards. The rescue of those most threatened

should, of course, receive highest priority, except where danger to rescuers is excessive and personnel are needed for other rescue operations.

Based on these considerations the strategic decisions can be made — specifically, the resources that should be allocated to each of the rescue operations. Only after all the strategic decisions have been made can the tactical ones be considered. Tactical decisions involve assigning positions to fire fighters and specific pieces of apparatus.

In addition to the direct rescue attempts, the officer in charge must consider protecting those exposures where potential risk to life is serious enough to warrant immediate attention.

Formulating Exposure Protection, Confinement, and Extinguishment Strategy: Strategies are not static; they are never "cast in concrete." Instead, to be most effective, strategy must be adapted constantly to new developments. For instance, improper ventilation of a structure can cause a fire to change course, requiring revisions to strategy or at least a quick review to determine whether the strategy is still appropriate. If it is not, other options have to be reevaluated, and the plan has to be altered accordingly.

Although the decision-making process might seem to be a lengthy and complex sequence, in reality it might take only seconds to consider all the data, to evaluate all the alternatives, and to make the strategic decisions. The same questions might be considered several times. For example, an officer would have evaluated the vertical and horizontal ventilating probabilities early in the attack, and again later in the attack.

If the decision was made initially to delay ventilation procedures, the same decision-making process might have to be repeated at a subsequent stage in the fire fighting operations. For various reasons, a strategy that has been decided upon and implemented can bring results that differ from those anticipated. These results can force reevaluation of the approaches; such reevaluation might again have repercussions on operational tactical decisions. Thus, the process repeats itself until the fire is under control.

However, the allocation of resources for one purpose — that is, to achieve one objective — cannot be made in isolation from the other objectives that have to be considered in an emergency situation. Every operation and each segment of an operation requires resources. The allocation of these resources must therefore be coordinated in order for each operation to receive an adequate share. It is the officer's understanding of this process, combined with the ability to perceive the relationship between a particular decision and the whole plan, that contributes to the overall success of fireground operations.

As a strategy evolves and portions of the total resources are committed to the various activities, the officer in charge must estimate whether resources for exposure protection, confinement, and extinguishment are sufficient for a direct attack against the fire, or whether they must be devoted in part or completely to protecting against fire extension until additional resources arrive.

If additional alarms have been sounded, reinforcements should be integrated into the overall plan as they arrive. This might call for a redirection of strategy from a defensive to a more offensive one, or to a more comprehensive attack on the fire than had been possible previously.

Strategies for exposure protection, confinement, and extinguishment revolve around the best methods of applying the required water flow to the fire. In this case, the line between strategy and tactics is not a clear one. Although consideration of elevated streams as opposed to hand streams, for instance, might be a strategic decision because it involves a fundamental choice about the way in which the fire attack should be approached, the ladder work required is a tactical consideration. In order to extinguish fires in buildings where nothing is stored, a heavy flow of water can be used. However, where contents might be damaged easily or the structure itself weakened by the increased load, a more judicious use of water should be considered so that losses are minimized. This consideration is very important during freezing weather, when ice formations can cause considerable damage.

Fireground Tactics

Tactics involve the implementation of strategy. They identify the who, what, and how in order to achieve an objective. Tactics prescribe the exact apparatus, its location, and the specific way that hoses will be run. Tactics dictate the specific assignments of personnel to the various tasks.

The formulation of strategy is usually the responsibility of the fireground commander. However, unless the fire emergency is so small and routine that it can be handled by a single company, the tactical decisions—implementation of the specific strategies—generally fall to the officers in charge of individual units. Several tactical operations can be employed at each fire incident, and several tactical operations can be carried out simultaneously during multicompany operations. Every company must be trained to carry out all basic operations and be prepared to contribute to tactical objectives when possible.

Tactical Functions[6]

The following tactical functions are prioritized in order of importance; however, in reality, search and rescue, exposure protection, confinement, extinguishment, and ventilation often occur simultaneously. Sometimes extinguishment alone can take care of all of these tactical functions.

Search and Rescue: Rescue is the first and most important consideration at any fire incident, and, until completed, it might preclude any fire control efforts. The fireground commander might have to initiate fire control activities to protect the rescue operation or to keep the fire away from potential victims.

Rescue operations range from simple, requiring only one or two fire fighters, to multiple-alarm operations. All involved or threatened occupancies should be searched thoroughly for occupants without delay, with companies specifically assigned to this task. Rescue operations can be complicated by the time of the incident, the type of occupancy, and the height and construction of the structure. Rescue is the only acceptable reason for exposing fire fighters to otherwise unnecessary risks.

Exposure Protection: The second fire suppression priority is to control the fire. This begins with limiting the spread of fire to the property initially involved. The most basic responsibility of fire departments, with respect to property, is to protect the community from large-loss fires. Failure to adequately protect exposed structures can allow a fire to extend beyond the building of fire origin. The problem of exposure protection can be complicated by closely spaced buildings, combustible construction, the type of occupancy, the lack of fire department access to the fire, and the lack of fire department resources. Exposure protection should be the major objective in defensive fire control situations.

Confinement: The confinement of a fire to its area of origin is often a complex problem. Fire control is achieved when a fire is successfully confined to a manageable area. All avenues of possible fire travel must be secured, and the fire must be surrounded (over, under, and around) for successful confinement. Factors that influence the success or failure of confinement operations are the type of fuel involved, the location of the fire, building construction features, the presence of built-in fire suppression systems, the availability of fire department resources, and an aggressive fire fighting approach.

Extinguishment: Offensive fire control strategies are aimed at controlling and extinguishing the fire where encountered by attack forces. Successful offensive operations are regulated by the type of fuel involved, the location of the fire and the degree of involvement, and the ability of fire control forces to apply sufficient extinguishing agents directly on the fire. In some instances, the use of special extinguishing agents are required.

In defensive operations, final extinguishment can be achieved only when the fire burns down to a size that can be extinguished by the responding fire department. Defensive tactics depend on the department's capability to apply large volumes of water or other agents to confine a fire and limit fire movement to surrounding buildings.

Ventilation: Ventilation operations involve the systematic removal of heat, smoke, and fire gases from the structure. In some cases, it is necessary to coordinate ventilation with rescue in order to protect occupants from combustion products and heat and to provide visibility and tenability during rescue operations. Ventilation is also necessary during confinement and extinguishment operations to aid in locating the fire, to provide safer working conditions for fire suppression personnel, and to reduce overall damage to structure contents.

Property Conservation: Salvage operations are conducted by fire suppression personnel to conserve property by minimizing damage to the structure and contents due to heat, smoke, and water. This involves rapid extinguishment, covering contents, and removing excess water. Salvage is an integral part of tactical operations and should commence as soon as possible to prevent additional damage to the structure and its contents.

Overhaul: Overhaul operations are required to completely extinguish the fire, place the structure in a safe condition, and aid in determining the fire ignition sequence. Overhaul might involve only a few personnel for a short period of time, or large numbers of personnel over an extended period. Extensive overhaul can require the use of special equipment beyond what is normally provided by the fire department. It is important that extensive overhaul not be commenced before a thorough investigation to determine the cause of the fire. Once the investigation is complete, overhaul should continue to ensure that the premises are left as safe as possible, and that all fires are extinguished.

Implementation of Commands

The more thorough the drills and the better the training, the more rapidly various tactics can be implemented and fewer instructions will be needed for fire fighters to understand what is required of them. In this way fire fighters can move immediately to carry out any tasks as soon as the instructions are given. As much as possible, orders should be in the form of general guidelines as to what course of action should be taken so that the specific decisions involved can be made by the fire fighters themselves. The following example shows the difference between the degree of instruction needed to implement a command for a poorly trained or new fire fighter and a well-trained or veteran fire fighter. An officer tells a fire fighter to find a way to get into a building that is on fire; the nearest door has four window panes.

1. For a least experienced, least trained fire fighter.	Get into the building; take a power saw with a carbide-tipped blade so you can cut the Lexan plastic windows. Cut the lower left pane so you can reach in and open the door from the inside. If that doesn't work, cut all of the panes so that you can climb in.
2. For a somewhat experienced, trained fire fighter.	Get into the building through that door; take the right cutting tool—those could be plastic windows.

3. For a more experienced, more thoroughly trained fire fighter.

Get into the building through that door.

4. For a highly experienced, highly trained fire fighter.

Get into the building.

When a fire fighter can implement a command without requiring detailed instructions, much time is saved. In addition, the officer in charge is free to concentrate on other problems by knowing that the fire fighter will not return for more step-by-step directions if, by chance, one stage in the plan of action was not communicated adequately. The advantages of good training produce more rapid development and implementation of strategies, swifter decisions about tactics to be used, and improved communications of those tactics.

Ultimately, fire fighters benefit psychologically from the mutual understanding and close working relationship that come from being a member of an efficient, well-functioning, competent team.

OVERHAUL AND SALVAGE

Overhaul and salvage operations, while part of the overall strategy, constitute a different stage in fireground activities. The excitement of the emergency has diminished somewhat by the time search and rescue operations have been completed and the extinguishment streams are in operation. If some fire fighters are available, they can be directed to start salvage operations.

Overhaul Operations

Overhaul ensures that a fire is completely extinguished. Overhaul operations also enable a department to search for evidence of the cause of a fire. Hot spots are checked to make certain the fire is not spreading behind walls and between ceiling spaces, and that anything that is smoldering is doused with water. Even though there may be no visible burning, fire fighters might still encounter hazards, such as toxic fumes and flammable or otherwise hazardous materials, that have been exposed to water and heat. Sometimes hydraulic overhaul is the best method to use on abandoned buildings so that time can be saved in lieu of extra water.

Even though overhaul and salvage operations are basically different from fireground activities in that they demand their own strategies, tactics, and differing considerations, the decision-making process that an officer must follow is essentially the same as that followed for fireground activities. Both require that the officer in charge consider how to use human resources best, how to minimize damage, and how to return the structure to its owner in as good a condition as possible.

Salvage Operations

Salvage procedures include all operations required to protect a property from unnecessary damage caused by excessive water or other extinguishing materials. Salvage operations include covering objects with salvage cloths and removing water from the property so that it doesn't seep through floors and cause damage to the contents of lower floors. In this way a building can be restored to a reasonable condition before the fire fighters leave.

Strategic Factors in Overhaul and Salvage Operations

Strategic factors for overhaul and salvage operations are often somewhat similar. Following are some of the strategic factors to be considered for both operations:

1. To what extent can and should the human resources at the scene be used to carry out overhaul and salvage operations, especially if they are fatigued?
2. To what degree can damage be prevented by quick action?
3. At what point should units be freed so they are available for other emergencies and duties? When should supplies be replenished, hoses examined and stored away, and apparatus and equipment checked?
4. To what extent should personnel be required or encouraged to work overtime? Fireground operations are costly. Although this might be of minor consideration in comparison to the cost of fire damage, as soon as a fire is under control the question arises about the budgeting of time.
5. How long can or should volunteer fire fighters reasonably be kept at the scene?
6. Is the building in the best possible condition for return to the owner (cleaned up and closed up so that vandals cannot enter easily)? Overhaul and salvage operations provide evidence to both the people who own the property, and those who see it, that the department carries out its responsibilities in an efficient, effective, and considerate manner, with the best interests of the public in mind.

Tactical considerations for overhaul and salvage operations can also be similar, and include the following:

1. Which companies should be assigned to salvage, which to overhaul, and when?
2. Where is action needed, in what sequence, and who should be assigned to it?
3. Who should be assigned to check out equipment and supplies?

Although the strategic and tactical thinking process involved in salvage and overhaul operations is similar to other phases of fireground operations, it is applied under entirely different, less urgent circumstances. Although the leaders and subordinates are the same, a different leadership style is required because the work situation is different.

Leadership Styles During Overhaul and Salvage Operations

During overhaul, clean-up, and preventive salvage operations, the time pressures on the fire fighters are nowhere near as great as they were before the fire was under control. Overhaul and salvage, therefore, call for a different goal-setting/decision-making style. Substantially more consultation is warranted. Competent fire fighters and lower-level officers can be given considerably more freedom in deciding what should be done, how it should be done, and in what order.

In overhaul and even more so in salvage operations, officers and other managers have a significant potential for developing subordinates and for providing them with substantially greater job satisfaction if they switch to a more participative leadership style the moment the situation allows. It should be remembered that, with a well-disciplined and organized team, even the commands during fire fighting are, in effect, participative decisions; they are, however, primarily one-way communications. In order to conserve as much time as possible, the lower-level officer or fire fighter would not express any reservations or problems unless they were very serious. Once the emergency is over, however, the lesser problems become more important in relation to other aspects of the task, and failure to provide an easy outlet for discussion can stifle the desire of lower-level officers and fire fighters to perform their duties as enthusiastically as possible and in the way they deem best.

ORGANIZATION FOR FIREGROUND OPERATIONS

Two fireground command structure systems are currently in use in the American Fire Service: the Incident Command System (ICS) and the Fireground Command System (FCS).

Incident Command System (ICS)

The Incident Command System was developed as a result of experience gained during woodland fires that consumed large portions of southern California in 1970. This system consists of a flexible organizational structure, fixed position titles and descriptions, and prescribed operational functions that must be addressed during an emergency situation. ICS is designed to allow smooth operations and efficient interaction at the scene of an emergency, regardless of its magnitude, location, or cross-jurisdictional nature. Using ICS operational forces can work together effectively and efficiently, regardless of how many people, agencies, or communities are involved. This is accomplished through the use of common operational methods, terminology, functions, and position responsibilities throughout the course of an incident.

Under the ICS structure, someone is responsible for each of the functions deemed necessary to control the emergency at hand. In this way, operational control is distributed among a number of people, with responsibility tracking directly back to the single person responsible for overall command (see Figure 10.5). Because of the methodical nature of ICS, the incident commander is less likely to overlook a particular task or function, or suffer from information overload because of working with too many facts, figures, or people. Areas of responsibility that might be addressed during an emergency where the Incident Command System is in use include:

1. **Incident Command**: One individual must be responsible for directing the operation.
2. **Hazard Sector**: The area where the actual operation is being conducted. (At a major emergency, there could be multiple hazard sectors.)
3. **Logistical Sector**: Responsible for resupply of resources, equipment, and personnel.
4. **Communications Sector**: Responsible for providing adequate communications capability.
5. **Water Supply Sector**: Responsible for ensuring that adequate water is available to handle the incident.
6. **Emergency Medical Services (EMS) Sector**: Responsible for providing EMS services.
7. **Public Relations Sector**: Responsible for communicating with the media and the public.
8. **Staging Area Sector**: Area where incoming units gather for eventual use at the emergency scene.

An incident can require the use of some or all of these sectors. Additional sectoring can be utilized if required by special geographic or local circumstances. The number of sectors is a factor of the size of the emergency: Larger incidents require a greater commitment of forces and more sectors. The ICS system has been mandated by the federal government, under the Superfund Ammendments and Reauthorization Act of 1986 (SARA), for use during hazardous materials incidents. Progressive fire departments have adopted it for use at all incidents. The following design requirements are specified for the Incident Command System, depending on the size of the incident to be managed.[7]

- Must provide for the following kinds of operations: (a) single jurisdiction/ single agency involvement, (b) single jurisdiction with multi-agency involvement, and (c) multi-jurisdiction/multi-agency involvement.

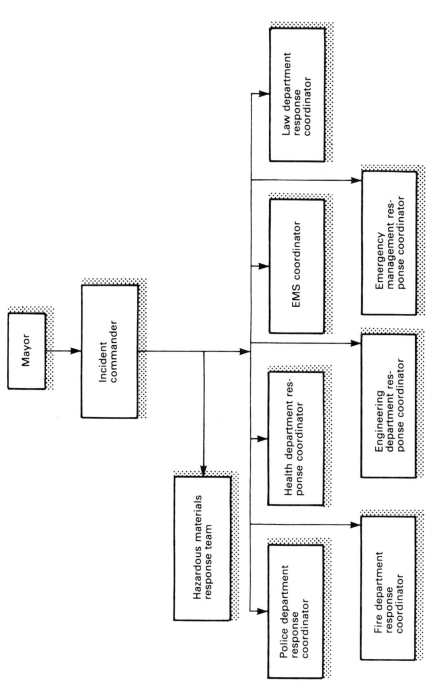

FIGURE 10.5 *Incident Command System used in Newark, New Jersey, for responding to situations involving hazardous materials.*

- Organizational structure must be able to adapt to any emergency or incident to which fire protection agencies would be expected to respond (e.g., fires, floods, earthquakes, hurricanes, tornadoes, tidal waves, riots, spills of hazardous materials, and other natural or human-caused incidents).
- Must be applicable and acceptable to users throughout the country.
- Should be readily adaptable to new technology.
- Must be able to expand in a logical manner from an initial attack situation into a major incident.
- Must have basic common elements in organization, terminology, and procedures. This allows for the maximum application and use of already developed qualifications and standards.
- Implementation should have the least possible disruption to existing systems.
- Must be effective in fulfilling all of the above requirements and yet be simple enough to ensure low operational maintenance costs.

Fireground Command System (FCS)

The Fireground Command System was developed by Chief Alan V. Brunacini of the Phoenix, Arizona, Fire Department. This system uses a structured approach to emergency operations that is similar to the Incident Command System. By defining operational guidelines and establishing standard operating procedures, this system establishes responsibility for all anticipated emergency operating tasks.

The Fireground Command System goes further than the ICS system because it is designed to apply basic management principles to the hectic nature of fire fighting operations. As Chief Brunacini states in his text, *Fire Command*, "The entire command system is an attempt to somehow intellectualize a fast-moving and violent event."[8]

To achieve this end, Chief Brunacini has standardized fire department response to emergency operations so that each member knows what role to play, what procedures to use, and when the procedures should be applied (see Figure 10.6).[8] His purpose is to make as many decisions as possible a routine part of the system.

The ICS system and the Fireground Command System share a number of similarities:

- Both are designed to operate at all levels of emergency operation.
- A fixed responsibility for command is established by the initial arriving fire officer.
- Resources are evaluated and used in an orderly fashion.
- Support functions are specifically assigned so that they are performed during the stress of emergency operations and not overlooked by a busy fireground commander.

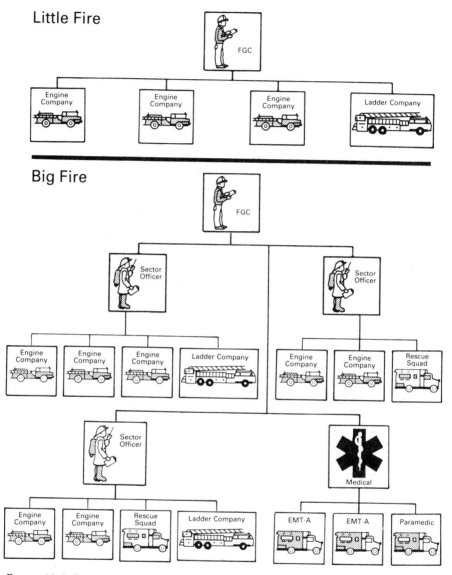

FIGURE 10.6 *Organizational differences between little and big fires under the Fireground Command System.* (Modified from Figure 3.5.3 of *Fire Command,*[9] p. 89, copyright © 1985 by Don Sellers, AMI.)

Overall responsibility for command of an emergency is vested in the fireground commander (FGC). Depending on the size and magnitude of an incident, the FGC can be a lieutenant, captain, district chief, or chief of the department. The Fireground Command System is designed to stress the need for assumption of command and use of strategy over the actual conduct of tactical operations. The fireground commander, regardless of rank, must maintain an overall view of the situation.

Responsibility for each aspect of the emergency is assigned to a sector commander. This allows for better operational command. The various sector commanders must be allowed to function within their operational sector, according to the goals and objectives set by the fireground commander. This setup allows for a wide range of tasks to be accomplished simultaneously and allows for better command and control. The use of standard operating procedures for routine procedures frees the fireground commander to manage the emergency and concentrate on any exceptional problems encountered.

It is crucial to remember the importance of sectoring to the Fireground Command System (see Figure 10.6). Brunacini stresses the following as advantages to the sectoring system of fireground command.[8]

- A reduced span of control makes operations more manageable.
- Better communications are possible because fewer radio interactions are required.
- A standard system of dividing major incidents into effectively sized units is provided.
- More emphasis is placed on support functions.
- Closer supervision of operating units facilitates greater fireground safety.

Although each system operates in the same general way, some minor differences exist. Where the Incident Command System is generic in language, positions, and roles, the Fireground Command System is more specific and structured in its approach. While the ICS can function under any sort of emergency scenario, such as a major rail incident, hazardous materials release, or forest fire, the Fireground Command System is more specifically attuned to the needs of a structural fire fighting operation. The Fireground Command System concentrates mainly on decision making, command and control, and review and evaluation.

Good organization facilitates the effective implementation of all fire department activities, particularly those related to fireground operations. Good organization results primarily from two of the linking elements — coordination and rules — which were discussed briefly in Chapter 4, and which are dealt with more specifically at the end of this chapter. Like any system, the Fireground Command System is best utilized where all members of the organization are convinced of its usefulness and are well-drilled in implementing it.

Fireground Communications

Good communications are paramount on the fireground where, in order to hold misinterpretation to a minimum, directions must be precise. Because time is of the essence on the fireground, conciseness and clarity in communicating are essential when giving directions at any level. Unfortunately, there are many barriers to good communications that can make clarity difficult to achieve.

Successful verbal communication depends on the ability of the speaker to use words that appropriately express the thought that is to be transmitted to the listener. The speaker must be able to choose the correct words in the time available for explaining the thought, and must also think about how the thought should be presented to the receiver in order for it to be received in the best possible way. Sometimes, words used can mean something slightly different from what the speaker intends. At other times, words can be substantially different because the speaker might have been distracted either by an external element or by other thoughts.

In the brief moment before the message reaches the receiver, several things can happen. The voice level could be so low that the receiver cannot hear the full message. Or, there could be loud, interfering noises. In most instances the words are accompanied by a facial expression or a gesture. These nonverbal cues become part of the message; they can change the meaning of the message by reinforcing or weakening it. For example, a different meaning is carried by words that are spoken with a smile than by ones accompanied by a frown.

When the words reach the listener, they arrive as a complete package of words, gestures, and other symbols—including the relationship between the speaker and the listener and the situation that surrounds them at the moment. The possible distractions—visual or audible—in the environment, including other people who might be speaking at the same time, diminish effective communication. Therefore, what the listener hears and sees of the message might be only part of what the speaker transmitted. Misinterpreted and misunderstood communications on the fireground can be avoided when:

- There is a good understanding of the communications process by both the officers giving the orders and the fire fighters receiving them.
- Joint drills have been conducted, with attention to standardized orders or instructions to ensure that the same meaning exists for both the senders and receivers.
- There is sender-receiver feedback on the way the message is understood by the receiver.

The Meaning of Words

The degree of understanding achieved from a verbal or nonverbal order depends on the symbols—the words, sounds, codes, or mental pictures—used to relay the order as well as the way they are used. Words can have widely different meanings in different situations and for different people. Understanding the meanings of words depends heavily on such things as previous experience with particular words, knowledge about the way others use the words, the environment (such as expectations about the other person's attitude), and the context in which the words are used. For example, the word truck can produce images that range from a toy truck to an ice cream truck, from a tow truck to a delivery truck, or from an emergency repair truck to a pumper.

Words are the symbols for thoughts that are often highly complex. Therefore, single words are rarely adequate. Complete sentences add more meaning and specificity to an order or message. Some words are more precise or general than others, and some can have several meanings. Also, to further complicate the transmission of an order or a message, there are some words that sound alike. For example, the word two has a very precise meaning, unless misunderstood to be another word such as too or to.

Ladder of Abstractions

Sentences that are used for transmitting orders or messages are more effective when their meanings are made as specific as possible. The ladder of abstractions concept, which is used by semanticists and linguists, illustrates how the meaning of an order or message can be made clearer by increasing the degree of specificity (see Figure 10.7).

With experienced people, where there is a high level of mutual understanding, instructions can often be given in fairly broad terms—high up on the ladder of abstractions. With less experienced people or with those who do not usually work closely, instructions or messages have to be more detailed to be sure that they are clearly received. For example, a new recruit might feel insecure unless all the necessary details about how to enter a building are spelled out. However, a seasoned, well-organized fire fighter might not need—and might even resent—step-by-step instructions.

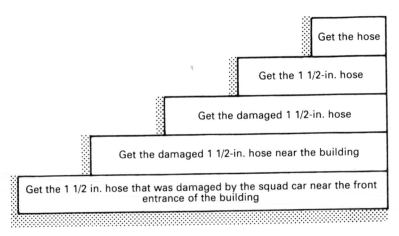

FIGURE 10.7 Ladder of abstractions shows an increasing degree of specificity to help prevent misunderstandings.

Specialized symbols are an excellent means for eliminating excessive words from messages. Fire departments often develop sets of symbols—numbers, codes, or terminology—so that the information communicated is clear, precise, and quickly translated into action. In the fire service, numbers can be assigned to apparatus, companies, stations, or even sections of a fire scene so that there will be no doubt as to which piece of equipment or apparatus is being referred to. Some departments also assign numbers to officers in order to facilitate radio communication. Numbers or letter codes are also used to convey various standard messages such as those concerning false alarms, the status of companies, the fire situation, and requests for additional personnel.

Specific terminology or jargon, which is often unintelligible to all but those who use it, develops in most organizations. Such terminology enables people to communicate with each other in terms that have a narrow and specific application. The terms *BLEVE* (boiling liquid-expanding vapor explosion) and *fire loading* (the weight of combustibles per square foot of floor area), for example, mean little or nothing to people outside the fire service. Some departments use the terms *working fire* or *all hands* to indicate a serious fire that might require a multiple-alarm response.

Giving Assignments and Instructions

In giving assignments and instructions on or off the fireground, or in reporting back, it is important to organize the information to be communicated so that it will be relayed in a logical sequence that is clearly understandable. This can usually be accomplished by:

1. Organizing the information.
   - Identifying the main points (topic, activity assigned, etc.).
   - Pointing out the relevant details for each main point.
   - Identifying the order in which the main points should be presented.
2. Directing the information to a subordinate or reporting back to a superior officer.
3. Obtaining feedback—making sure the information was understood.

Using this process does not necessarily take more time than it does to transmit messages in a less carefully organized way because once such use becomes a habit, the thought processes involved are almost instantaneous. The benefits of such habits can be substantial.

Linking Elements and the Company Officer's Role on the Fireground

There are several important areas relevant to the Linking Elements concept (see Chapter 4) that directly affect the role of the company officer on the fireground. These areas include: 1) goals and leadership style, 2) enforcement of rules, 3) post-emergency critique, and 4) sample goals for fireground command.

Goals and Leadership Style

The company officer must be able to use a wide range of leadership styles. Different styles are required at the beginning and through the climax of the emergency than are required during overhaul and salvage operations. For example, it is rarely advisable to hold a conference on the fireground immediately after size-up to discuss the next steps that should be taken. Instead, the fire officer must be decisive and quick about laying out attack strategy and implementing it immediately. However, this does not mean that participative decision making and goal setting are totally inappropriate; a great deal of participative goal setting takes place with a smoothly coordinated team, although at first this might not be apparent.

Sometimes, something that might appear to be a command, in reality, is not. If an officer in charge and the individual line officers have the kind of understanding characteristic of a well-trained team, there will be deeper meanings to the commands. For example, the instructions or orders from the fireground charge officer to a line officer might sound brief, but could be highly complex. Both officers are aware, if the working relationship between them is thoroughly professional and competent, that they have entered into a contract. The subordinate officer has accepted the goal given by the charge officer's instructions or orders, and can now be held accountable for working toward it. The officer in charge has the right to expect that the subordinate officer will respond as soon as the instructions are given. If the subordinate officer feels that a goal is unrealistically high or is beyond the capability of the team to achieve it, then it is that officer's responsibility to say so. By accepting the instructions or orders, the subordinate officer has assumed the responsibility to:

1. Lay out the tactical steps to achieve the goal.
2. Change the tactical steps as necessary to achieve the goal.
3. Immediately notify the officer in charge if the resources are inadequate to meet the goal. For instance, considerable notice should be given if a team is reaching the point of exhaustion, or of any other matter related to fire fighters' safety.

Thus, even though most of the goals are decided by the officer in charge, more participative decision making is practiced on the fireground by an effective team. The effectiveness that results from a sound working relationship between the officer in charge at the fireground and subordinate officers should also result from a sound working relationship between company officers and fire fighters. Although the ultimate responsibility for coordinating the fire fighting effort rests with the officer in charge, responsibility must also be delegated to line officers and fire fighters in order to ensure the close coordination of effort from all members of the company.

Enforcement of Rules

The enforcement of rules on the fireground is an important responsibility of an officer in charge. On the fireground there is little time to explain rules. A thorough understanding of the reasoning behind rules must take place before an emergency. When an officer gives instructions to withdraw or accept relief, for example, a fire fighter who resists must be aware that such resistance is a major breach of the command authority, even though such devotion to duty might seem exemplary.

Obviously, to achieve compliance with an order, the officer in charge cannot use excessive force on the fireground. Firmness helps to ensure that instructions are made with serious intent and, through prior training, it should be known that disciplinary consequences will result from instructions not being followed.

Post-Emergency Critique

Most fire fighting teams conduct critiques after each run (except the most routine ones) to review strategy and tactics and to form conclusions for improvements. Such conclusions can have limited application if they concentrate, as they often do, on fire fighting strategy and tactics and do not take into consideration other elements that contribute to a more effective operation. For example, any indication that the goal-setting process is not understood by everyone can become the foundation for team training and practice sessions. Such training and practice could help fire fighters better understand the principles of delegating goals, which is an important part of effective team work, as distinguished from a work group that continually depends on instructions from its leader.

In critiques of what occurred during a run, many opportunities exist to allow the fire fighting team to suggest methods for improving effectiveness. To help accomplish this, an officer can:

1. Allow members of the team to express their views.
2. Thoroughly explore these views to give credit for any ideas that would be beneficial in the future.
3. Plan, jointly with the team, training and drills that would be beneficial.
4. Agree on objectives that should be set.

There are other little-used facets to the critique that can also be valuable. Conclusions can be drawn about methods that can be used to enhance coordination, cooperation, or rule adherence. There is also a need to analyze whether, and to what extent, an emergency has helped cement and increase team spirit, or to what extent it might have done damage to the cohesiveness of the team. The extent to which the goal-setting process has worked is another important subject that should be reviewed during the critique of every emergency. Finally, a discussion can include how an emergency might have added to the satisfaction team members receive from their work and methods to improve work-related satisfaction in a more general way.

Every emergency provides many opportunities for the company officer to analyze, either alone or jointly with the team, what impact the emergency has had on the effectiveness of that team. From this analysis, changes can be made that will help the team to perform its mission more effectively in the future.

Sample Goals for Fireground Command

Following are some sample goals for the fireground commander, presented here as guidelines for company officers when developing fireground goals:

Strategic Goals:

- Develop improved techniques so that the total response time needed to start actual fireground operations is reduced by 10 percent.
- Establish coordination procedures that will increase effectiveness of mutual aid companies through better communications during response and through clearer delineation of responsibilities.
- Develop standards for overhaul procedures.
- Develop standard times for all major hose evolutions.

Operational Goals:

- Reduce tie-up time by 10 percent by a specified date.
- Establish revised regulations for use of airpacks and ensure adherence.
- Reduce excess water usage in private home fires to cut down on water damage.
- Expand coverage of post-fire critiques to include setting goals to meet training needs uncovered at fire fighter and officer levels.
- Include paper-and-pencil fireground simulations in training sessions.

Operations on the fireground are truly a life and death matter. The modern fire officer must be aware of the basic principles and practices that guide the conduct of operations at the fire scene.

Mastery of both the strategic and tactical segments of departmental operations is essential to success on the fireground. The ability to muster sufficient numbers of trained personnel and operational equipment must be increased through knowledge, education, and drills. Operational concepts must be developed and codified so that all is ready for the outbreak of a hostile fire.

ACTIVITIES

1. Write your own definitions of the terms *strategy* and *tactics*, emphasizing the major differences between the two. Which decisions must be made first?

2. Strategy and tactics contribute to high-level performance on the fire-ground. In outline form, describe the factors involved in each of these activities, including in your descriptions the reasons why they contribute to the effectiveness of fire fighting operations.

3. At the fire scene the definition of the problem and the data come from three distinct and separate analyses. List these analyses and describe how the basic decision-making process can be used to help make each analysis.

4. When formulating rescue strategies at the fireground, what factors need to be considered by the officer in charge?

5. Define overhaul and salvage operations and discuss the differences between them.

6. Describe the differences and similarities between the Incident Command System and the Fireground Command System.

7. (a) When giving assignments, instructions, and orders on or off the fireground, why it is important to organize the information to be communicated?

   (b) Explain how the concept of ladder of abstractions can help sharpen messages and instructions.

8. What is the difference between verbal and nonverbal communication, and why is each one of major importance when giving instructions?

9. List and explain the four areas that affect the role of the company officer on the fireground.

REFERENCES

[1]Cote, A. E., ed., *Fire Protection Handbook*, 16th edition, National Fire Protection Association, Quincy, MA, 1986, pp. 15-24, 15-25.

[2]Cote, A. E., ed., *Fire Protection Handbook*, 16th edition, National Fire Protection Association, Quincy, MA, 1986, p. 15-25.

[3]Brunacini, A. V., *Fire Command*, National Fire Protection Association, Quincy, MA, 1985, p. 91.

[4]Hill, R. M., "Fire Combat," *Fire Command!*, Vol. 41, No. 8, Aug. 1974, pp. 38–42.

[5]Kimball, W. Y., *Fire Attack 1: Command Decisions and Company Operations*, National Fire Protection Association, Quincy, MA, 1966, p. 88.

[6]Cote, A. E., ed., *Fire Protection Handbook*, 16th edition, National Fire Protection Association, Quincy, MA, 1986, pp. 15-25, 15-26.

[7]*Incident Command System*, Fire Protection Publications, Oklahoma State University, Stillwater, OK, 1983, pp. 5–6.

[8]Brunacini, A. V., *Fire Command*, National Fire Protection Association, Quincy, MA, 1985, 259 pp.

[9]Brunacini, A. V., *Fire Command*, National Fire Protection Association, Quincy, MA, 1985, p. 89.

11

Management of Physical Resources

The most valuable resources in any fire department are the people who staff its agencies and equipment. Yet no matter how well-trained the employees or how well-staffed the fire department, people cannot do their jobs without the necessary physical resources.

There are basically three types of physical resources available to a fire department: 1) the facilities (the real estate and buildings), 2) the apparatus, and 3) the equipment and supplies. These resources, in addition to personnel, enable a fire department to function and fulfill its objectives. A department's overall effectiveness and the degree to which it can control, extinguish, and help prevent fires is greatly influenced by the management and coordination of these resources.

PROBLEMS IN MANAGEMENT OF PHYSICAL RESOURCES

The constantly changing nature of the job of fire fighting and the updating and modernizing of facilities, apparatus, and equipment present many unique management problems to fire department administrators. In order to comprehend the complexity and extent of some of these problems, it is necessary to understand how fire fighting apparatus and facility needs change as technological advances bring new construction materials and hazardous substances into more common use. For example, the increased use of plastics and their many derivatives for construction purposes, creates new challenges for fire fighters. The risks involved in storage and transit of hazardous materials, which has led to the imposition of local, state, and federal regulations, have created new demands on fire departments. The advent and popularity of high-rise living and working has complicated the task of fire fighting. The severity of economic loss and loss of life associated with arson-related fires have created the need for new communication and detection equipment and for more effective inspection and investigative procedures.

Each of these considerations adds to the complexity and scope of fire department management problems and has impact on facility, apparatus, and equipment needs. Continual changes in the physical resources required to do the job are therefore necessary. These changes might involve purchasing aerial ladders to cope with an increase in tall building construction or they could involve decisions about the location and construction of a new station or modification of an existing one. Expenses involved in the purchase of an aerial ladder could require the postponement of a new station or, in other cases, could necessitate remodeling a station to make room for it. In all situations, it is the responsibility of management to establish appropriate priorities.

The decisions that have to be made in order to establish and meet a department's physical resource needs are often guided by many existing standards and laws as well as standards or laws being considered as state or national legislation. The National Fire Protection Association (NFPA) sets standards for nearly every facet of fire fighting. Although these standards are too numerous to list in this text, some that relate to fire service management will be discussed in this chapter.

Effect of Grading Schedules on Physical Resources[1]

The *Grading Schedule for Municipal Fire Protection*,[2] was developed originally by the National Board of Fire Underwriters (NBFU), continued by its successor, the American Insurance Association (AIA), and then by the Insurance Services Office (ISO). The schedule provides a guideline for municipalities to classify their fire defenses and physical conditions. Gradings obtained under the schedule are used in establishing base rates for fire insurance purposes. The schedule has always been subject to change, and sweeping changes were made in the 1980 edition with the development of a revised *Fire Suppression Rating Schedule*.[3]

The *ISO Fire Suppression Rating Schedule* (FSRS)[3] defines different levels of public fire suppression capabilities. It includes ten different Public Protection Classifications, with Class 1 receiving the highest rate recognition and Class 10 receiving no recognition.

In 1975 the ISO implemented the *Commercial Fire Rating Schedule* (CFRS),[4] which was a major revision in the method used to develop individual property rate relativities. The CFRS reviews and correlates construction, occupancy, exposures, and private and public fire protection (represented by the Public Protection Classification number). This correlation allows development of an equitable rate relativity applicable to the individual property.

The *Fire Suppression Rating Schedule*[3] is designed to assist in an objective review of those features of available public fire protection that have a significant influence on minimizing damage once a fire has occurred. This revision ties very logically to the review of contributive and causative hazards that can be performed with the *Commercial Fire Rating Schedule.*[4]

Grading schedules are important to fire department managers because of the pervasive effect of these schedules throughout a fire department organization. A fire department is subject to close analysis and grading by representatives of the Insurance Services Office. Although ISO is quick to point out that their grading schedule is used only for determining insurance rates in a community, chief fire executives have traditionally built their operations around the tenets of the *ISO Grading Schedule.*[2]

All aspects of the management of physical resources are influenced by the grading schedule, and many of the improvements in the fire service are a result of the grading schedule's emphasis on personnel, equipment, and water supply capability. Table 11.1 shows one way to evaluate a fire department's capability to respond to various levels of hazard in a community.

By having a standard with which to make comparisons, a fire chief can determine whether the fire department is capable of handling different types of emergencies. This is particularly true in terms of personnel response to various emergency scenarios.

TABLE 11.1 Evaluation of fire department response capability.

High Hazard Occupancies (Schools, hospitals, nursing homes, explosive plants, refineries, high-rise buildings, and other high life hazard or large fire potential occupancies)
    At least 4 pumpers, 2 ladder trucks, 2 chief officers, and other specialized apparatus as may be needed to cope with the combustible involved; not less than 24 fire fighters and 2 chief officers.

Medium Hazard Occupancies (Apartments, offices, mercantile, and industrial occupancies not normally requiring extensive rescue or fire fighting forces)
    At least 3 pumpers, 1 ladder truck, 1 chief officer, and other specialized apparatus as may be needed or available; not less than 16 fire fighters and 1 chief officer.

Low Hazard Occupancies (One-, two-, or three-family dwellings and scattered small businesses and industrial occupancies)
    At least 2 pumpers, 1 ladder truck, 1 chief officer, and other specialized apparatus as may be needed or available; not less than 12 fire fighters and 1 chief officer.

Rural Operations (Scattered dwellings, small businesses and farm buildings)
    At least 1 pumper with a large water tank (500 or more gal), one mobile water supply apparatus (1,000 gal or larger), and such other specialized apparatus as may be necessary to perform effective initial fire fighting operations; at least 6 fire fighters and 1 chief officer.

Additional Alarms
    At least the equivalent of that required for Rural Operations for second alarms; equipment as may be needed according to the type of emergency and capabilities of the fire department. This may involve the immediate use of mutual aid companies until local forces can be supplemented with additional off-duty personnel.

The insurance costs associated with ISO ratings can sometimes have a significant influence on community development. There have been cases where industries seeking locations for new plants have avoided a community where the insurance rates were excessively high. The municipality involved thus lost tax revenue that could have helped pay for needed fire defense expenditures.

The remainder of this chapter deals with managerial methods that apply to the three types of physical resources available to fire departments (buildings and location, apparatus, and equipment). Chapter 12 includes information on the use of budgets as tools of management.

MANAGEMENT OF FACILITIES

A fire department's facilities can include buildings or areas for housing of personnel, storage of equipment, administrative offices, communications functions, training facilities, maintenance equipment, and supplies. In smaller organizations these functions usually are contained in one building; larger organizations, however, might use several facilities in different locations.

The Fire Station

The fire station is the single, most vital unifying force within a fire department. It not only provides housing for the department's apparatus and equipment, but also might house department members. The fire station, as the center of a community's fire fighting operations, is a vital symbol of the protection of lives and property.

The importance of a fire station's upkeep and location involves management decisions by either the chief or another officer or bureau whose specific duties include handling all matters related to the station. In volunteer departments a committee representing the membership might manage the building and, within the scope of its power, might even be able to recommend the rebuilding of a new station.

If there are no inherent problems with the site and capabilities of an existing fire station, it is the responsibility of management to properly maintain the present building so that it will remain functional in the future. If the present building is not adequate to meet fire fighter and/or community needs, and if funds have not been budgeted to build a new station in the near future, then department management must "make do" with the facilities and initiate ideas to alleviate some of the problems that necessitate rebuilding. For example, management might realize that the department needs another pumper in order to handle any fires in the community even though a shortage of space would not permit housing another pumper. If the station is near a municipal facility that houses large trucks, management might be able to park the new pumper at that location until a new station can be built. Storing the pumper at a municipal facility would be a simple, although temporary, solution.

If management discovered that the protection capabilities of the present fire station were insufficient because of the community's growth the construction of a new fire station would be considered a necessity, and major emphasis would be placed on obtaining approval to build it. A fire department's top managers rely on statistics (see Table 11.2) in order to conclude that another fire station is essential and to convince the necessary authorities. Once the decision has been made to build a new station, many related decisions have to be made. These primarily concern the location and design specifications of the station.

Location of the Station

The number and location of new fire stations must be reevaluated continually because the buildings and the population of a community change. The number of stations a department will require to accomplish its function is, like everything else, a balance between the costs of the buildings and their maintenance on the one hand, and the need for more stations on the other. If a station is located near the high response section of a community—such as a heavily populated area of multi-occupancy or wood-frame structures—then station relocation would be inappropriate. Station relocation would be more feasible if a station is located in a rural area that is a considerable distance from the normal population flow and from urban housing and development.

TABLE 11.2 Number of apparatus needed to provide the fire flow recommended by Insurance Services Office.[5] All built-up areas should have an engine company within 1½ miles and a ladder/service company within 2½ miles. Response areas with five buildings that are three stories or 35 ft or more in height, or with five buildings that have a required fire flow greater than 3,500 gpm, or any combination of these criteria, should have a ladder company.

Required fire flow (gpm)	Number of engine companies needed	Number of ladder companies needed
4,000–4,500	4	1
5,000–5,500	5	2
6,000–6,500	6	2
7,000–7,500	7	3
8,000–8,500	8	3
9,000–9,500	9	4
10,000	10	4
11,000	11	4
12,000	12	5

The location of a station in a community directly affects the total response time needed to combat fires effectively. For example, although a fire station is centrally located in a community, the majority of the fires might occur at substantial distances from the station. Therefore, an evaluation of the time from receipt of an alarm to the arrival at a fire plays an important part in deciding the need for relocating a fire station. The total time is the sum of the time it takes to complete each of the following seven fire fighting processes.

Detection: This is the time it takes to detect a fire, which depends on the number of people who are in the vicinity of the fire, how rapidly they respond, and the time of day. Automatic fire detection systems, such as smoke and heat detectors, give early warnings of fire and save considerable response time. Some detectors are connected directly to a fire station through a central station signaling systems, while others sound only in the building in which there is a danger. In the latter case, detection time depends on human response.

Alarm: This is the time that elapses between detection of the fire and the transmittal of the alarm to the fire station. It depends on availability of alarm boxes or telephones, their reliability, the extent of automation, and the speed of transmission.

Dispatch: This is the time required to record information and send personnel. If information is recorded automatically and if dispatchers have the most modern communication equipment, the time needed for dispatch is reduced.

Turnout: This is the speed that personnel — paid, off-duty, and volunteers — can report for duty, board apparatus, and leave the station for the fire. Turnout depends on the location of the personnel at the time of the alarm — whether at the station, at work, or in their homes.

Response Time: This is the travel time from the station to the fire. It depends on the station's location and the topographic, traffic, and weather conditions. When traffic is particularly heavy, the police department might be needed to aid in traveling to the fire and in beginning evacuation.

Attack Preparation: This is the time that is necessary for laying hose and placing ladders and rescue equipment. The time might vary according to the methods of attack employed.

Extinguishment: This time depends on the type of fire and the surrounding conditions. Fires often require varying methods of attack and extinguishment, and time must be allowed for making decisions about the particular fire fighting process to be employed.

In addition to total time, the growth of a community also adds new considerations and problems in locating or relocating a fire station. Community expansion, such as new roads, bridges, or housing developments, take time for completion and affect the normal routing and traffic flow. Fire departments should be aware of such projects in order to map out quicker alternate routes in case of fire. Then, after the construction is finished, come more people, higher buildings, and so on. Expansion in a community creates ever-changing fire protection needs.

Fire department managers should also be aware of the "minor" changes in a community — those changes that can occur so gradually that most people are barely aware of them. For example, vacant lots are filled in, industrial interests are relocated, a small farm is sold to a real estate developer, and zoning ordinances are changed to attract more business and people. Such changes directly affect fire spread and fire fighting abilities. They should be taken into consideration by fire department managers when relocation considerations are being made.

Design Specifications of a Station

If a department finds that constructing a new fire station is necessary, a good public relations program should be formulated in advance of announcing the need for a budgetary decision. This requires good communication between the fire department management and the general public so that it is clearly shown that a new fire station is in the best interests of a community.

The reaction of the voting community and the political power for the decision to build a new station depends on several factors: 1) the professionalism exhibited by the fire department, 2) the ISO rating of the present fire station, 3) the proposed location of a new station, 4) the public's understanding of the need for new construction, 5) the manner in which the proposals are presented, and 6) the amount of money involved.

Once a location for the station has been determined, management can focus on the design needs of the new station. Some of these needs might already be known. If a station is run by volunteers, is there a possibility that the station will require full-time, paid fire fighters in the future? If the area served by the fire department has no high-rise buildings, are tall buildings likely to be constructed? If so, could the new station accommodate the specialized apparatus required for fighting fires in such buildings?

Although questions about future changes necessitate discussion with municipal officials and others, the ultimate decisions about the fire department, its design, and its general needs are decided by fire service management and its advisors. Management needs to be aware of all considerations in order to communicate them to the architect selected to design the new station. Traffic flow, terrain features, area characteristics, weather peculiarities, communications needs, personal needs of fire fighters, space and storage needs for apparatus, equipment, and supplies, and space requirements for offices, parking facilities, living quarters, and training facilities must be thoroughly researched and understood (see Figures 11.1 through 11.4).

Other important areas of consideration by management when planning station specifications include the heating and ventilating needs of the station and the setup of the watch-desk area. The design of the station should

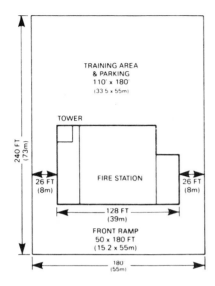

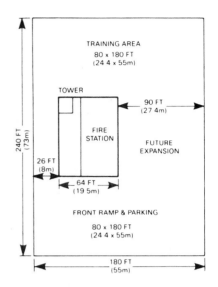

FIGURE 11.1 *Plot plan for a typical district fire station for urban and suburban services. Minimum recommended plot size is 43,200 sq ft. (Source: Fire Protection Handbook[6])*

FIGURE 11.2 *Plot plan for a typical rural fire station. Minimum recommended plot size is 43,200 sq. ft. (Source: Fire Protection Handbook[6])*

incorporate a heating system that is able to recover rapidly after apparatus responds, especially during the winter when the doors to the station are not closed immediately. In addition, adequate ventilation of the station should be provided in the apparatus room before the doors are opened to avoid building up carbon monoxide during the usual engine warmup, drilling, or servicing.

The proper setup of the watch-desk area is of major concern to management because it is where alarms are received. The watch desk should be in the form of a desk-console arrangement with wall space for maps, schedules, and instructions, and with ample space for the necessary radio equipment, alarm control devices, floor controls, and traffic signal controls. The watch-desk area should be as soundproof as possible and should allow for clear visibility of the entire apparatus room. A desirable location for the watch desk is near the front entrance of the station — the point where visitors enter and seek information.[6]

MANAGEMENT OF APPARATUS

Whether or not a fire department decides to construct a new fire station, it is necessary for management to continually analyze and evaluate the effectiveness of the apparatus in terms of its ability to combat the diverse and everchanging fire types in the community. The Insurance Services Office (ISO) grading schedule and survey is useful in determining whether to maintain

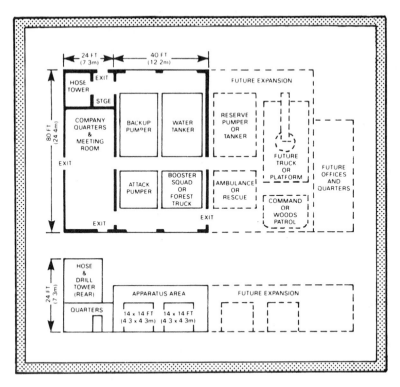

FIGURE 11.3 Elevation and plan view of a typical urban fire station. (Source: Fire Protection Handbook[6])

present apparatus or purchase additional and/or newer equipment. Specific recommendations for apparatus might come from the battalion or company level of a particular department or from the fire fighters who use the equipment. A well-managed department could rely on the experience of the fire officers and fire fighters because they have specific knowledge of inadequate features on existing apparatus. Fire fighters might request extra facilities for preconnected hose, additional intakes, or larger compartments for a newer piece of apparatus. They might suggest relocating various appliances and controls, new facilities for storing respiratory equipment, new locations for lights, or greater availability of lights and generators. Such first-hand recommendations for improving fire fighting capability and efficiency should be given to a superior officer or directly to the chief so that better decisions can be made concerning a station's needs and appropriate apparatus.

Purchase and Replacement of Apparatus

In addition to ISO grading schedules, fire department management is also guided by NFPA standards in its decisions about apparatus. Directly applicable

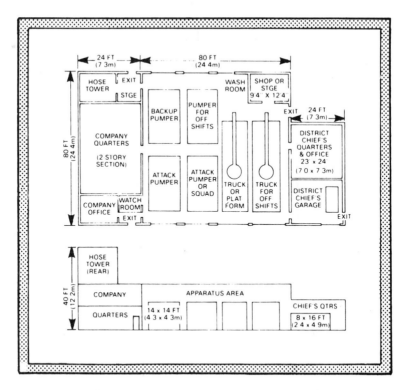

FIGURE 11.4 *Elevation and plan view of a typical rural fire station.* (Source: *Fire Protection Handbook*[6])

to apparatus decisions is NFPA 1901, *Standard for Automotive Fire Apparatus.*[7] NFPA 1901 enumerates various pumper specifications and equipment that should be carried on particular pumpers (see later in this chapter). Chapter 2 of NFPA 1901 discusses contractor responsibilities for fire department apparatus, purchaser responsibilities, design of engines, carrying capacity, and the cooling, lubrication, fuel exhaust, and electrical systems of pumpers. The guidelines contained in NFPA 1901 provide the essential requirements that must be adhered to by the department. In addition to these items, various other component parts of pumpers are summarized:[7]

> 2–3.3.1 The apparatus body design shall be rugged with suitable ventilation and drains where needed and with good visibility to front, sides, and rear. Bodies shall provide readily accessible facilities for carrying hose, appliances and equipment and riding space for the personnel.
> 2–3.3.2 Front and rear hooks or rings shall be attached to the frame structure to permit towing of the apparatus . . .

When determining the particular kinds of apparatus needed by a department, management should also consider: 1) the need for effectiveness – to prevent and extinguish fires more effectively, and 2) the need for efficiency – to perform the mission of prevention and extinguishment at the lowest possible cost. While the needs might seem to indicate that the latest piece of equipment should be purchased and that the oldest piece of apparatus should be sold, closer examination of apparatus efficiency and future needs might reveal otherwise.

For example, in a small community the average age of apparatus might be as high as eight to ten years. The newest engine might be at least three years old. When considering the ages and capabilities of these pumpers, the department should not consider only the greater acceleration provided by a new pumper in extinguishing a fire; the older pumper is not likely to be the first-in engine. An older pumper would be used as a backup unit when newer engines were not sufficient to cover a specific fire.

The managerial concern then becomes not how much better the newer engine can fight a fire, but how often the old engine is used in a fire attack? If the old engine is used regularly in a fire attack, how much damage could probably be prevented if a more modern engine were used? Determining the benefits that a more modern engine will bring is a difficult question to answer. The following questions, and less important ones, such as fuel efficiency and equipment layout on the engine, have to be considered in making the decision.

- How much higher is the annual maintenance cost on the old engine?
- When is it likely that the old engine would be so outdated that it would have to be scrapped, and how much less would its resale value be at that time compared with today's value?
- How long will it be before the newest engine will be outdated, making fire attack less effective than it would be if a newer engine could assume the lead position?
- Will the new equipment require fewer personnel?

In the world of general industry, equipment replacement decisions are difficult because so many complex questions are involved. Such decisions are usually made by considering long- and short-term profitability. The basis for the purchase of a new piece of equipment usually is whether or not it will "pay for itself" in a specified period of time. In industry, the following factors are considered to determine whether a new piece of equipment is worth buying:

- How much more will it produce than the older equipment or, if it is totally new—for a new product or service—how much will it save over doing the job by hand, or how much profit will be earned from the product or service?
- How many years will it be used—and usable; in other words, how long will there be a demand for the product or service and, if that demand will be for many years, how long will the equipment or service last, and what will its depreciation factor be?
- How fast is technology moving? How long will it be before much more productive equipment will be available so that competitors with newer equipment will have a greater advantage?

- What will be the replacement cost (what will new equipment probably cost) when the older equipment becomes worn out?
- How much will the equipment bring, as second-hand equipment, if it has to be sold earlier than expected?
- How much will it cost to operate the equipment? How much personnel time will be needed to operate it, and how much material?
- How much will the utilities (electricity, gas, oil, etc.) cost?
- How much will it cost to maintain the equipment in satisfactory working condition?
- What is the interest rate? How much would the organization save in interest charges if it did not buy the equipment? Most companies have mortgages, bank loans, or outstanding bonds on which they pay interest. If equipment is not purchased, these loans could be repaid, partially or fully, and interest would be saved.

As difficult as it is to obtain valid answers to many of these factors in the world of general industry, it is often more difficult to obtain valid answers in the fire service. For example, in view of the possibility that a life might have been lost without a new piece of apparatus, how should one evaluate the probability that the person would instead have suffered a serious or fatal injury? Most people would agree that an aerial ladder is justifiable equipment if it can be credited with saving a life; however, is it justifiable equipment if it prevents third-degree burns over most of an arm? These questions are vastly more difficult than those faced by general industry because, in most instances, they involve moral and social issues. Thus, traditional business analysis, in the strict sense, does not always apply to fire service apparatus replacement decisions.

Selection of Apparatus and Equipment Based on Fire District Influences

When ISO engineers evaluate a fire department, they compare its features (e.g., buildings, apparatus, equipment, competence) with the established standards. These standards recommend location of stations and distribution of companies (apparatus and personnel) based on response time under normal conditions.

Table 11.2 (see page 270) relates the number of apparatus needed within a given area to the required fire flow. Fire flow, which is the gallons of water per minute (gpm) that the water supply is capable of delivering, is determined by the size of the community, population density, and related factors.

Fire departments do not strictly adhere to the apparatus guidelines shown in Table 11.2 because they must consider their particular districts in relation to three local conditions: 1) the size and type of district, 2) the hazards in the district, and 3) the types of fires in the district.

Size and Type of District: Despite the fact that two fire departments might have the same number of people to protect, their individual needs could vary greatly due to the particular area and type of district served by each. For example, districts that have areas in which the population is widely dispersed might have to pay particular attention to the driving characteristics of the vehicles they purchase, with particular emphasis on a faster response time.

On the other hand, a district with steep grades, narrow winding roads, or difficult terrain might be especially interested in a vehicle's shifting characteristics. In this case, a four-wheel drive vehicle with extra-large tires or a tanklike base can reduce response time despite difficult driving conditions. Or, reduction in overall dimensions might make it easier to maneuver around curves. These districts might also consider purchasing pumpers without the forward-cab design, which would give improved maneuverability that would outweigh the advantage of having fire fighters ready for action immediately upon arrival. If many minutes would be saved by eliminating certain features, the extra time saved should more than offset the time it would take for fire fighters to don breathing apparatus at the fire scene.

Fire departments in rural areas need large water tank trucks, portable suction basins (which allow tank trucks to unload their water next to the pumper and go back to the nearest hydrant or static source for more), portable pumps, and suction hose because most of the water would have to come from a static source, such as a pond, or from water carried to the fire scene. Brush-fire trucks or ladder trucks in rural areas often have auxiliary booster pumps with capacities of less than 500 gpm. Auxiliary pumps are useful on small, nonstructural fires.

Fire departments in urban or suburban areas have to consider the advantages of different aerial devices so that buildings over three stories high can be protected adequately. In addition, they must take into account factors required in the use of mechanized aerial devices (such as obstacles above roadways, width of streets, and parking spaces available near buildings). The number of people who could be rescued, potential use of such equipment, and frequency of use should be major considerations before any purchase. In a district where many fire hazards exist, or where the fire department is frequently called in to help in other emergencies, additional rescue vehicles might be needed.

Hazards in District: Some other hazardous conditions that bring about the need for additional companies and fire department personnel are: 1) numerous wood-shingle roofs, 2) large concentrations of closely spaced, wood-frame buildings, 3) large blocks having structures weak in fire resistance and lacking adequate private fire protection, 4) large, individual structures with inadequate private fire protection, 5) narrow streets and traffic congestion, including parked cars, and 6) severe climatic conditions such as frequent droughts or heavy snows.

All of these conditions are usually considered in the ISO survey and are taken into account in establishing the grade classifications. However, a fire department's management might also have a valid perspective that differs from the conclusions of the ISO survey; in such instances, the department is likely to be successful in taking its case to the authorities only if it can objectively show why the need is more or less serious than ISO engineers found it to be.

Types of Fires in District: In suburban or semirural areas where there is a high incidence of brush fires or fires in rubbish dumped in vacant lots, management might consider purchasing a grass or brush fire truck instead of a regular pumper, or they might consider such a vehicle as an addition to the standard pumper fleet. Equipped with booster pumps, these trucks are better adapted to fighting small fires than regular pumpers. They are less expensive than regular pumpers because they can be built from regular commercial truck chassis. Grass or brush fire trucks are easier to drive and faster to place in position than are regular pumpers, and they eliminate the possibility of taking a standard pumper away from fighting a structural fire.

Although districts with flammable liquid fire hazards are likely to have specially equipped apparatus for delivering foam or other chemical extinguishing agents, most districts will be confronted with explosives or flammable liquids fires at some time. Gasoline station tanks must be filled from commercial gasoline tankers. Such tankers often catch fire when they overturn on a slick surface or at an angular bend in the road. A fire department should be equipped to fight such fires, and its apparatus must carry an adequate number of extinguishers with the capacity to deliver foam.

Major Types of Apparatus

Once the various fire district influences have been determined, management can consider the specific types of apparatus that will be needed and the specification requirements for each piece.

Vehicles for Specialized Purposes: Although standard pumpers and ladder trucks carry their own supply of specialized equipment for dealing with specific hazards and situations (such as vehicle rescue and salvage operations), many of the larger fire departments find use for special-equipment vehicles that are outfitted for one specific type of operation or purpose. Such special-equipment vehicles can be trucks that carry extra hose and nozzles to lend a greater degree of flexibility to fire fighting operations, trucks with large capacities to generate power and lighting to supplement portable generators on standard equipment, or trucks that are specifically designed for specific hazards.

Some community airports and industries having unusually high flammability risks maintain their own fire fighting units. These occupancies require adequate pumpers primarily equipped for fighting specific types of fires. Whether or not to obtain and use specialized types of vehicles and equipment is a management decision.

A municipality that has a large waterfront area with commercial docks or marinas might purchase one or more fireboats that are specially equipped with turrets that can throw heavy streams, or include an elevating platform (see Figure 11.5). Because fireboats represent an enormous financial investment in relation to their limited use, districts with small areas of waterfront might purchase a used fireboat or make arrangements with neighbors for joint purchase and use.

FIGURE 11.5 *Large waterfront area protected by an elevating platform on the fireboat.*
(Courtesy of William Lyon MacKenzie, Toronto Fire Department, Toronto, Ontario)

In certain dry climates with heavily wooded areas, forest and brush fires present a serious hazard. Departments confronted with this problem usually either have their own special equipment or they make arrangements for leasing forest fire protection devices. In these situations, aircraft and helicopters are used extensively in the control of forest fires, particularly by the National Forest Service. Experiments are also being conducted in the use of large-capacity foam trucks on such fires.

In addition to the specific instances that require specialized vehicles, a department might consider designing its own apparatus from a piece of used equipment. Under some conditions, used equipment can be a wiser purchase than a new piece of equipment — particularly when limited funds are available. For example, a locality might use a specialized piece of apparatus so infrequently that large expenditures on new apparatus cannot be justified. Or, a department might find that it needs an extra backup piece of standard equipment to replace one that can no longer be maintained economically. The purchase of used apparatus or the rebuilding of the chassis of an older piece of apparatus might be a satisfactory solution to a serious problem.

Specification Decisions: Once it has been established that a major piece of apparatus is needed, be it for specialized purposes or not, fire department management must decide on the design specifications, which are influenced by the intended use. For example, management might choose an apparatus with special fire pump capabilities, with an elevating platform, or with a special capacity water tank. Many fire departments use NFPA 1901[7] as a general guideline for making decisions concerning design specifications.

MANAGEMENT OF EQUIPMENT AND SUPPLIES

In addition to providing as functional a fire station as possible and an efficient range of apparatus, it is also a management responsibility to decide on the necessary equipment to be used both at the station and on the apparatus. NFPA 1901, *Standard for Automotive Fire Apparatus,*[7] can be used as a guide for setting standards for the basic equipment to be carried on apparatus (e.g., ladders, nozzles, hoses, various tools, etc.). Sound management decisions concerning such equipment enables a department to operate with utmost efficiency. Such decisions apply to the use of all types of equipment, including personal equipment used by fire fighters, communications equipment, auxiliary equipment, and used equipment.

Personal Equipment

Most personal equipment is intended to provide protection to fire fighters in the performance of their work. Respiratory equipment and protective clothing are two areas of major concern to management. Breathing apparatus is needed to protect against the danger of inhaling noxious fumes, and protective headgear, footwear, and clothing help protect the body from the most adverse environmental conditions, such as extensive heat and cold, and from exposure to radiation contamination, chemicals, and water. Helmets also help safeguard against injury from falling objects.

To assist fire departments in meeting their personal equipment needs, NFPA has developed a number of standards for use in selecting and using personal safety equipment. Following is a list of relevant NFPA standards:

- NFPA 1971, *Standard on Protective Clothing for Structural Fire Fighting.*
- NFPA 1972, *Standard on Helmets for Structural Fire Fighting.*
- NFPA 1973, *Standard on Gloves for Structural Fire Fighters.*
- NFPA 1974, *Standard for Protective Footwear for Structural Fire Fighting.*
- NFPA 1975, *Standard on Station/Work Uniforms for Fire Fighters.*

- • NFPA 1981, *Standard on Open-Circuit Self-Contained Breathing Apparatus for Fire Fighters.*
- • NFPA 1982, *Standard on Personal Alert Safety Systems (PASS) for Fire Fighters.*
- • NFPA 1983, *Standard on Fire Service Life Safety Rope, Harnesses, and Hardware.*

Although some fire departments believe that uniformity of personal equipment is of greater significance than adaptation to personal preferences and needs, the more enlightened departments allow fire fighters increasingly greater freedom in matters pertaining to equipment selection. Personal equipment for use in rescue operations, such as life nets and life guns, is an area where personal preference can be important. Although some fire fighters feel that ladders are easier to use than life nets in rescue operations, others feel that life nets are more valuable for rescuing people in three- or four-story buildings. Life guns, which are used for shooting rope to people in distress, usually have limited use in water rescues and rescues from cliffs or canyons; however, if fire fighters feel that either life guns or life nets are useful for their jobs, management should give serious consideration to such requests.

Personnel Safety Equipment

It is essential for fire department management to recognize the importance of safety in the management of their physical resources. During the past decade, safety has assumed a prominence not previously known. Concern for protection of the individual evolved to the point where an NFPA standard was developed to address the personnel safety issue. NFPA 1500, *Standard on Fire Department Occupational Safety and Health Program,*[8] set for the first time minimum safety standards for the fire service.

Fire department managers can benefit from the provisions of NFPA 1500 with regard to such issues as protective equipment and clothing, vehicles, and other equipment. This standard provides a measure by which the safe management of a department's physical resources can be judged.

Communications Equipment[9]

The most important aspect of fire department communications is the facility where calls for assistance are received and action is taken. Large communities might require one large center and possibly satellite centers to handle message loads, while smaller communities might require only a watch desk located in a fire station. In addition to receiving calls for assistance, the alarm center must be capable of handling all radio communications for the department, keeping a continuous record on the status of all companies, handling communications to each station, and maintaining current files and maps of streets. It must also have the personnel resources for the required record keeping.

Communication Center Design

The design of communication centers should focus on the operations room where all calls and alarms are received, and from which all alarms are transmitted to companies or stations. A desk or console might be provided for the dispatcher or dispatchers on duty. Console design must be functional so that all necessary operations can be performed efficiently. The operations room might contain all equipment necessary for the receipt of calls from the public, receipt of alarms from street boxes, a department telephone switchboard if necessary, radio transmitting and receiving equipment, tone alerting equipment, and computer terminals and video display units, if used.

Equipment requirements are dictated by the size of the operation and the type of services that are provided. Centers in communities that have community-wide alarm systems require space for alarm equipment and standby batteries. Space is also required for radio and telephone equipment. If computer-assisted dispatching is used or anticipated, additional space is required.

Communications Equipment Specifications

The purchase of communications equipment is an important management responsibility. Such purchasing often requires a large outlay of funds, especially if the communications center is to be completely or even partially modernized. There are many different communications needs in a fire department, all of which require equipment that must operate with minimum interference so that emergency and urgent messages will be transmitted and received on a priority basis. Following are some of the needs, or demands, that should be fulfilled by a communications center.

1. The public must have 24-hour access to headquarters to initiate an alarm or to obtain information.

2. Headquarters must be able to contact its fire fighting personnel, either in the fire station or in their homes.

3. Headquarters must be able to communicate with personnel on the apparatus.

4. The chief officer must be able to communicate with remote units and sometimes with individual fire fighters.

5. There should be a means for communication between pieces of apparatus and between apparatus and individual fire fighters.

6. Officers must be able to contact headquarters to request aid or further instructions on how to control a fire.

7. There must be a regional intercommunications system for mutual aid calls.

8. All these systems must operate with minimum interference so that emergency and urgent messages are easily understood.

There are several different ways to satisfy these communications needs. Some methods are more efficient than others, or cost less, or are more suited to existing conditions. Which one to select, therefore, requires careful analysis of the specific advantages, drawbacks, and equipment requirements of each. The following information outlines some of the important concerns for management when considering ways to satisfy the communications needs of a department.

Public to Fire Department: Most people still communicate with fire departments by public or private telephones. However, someone who discovers a fire can also use public alarm boxes (see Figures 11.6 through 11.8), which can be wireless or interconnected with wires. Wireless boxes are transmitters that operate from batteries; some operate with solar energy devices or with small hand-cranked generators.

Battery-operated transmitters emit a signal if the battery needs replacing. Alarm boxes that are connected by wire circuits to a communications center usually have several different boxes connected to the same circuit. These separate circuits can be tested; if one is not operating properly, the defective alarm box can be traced by checking each box in that circuit.

Alarm boxes are usually situated outside public facilities in heavily populated areas and in areas where private or public telephones are not available or not available at all times (such as industrial areas, which are deserted during the night). Even in those areas where public telephones are readily available, increasing incidences of vandalism often make them inoperable.

In addition to alarms and requests for emergency assistance that are received by telephone, alarms are radioed in by the police, by fire department vehicles

FIGURE 11.6 (Left) A coded telegraphic-type box. (Right) An interior view of the telegraphic alarm box, showing the actuating lever (arrow) that normally protrudes through the hole shown on the inner door at right. When depressed, the handle releases the spring-wound mechanism and sends a coded signal from the code wheel shown at center. (Courtesy of Gamewell Corp.[10])

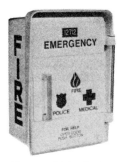

FIGURE 11.7 *(Left and Center) Typical battery/dc-powered coded radio-type alarm boxes equipped for multiple messages (fire, police, ambulance, etc.).* (Courtesy of King Fisher Co.) *(Right) A user-power-coded radio box. This type of device must incorporate an automatic test feature to meet standard requirements.* (Courtesy of Signal Communications Corp.[10])

FIGURE 11.8 *(Left) A voice-telephone alarm box, series type, for handset operation only. (Right) A combination telephone and coded telegraphic-type alarm box.* (Courtesy of Gamewell Corp.[10])

in the field, by first-aidsquads, and by private persons with citizen-band radios. An ever-increasing number of alarms come from automatic alarm systems installed in homes, factories, and offices. Such systems have direct connections to fire departments or to private fire protection service organizations that immediately relay the alarms to the fire departments.

The initial fire alarm information is not always received by the fire department. Most small departments rely on the police department to accept emergency calls. Often the police operate a comprehensive communications center intended to service all of the emergency needs in the area. In these instances, there should, obviously, be a direct link between police stations and each fire station.

Of course, the greatest communication needs are during a fire or other emergency, such as a hazardous materials spill. A fire department, depending on the size and available resources, might staff a communications center on a continual basis. Once a fire alarm has been received, a communications center provides many services to the fire department, including the following:

1. Dispatches apparatus. This is usually a routine task; however, in large communities where multiple fires can occur, the dispatching of apparatus might require difficult decisions involving priorities.

2. Provides information to the officer on the lead engine about locations of hydrants, special hazards, sprinkler systems, and any other data that are available at the communications center or from the field.

3. Provides information to the command officer responding to the alarm.

4. Services the needs of responding apparatus for supplies or other assistance.

In large fire departments the communications center is an elaborate installation with the ability to convey simultaneously many instructions and receive many calls (see Figure 11.9). These larger centers use computers to store information—especially prefire planning data and information concerning availability of equipment or special resources—so that the responding units can be given important data while they are on the way. As prefire planning becomes more widespread and therefore more detailed, more elaborate communications equipment and procedures will be needed. The cost of personal computers has decreased enough that most fire departments should be able to afford them.

Headquarters to Personnel: Once an alarm is received, the fire fighters on duty or on call must be contacted at their station or in their homes. Volunteers who work in the area might be alerted by a general alarm. Many fire fighters have home radio-alarm systems to receive information about a fire. Paging systems ("beepers") have also assumed an important role in the alerting of volunteer personnel. Fire personnel can now be alerted wherever they might be within their community. This information can be sent directly from fire headquarters or can come from the police department. These paging systems should be tested regularly (usually at least once a day) to ensure proper functioning.

Headquarters to Personnel on Apparatus: Each piece of apparatus is provided with radio equipment so headquarters can communicate with the personnel on the apparatus. Higher-level officers might want information on the status of fire fighting operations, and a dispatcher must know what apparatus and personnel are available in the event that companies need to be dispatched to a fire or pulled from a fire that is under control in order to respond to another alarm.

The latest computer technology has made it possible for computers and cellular telephones to be mounted on fire department apparatus. The use of

FIGURE 11.9 *Communications center equipped with a status board (top center), controls for the status board to the left and right of the board, and radio controls near the base of the board. At lower left are city telegraph system recorders. A status board is a visual indication of the location of the various stations and the equipment housed in each station. Indicating lights at each location show the current disposition of apparatus, e.g., in service by radio, out of service, and so on. (Source: Fire Protection Handbook[11])*

such equipment keeps the radio frequencies clear for fireground communications and speeds the flow of data to and from the fire scene. Some of the most important strides have been taken in the area of response to incidents involving hazardous materials. On-board computers, tied into national databases, can generate a tremendous amount of chemical-hazard information very quickly.

Because the noise level is high when apparatus is in motion or pumping, the radio equipment must be loud enough so it is clearly audible above the noise. Sometimes multiple speakers and earphones are necessary.

Chief Officer to Remote Units and Interunit Communication: In case of fire, or when in the field, the command officer must be able to communicate both with headquarters and with the units. During a fire it is necessary that the command officer be in communication with the first response engine in order to obtain a preliminary report and to be as informed as possible upon arrival at the fire scene. Once at the fire scene, the command officer needs to be able to talk to officers and fire fighters already engaged with the fire in order to obtain current information.

Radio Communication Between Apparatus and Individual Fire Fighters: All apparatus carry radio equipment. Radio communication between fire fighters has been made easier by the introduction of light-weight portable radio sets, some of which are small enough to be carried on a belt or in pockets.

Personnel to Headquarters: The command officer needs to communicate with headquarters by radio in order to request further aid or information.

Regional Intercommunications System: Finally, there must be a system to call mutual aid when needed. Incoming requests for mutual aid must be processed. Especially important is a system that is capable of clear transmission without excessive interference so as to avoid serious delays.

The quality of communications significantly affects the total time needed to gain control of a fire. If each individual component of the communications system can be operated more efficiently, then the total time it takes from the sounding of the alarm to the extinguishment of the fire will be reduced. Thus, it is sometimes more beneficial for fire department management to consider investing money in upgrading its present communications system than it is to invest in new equipment and additional personnel. The modernization of a department's entire communications system, or the improvement of any component of it, can help increase overall efficiency.

To the competent officer who is alert to opportunities for improving operations, the management of all operational aspects concerning communications equipment offers interesting challenges. Communications equipment with improved features is constantly being offered by manufacturers. To take advantage of the latest developments in the area of communications equipment, fire department management must:

1. Keep informed of changes that could bring significant improvements if old equipment was exchanged for new.
2. Be able to evaluate the benefits of new equipment in factual terms when asking for authorization to purchase it.
3. Learn how to make best use of the equipment once it has been acquired.

Sometimes new equipment must be purchased all at one time, thus necessitating the preparation of capital budget requests. At other times, new apparatus can be phased in gradually by making smaller purchases every year. Management concerns related to equipment decisions involve the setting of goals in order to prepare evaluations for training, for self-study on using the latest equipment correctly, and for analysis on whether or not procedural changes can help make existing equipment more effective. Fire department management is also involved with inevitable decisions about whether to request new equipment in the current year, or whether to wait another year when, usually, still more modern versions will be available.

Auxiliary Equipment

Auxiliary equipment is composed of those tools, attachments, and small pieces of apparatus that are not an integral part of the vehicle body or hose. NFPA 1901[7] lists the standard equipment items that should, or in some cases might, be included on each specific piece. The NFPA listings are similar to the ISO lists that are used for the purpose of grading apparatus. Older apparatus might not have all of these items, and departments are sometimes downgraded for not having them. In such cases there is often no convenient way of adapting old apparatus to fit modern requirements.

The list of equipment specified in NFPA 1901[7] is only the minimum required. For example, a department that has frequent need for certain pieces of equipment should consider additions. Also, departments that are frequently involved in vehicle rescue work usually carry additional equipment, such as medical equipment and tools, to extricate people from wrecked automobiles and trucks. Rural and suburban departments not specially equipped with trucks to fight brush fires, but who are frequently called to grass and brush fires, might include such items as hay forks, buckets, metal rakes, back tanks, fire brooms, and portable pumps on their standard pumpers. Because hose in standpipe-protected properties sometimes rots because of age (or might have been cut or stolen by vandals), many fire departments carry portable kits containing 1½-in. hose that is connected to standpipes when responding to alarms.

Used Equipment

As previously mentioned in connection with fireboats, used equipment can sometimes be a wiser purchase than new equipment—especially when limited funds are available. Often a locality needs a specialized piece of apparatus so infrequently that large expenditures on new apparatus cannot be justified; or, an extra backup piece of standard equipment is needed to replace one that can no longer be maintained economically; or, a major accident could have made a piece of apparatus inoperative. The purchase of used apparatus in such cases can sometimes be the solution to a serious problem.

ACTIVITIES

1. Given the following fire flows, determine the number of fire apparatus needed to protect a community, according to the Insurance Services Office (Table 11.2).
   (a) 4,000 gpm?
   (b) 7,500 gpm?
   (c) 9,500 gpm?
   (d) 12,000 gpm?

2. Discuss the present location of your community's fire station in relation to the fires that have occurred recently.
    (a) Considering that it might be necessary to relocate the station, what are some possible relocation sites?
    (b) List the factors that should be considered when choosing a relocation site for a station.

3. Your fire department's new budget has just been approved and the "go-ahead" has been given to build a new station. As a manager you must submit your design specifications for the station to the municipal officials in order for them to obtain bids for the job. Using fire departments you are familiar with, make a rough sketch illustrating an ideal floor plan for a station. Label the rooms and areas diagramed in your sketch.

4. What questions should fire department management consider before making a final decision on the purchase of a new piece of apparatus? Why is it sometimes better for a fire department to consider the purchase of used apparatus or the rebuilding of a chassis?

5. Because many of the fires in your district are in tall buildings that have been built within the past few years, it is necessary for your department to consider the purchase of an aerial ladder or an elevating platform. However, the road from the station to the tall buildings downtown is too narrow and steep to handle the new apparatus. Describe how you would solve this dilemma, including the considerations you would need to evaluate to help solve it.

6. Your community has recently adjusted its zoning laws to encourage more industry. The first new industry to be built will be an oil refinery. How would you adjust the physical resources of your fire department to better cope with the new fire hazard and with other fire hazards that might become part of your district?

7. As an officer in your municipality's fire department, what factors should you consider when deciding whether or not to purchase each of the following items for your department?
    (a) An aerial ladder.
    (b) A new car for the chief.
    (c) A new stove for the fire station's kitchen.
    (d) A console desk for your communications center.
    (e) New uniforms for fire fighters.
    (f) An additional wing to the fire station.

8. Review the purposes of an efficient fire department communications system. Then examine the communications system of your community's fire department.
    (a) What kinds of systems are available for the public?
    (b) Are these systems adequate? Explain your conclusion.
    (c) As a fire department manager, how would you go about making necessary changes?

REFERENCES

[1]Cote, A. E., ed., *Fire Protection Handbook*, 16th edition, National Fire Protection Association, Quincy, MA, 1986, p. 15-95.

[2]ISO, *Grading Schedule for Municipal Fire Protection*, Insurance Services Office, 1980, New York, NY.

[3]ISO, *Fire Suppression Rating Schedule*, Insurance Services Office, 1980, New York, NY.

[4]ISO, *Commercial Fire Rating Schedule*, Insurance Services Office, 1975, New York, NY.

[5]Cote, A. E., ed., *Fire Protection Handbook*, 16th edition, National Fire Protection Association, Quincy, MA, 1986, p. 15-92.

[6]Cote, A. E., ed., *Fire Protection Handbook*, 16th edition, National Fire Protection Association, Quincy, MA, 1986, p. 15-61.

[7]NFPA 1901, *Standard for Automotive Fire Apparatus*, National Fire Protection Association, Quincy, MA, 1985, pp. 1901-9, 1901-10.

[8]NFPA 1500, *Standard on Fire Department Occupational Safety and Health Program*, National Fire Protection Association, Quincy, MA, 1987.

[9]Cote, A. E., ed., *Fire Protection Handbook*, 16th edition, National Fire Protection Association, Quincy, MA, pp. 15-63, 15-64.

[10]Cote, A. E., ed., *Fire Protection Handbook*, 16th edition, National Fire Protection Association, Quincy, MA, p. 16-8.

[11]*Fire Protection Handbook*, 15th edition, National Fire Protection Association, Quincy, MA, 1981, p. 15-2.

12

Management of Financial Resources

All fire department resources, other than those provided by certain volunteer fire departments, are purchased with public money. After obtaining the necessary funds, every fire department must be concerned with managing these financial resources in an effective and efficient manner. The proper use of financial controls is essential to help ensure responsible management of these funds. An understanding of budgets and budgeting techniques is, therefore, essential to operational success.

In organizations where budgets are used properly, they bring a form of discipline that forces careful planning and thereby starts the management cycle, or the process of setting realistic and meaningful objectives.

FIRE DEPARTMENT BUDGETS

A budget is a plan for future operations, expressed in financial terms. Basically, formulating a budget involves asking what a fire department intends to accomplish during a given year and how much it will cost.[1] A budget allocates financial resources to the different uses for which the money is intended. Because exact amounts cannot be known in advance, a budget reflects the decision on how much money to make available for each function. At the same time the budget is a forecast of how much will be spent for a particular use.

Progressive fire departments use the budgetary process to list the objectives of the department along with the financial resources necessary to achieve them. In this way, municipal officials and the general public can better understand the need for a fire department's expenditures and make more informed financial decisions. The fire department is also better able to defend its requests.

Available funds are distributed in such a way that a balanced mix of resources usually is available to address community fire protection needs. Through the use of a budget the distribution of funds is conducted in a planned and controlled fashion.

A budget is used much like a road map. The departmental objectives are set, priorities are determined, and financial plans are developed to reach those objectives. The completed budget then serves the same function as a road map, showing where the emphasis in fire protection expenditures is to be placed.

BUDGET TYPES

There are basically two types of budgets used in municipal fire departments: the expense budget and the capital budget.

The Expense Budget

An expense (or operations) budget contains costs of a recurring nature, such as salaries, fringe benefits, supplies, and small equipment purchases. This is the type of budget used most often by fire department management in daily operations.

Budgetary Systems

There are essentially two basic operating systems used in preparing and working with recurring expenses: the line-item system and the program system (a performance-based or functional system).

Line-Item System: In this type of budget, each particular expense is noted line by line (see Table 12.1). On each of these lines the amount that can be spent is entered next to the appropriate line. As the money is spent, it must be accounted for by a series of matching vouchers that indicate the amount spent and the dates of the transactions.

Because this system lists each expense separately, rather than incorporating many expenses under one broad category, it is difficult to determine how much of the budget is being spent on nonitemized functions, such as fire fighting, training, or support of community activities. An advantage of this system is that the total expense for specific items is readily shown. Line-item budgets have the added benefits of simplicity and low cost.

Program System: In this type of budget, expenditures are allocated for specific activities (see Table 12.2). A department will, for example, estimate the total expense (e.g., salaries, materials used, etc.) for performing a specific function over a given period of time. This estimated amount becomes the basis for measuring actual expenditures for that function. As the year progresses, a record is kept of the actual money spent.

TABLE 12.1 Sample line-item budget system.

Account no.	Classification	Current year amount	Actually spent in previous year
001	Apparatus repairs	$ 6,500	$ 5,876
002	Office supplies	2,000	2,000
003	Fire hose	9,000	4,500
004	Radio repairs	10,000	9,760
005	New radios	25,000	3,500
006	Janitorial service	15,000	12,500
007	Chief's vehicle	21,000	—
008	Computer system	6,500	—
009	Computer software	2,000	—
010	Fire fighting equipment	9,000	9,000
011	Breathing apparatus	21,000	12,500
012	Salaries and benefits	240,000	229,000
	Total:	367,000	288,636

TABLE 12.2 Sample program budget.

Department: Fire   Division: Fire Prevention
Program: Firesafety Education   Year: 1990
Objective: To provide firesafety education to all citizens
Measurement criteria: Number of classes taught

Salaries (2 personnel)	$37,700
Fringe benefits (2 personnel)	11,310
Vehicle acquisitions	4,800
Vehicle upkeep	1,500
Educational materials	3,500
Audio-visual materials	2,650
Office supplies	135
Total program cost	61,595

Officers involved directly with the budget can best evaluate the compatibility between the department's needs and functions and budgetary estimates. In those cases where a function is not directly concerned with emergencies, many departments seek to curtail such functions to adhere to budgetary constraints. This tendency should be avoided, wherever possible because the future value of such functions, e.g., public education, while not directly measurable, are nonetheless very valuable.

From year to year, budget allotments can be compared to actual expenditures and resources, and resources can be reallocated if necesssary to allow for emergencies or to adjust for unavoidable outlays that are higher than forecasted. A program budget requires more record keeping than a line-item budget, but it permits a department to consciously direct its work so that the activities that deserve higher priorities receive the appropriate attention. For example, if a department has decided that public firesafety education should receive high priority for 12 months and has allocated a certain number of hours to the project, the program budget will show on a monthly basis whether public education is being deprived of resources or whether it is receiving its share for the year. This helps in predicting whether the planned activities will be accomplished during the time allotted, or whether more resources might be needed for certain tasks.

Program budgets have the distinct advantage of providing management with a better control tool. Adjustments can be made when it is desirable or necessary to achieve departmental goals.

The Capital Budget

A capital budget contains expenditures for items that cost too much to be paid for in a single year. Funding must be spread over a number of years. Examples of large capital expenditures include a new fire station or new apparatus (see Table 12.3).

Capital budgets differ from expense budgets in one major area: Only a small part of each item in a capital budget is paid for with current tax revenues. The operation of a capital budget is somewhat similar to purchasing a car with a bank loan. The local government pays for a small part of the capital budget out of money it sets aside from tax receipts. The remaining balance is borrowed either from banks or through the issuing of bonds. Over the years, the borrower repays a fixed amount annually.

Because capital budgets usually involve only a few items, they are not considered to be working tools for a manager in the same sense as expense budgets. Although capital budgets represent an authorization for a department to buy needed equipment, they do not require regular entries into the department's budget registers or evaluation of good operation of a department.

THE BUDGETARY PROCESS

"Fire administrators and city officials in general are well aware that the process of developing, presenting, justifying and monitoring a budget is. . . a

TABLE 12.3 Sample capital budget.

Account no.	Classification	First year	Second year	Third year	Fourth year
001	Station two	$150,000	150,000	150,000	150,000
002	Class A pumper	50,000	50,000	50,000	50,000
003	Aerial ladder	100,000	100,000	100,000	100,000
004	Air compressor unit	35,000	35,000	35,000	35,000
005	Rescue vehicle	75,000	75,000	75,000	75,000

turbulent, complex and sometimes chaotic process."[2] The mastery of this process is extremely important for fire department operations. Without sufficient funds, there is a poor link between the fire protection needs of a community and the operational needs of its fire department. Budgets thus serve many useful purposes, including the following:

- Guides or forecasts that can help make planning easier.
- A communications link, joining the department with the public and officials.
- Records that show how fast available funds are being spent, thus permitting better planning of activities during the last weeks and days of the budget year.

Because budgets are important management tools, every fire officer should understand the purposes they serve and the basis for formulating them. Fire officers must also be taught that fiscal responsibility (management's ability to live within a budget) is a crucial element in maintaining public trust.

Except in the case of a fire district, the fire department budget is a portion of the municipal budget. Personnel costs, including direct compensation and all benefits, generally are the most significant costs for most municipal fire departments, accounting for approximately 90 percent of the total expenditures of a full-time paid fire department. Personnel costs of partly paid, partly volunteer fire departments compose approximately 40 to 60 percent of their total budgets.[3]

The remaining funds are allocated to cover the costs of operating expenses such as heat and light, for the fire stations; gas or diesel fuel for the fire apparatus and other vehicles; maintenance supplies; minor equipment such as breathing apparatus; and fire fighting tools, office supplies, repairs to buildings and grounds, and so on.

Progressive fire departments use the budgetary process as a forecasting tool to determine the allocation of resources among the various segments of the agency. These departments list the objectives of the fire department along with the financial resources necessary to achieve them. In this way, the general public and municipal officials can better understand the need for a fire department's expenditures and make better informed fiscal decisions. The fire department can also defend its requests more effectively.

Formation of the Budget

Considerable time and thought is needed for developing a budget request to help ensure that it will be received favorably, especially if it includes significant increases from the previous year. If ideas and opinions are sought from various groups within the department, these contributions will help focus the budget on priorities for fire protection in the community. Budgeting is essentially a four-part process: 1) formulation, 2) transmittal, 3) approval, and 4) management.

Formulation

During the formulation phase, fire department managers review past budgets to see how well estimated outlays compared to actual expenditures. Variations are studied to achieve better predictions for the future.

During this time, suggestions are solicited from each division, bureau, or level of the fire department so that all useful ideas can be considered. Involving various groups also helps to achieve a better understanding of budgetary decisions because people feel that they have participated in the process. The specific knowledge of those responsible for implementing the budget decision can bring better prioritization and more accurate estimates. These groups can thus add detailed support and sound justification, both important elements when a budget is being considered by municipal authorities.

While a budget request is being developed, a proposed budget sheet sometimes is used. The proposed budget contains several columns. These show how much money was budgeted in the previous year, how much was actually spent, and how much is being requested for the current year and (usually) how much greater this is than the previous year's request. Where necessary, explanations and supportive data are attached to the budget in an appendix. While the layout is fairly standard, many fire departments use modifications to fit their individual preferences. The use of this type of format allows for a clear and logical approach to budgeting. Each request is based on careful reasoning and fortified by the relevant supportive information. Use of a proposed budget can prevent costly errors or omissions in budget development.

Transmittal

Once the preliminary budget has been prepared, it is transmitted to the local governing body. At this point the budgetary request should be thorough enough to be self-supporting in the event that department personnel are not available to explain it, answer questions, or defend it. Unanswered questions can do considerable harm to the message of a preliminary budget. The message itself should, therefore, communicate all important points supporting the budget request. Still, it is essential for fire department management to be available to assist the governing body by answering their questions.

A basic principle used in municipal fire protection master planning assumes that the proper level of fire protection for a community is the amount of fire protection for which citizens are willing to pay. However, managers of progressive fire departments will seek to inform their elected representatives of the probable total costs of fire risk and fire protection at different levels of fire department funding. In other words, the fire department managers, as experts, should provide estimates of potential fire losses at the requested budget and at other budgetary levels.

Approval

Once a budget has been estimated, management is required to submit it to a finance officer or a finance committee. These estimates are then given to the town or city administration.

When a departmental budget has been approved by the town or city administration, it must then be approved by the town or city council; in some municipalities, it must be approved by a financial town meeting. Some municipal charters allow the council to reduce a budget but not to increase it. Once approved, the budget takes effect at the beginning of the fiscal year and becomes an instrument of control that shows a department how much it can spend during a particular time period. If not approved in time, it is customary to permit expenditures at the same rate as the previous year.[4] As stated previously, this process can be altered somewhat for volunteer departments who raise funds themselves and for departments that obtain grants for special projects from the state, the federal government, or from a private foundation.

Management

Once a budget has been approved, fire department administrators must, of course, attempt to manage the department within the budgeted guidelines. Excessive spending, or even significant underspending, are signs of shortcomings in a department's administrative competence. This can lead to credibility problems and more critical reception of future budgetary requests.

Budget Worksheets: In order to help management work as effectively as possible within an allocated budget, budget worksheets are sometimes used. Budget worksheets usually show a record of expenditures for a current year, and can either be distributed to officers in a particular department or kept solely for the chief's use. Although departments organize budget worksheets according to their individual needs, most worksheets are set up like the sample shown in Table 12.4. Typically, one column is used for the monthly budget and another column is used for recording the amount actually spent. Additional columns can be plotted to show the difference between the two, or to show previous years' budgets and expenditures.

Long-Range Planning: When preparing budgets for the financial management of a department's capital resources, consideration must be given to the long-range use of such resources — one major reason being that to purchase all new apparatus would be impractical. To do so could mean that the expense of such new products would soon outweigh a department's ability to fund many important activities, such as fire prevention work.

TABLE 12.4 Sample budget worksheet that is prepared on a monthly basis.

				January					
Item	Budget this year	Actual this year	Difference (+)(−)	Budget last year	Actual last year	Budget to date	Actual to date	Last year budget to date	Last year actual to date
Contractual services									
Main. bldg. & grounds									
Etc.									

In order to formulate long-range budgetary goals it is necessary to consider all possible future expenses and renovations relevant to physical resources by predicting future problems and needs that might arise. Because the entire department is affected by all budgetary decisions, management should ensure coordination among all levels of the department and should allow for expression of individual needs and recommendations. Through the coordination of all departmental levels, the department is better able to work as a solidified unit in accomplishing its primary goal — protecting life and property.

ACTIVITIES

1. Discuss some of the negative and some of the positive aspects of utilizing group planning in forming a fire department budget. Defend your choices in each case.

2. Explain the benefits of a budget system as a planning tool and as a control device.

3. Write a brief explanation of: 1) a line-item budget system and 2) a program budget system. Prepare a simplified example of each.

4. List and discuss the steps used by fire department managers during the formulation phase of the budgetary process.

5. List and discuss the purpose of: 1) budget worksheets, and 2) long-range planning.

REFERENCES

[1]Carter, H. R., "Budget Justification, Your Fight for a Piece of the Pie," *Fire Command!*, August, 1986, p. 45.

[2]Burkell, C. J., "Budgeting with Objectives," *Fire Chief*, September, 1983, p. 35.

[3]Cote, A. E., ed., *Fire Protection Handbook*, 16th edition, National Fire Protection Association, Quincy, MA, 1986, p. 15-17.

[4]Cote, A. E., ed., *Fire Protection Handbook*, 16th edition, National Fire Protection Association, Quincy, MA, 1986, p. 15-18.

13

Fire Service Personnel Management

Private industry uses labor, material, and capital to produce goods or services that it sells in order to make a profit. Likewise, federal, state, and municipal governments use labor, material, and capital (obtained from taxes) to provide services to the public. In both situations the key resource is people, and the administration of this resource is a basic responsibility of management if the goals of the organization are to be accomplished.

In effect, personnel administration is concerned with maintaining effective human relations within an organization. As such, personnel administration is an integral part of the job of all people in supervisory capacities and is as much a part of their job as the work that has to be done.

ORGANIZATION FOR PERSONNEL MANAGEMENT

To assist management in the personnel function, many large organizations have a separate department staffed with personnel specialists. However, because most local governmental units cannot afford a separate personnel department for the fire service, the personnel function might either be in a personnel office for all departments or one of the responsibilities of a single fire department officer. In many instances, fire departments rely on the Civil Service Commission's personnel procedures for guidance. In other fire departments the personnel function might be the responsibility of the fire chief and the fire director or commissioner.

Whether it is the part-time responsibility of a single individual or the full-time responsibility of a fully staffed unit, the personnel activity of any organization has many specific responsibilities in three general areas: 1) routine procedures, 2) labor relations activities (whether the department is unionized or not), and 3) advisory activities for management.

Routine Procedures

Routine procedures include hiring, placing, and terminating employees; monitoring employee services; administering salaries, wages, and other compensation; administering fringe benefits; and administering career development programs, including performance evaluations.

Labor Relations Activities

Labor relations activities of a personnel department include recommendations on policy, a role in employee grievance handling (particularly in nonunion organizations), consultation with line managers on disciplinary actions, and contract negotiations if a union represents some or all of the employees.

Advisory Activities

The personnel department also has the responsibility to advise all levels of management on human relations policies, communications needs, and scheduling of personnel. The department maintains close contact with the needs of people in the organization so that it can recommend policy and procedural changes whenever it becomes necessary or advisable.

FIRE DEPARTMENT PERSONNEL POLICIES

The personnel policies of a fire department are subject to many influences, including union contracts and policies; federal, state, and local regulations; the fire commissioner or director; the fire chief; and the general public (taxpayers). Departmental officers play an important role in the implementation of these policies, whether or not a separate personnel division exists. If a department has such an office, the company officer's task is somewhat less demanding because policies and procedures are likely to be more clearly defined and because more support and advice is available. More of the responsibility for good personnel relations rests with the officer if there is no central personnel office even though these functions are performed by an office with responsibility for all employees of the municipality or government unit. In such a case, personnel services to the department are less likely to be specifically relevant to the department's needs.

Personnel Management Functions

Even though there are some personnel functions that are solely the responsibility of personnel professionals, the following functions are included here to provide an overview of personnel administration:

1. Equal employment opportunity.
2. Selecting, hiring, and placement.
3. Salary administration.
4. Fringe benefits and employee services.
5. Record keeping.

Equal Employment Opportunity

Local governmental organizations, including the fire service, must operate within the guidelines of federal and state statutes. One of the most significant pieces of legislation affecting all personnel functions is the prohibition against discrimination on the grounds of race, color, religion, sex, national origin, or age. This statute applies not only to hiring and firing practices, but also to all aspects of employment opportunities.

The Civil Rights Act: Originally, the Civil Rights Act of 1964 and its subsequent amendments and executive orders applied only to federal organizations and to those companies doing business with the federal government. Then, many state legislatures, following the lead of the federal government, passed equal opportunity laws that applied the same principles to local businesses and governmental bodies. In summary, Title VII of the Civil Rights Act of 1964 states that it is unlawful for an employer:[1]

1. To fail or refuse to hire, or to discharge any individual, or otherwise to discriminate against any individual with respect to that individual's compensation, terms, conditions, or privileges of employment because of an individual's race, color, religion, sex, national origin, age, physical or mental handicap, or status as a disabled or Vietnam-era veteran; or,
2. To limit, segregate, or classify employees (or applicants for employment) in any way that would deprive or tend to deprive any individual of employment opportunities, or otherwise adversely affect that individual's status as an employee because of such individual's race, color, religion, sex, or national origin.

Affirmative Action Programs: The Age Discrimination in Employment Act of 1967 added age to the list of prohibited discriminators, and in 1972 Congress amended Title VII extending coverage to most governmental activities. The legislation encouraged employers to prepare plans to actively seek out minorities and women who were qualified to be hired and/or promoted. Those employers doing business with the government who violate these laws or do not prepare federally approved affirmative action plans are subject to federal court suits. Such suits could be entered by the Equal Employment Opportunity Commission.

Affirmative action programs require that criteria for selection or promotion must be essential to the job. This does not mean that the standards must be lowered in order to provide employment for women and minorities. For example, if a job requires a fire fighter to carry a physical load a certain distance, then a person applying for the job could be asked to demonstrate the ability to do that job (see Figure 13.1). However, tests that measure abilities not necessary for the job cannot be used. Therefore, intelligence tests cannot be given, and questions about marital status or personal plans cannot be asked, unless the employer can show proof that the test or questions really measure qualities that are essential to the job.

Those employers who are required by law or regulation to prepare affirmative action plans must submit the following to the respective agency (often the Equal Employment Opportunity Commission):

1. A statement of commitment.
2. A specific allocation of time and money to implement an affirmative action program.
3. An analysis of the present organization to determine whether discrimination exists.
4. Specific plans to rectify the imbalance if discrimination exists.
5. Goals at all employment levels and timetables for accomplishing them, with procedures for measuring how well they are being achieved.

FIGURE 13.1 Recruits participate in a training program for full-time fire fighter positions. (Courtesy of Ken Yimm, Palo Alto Times)

Typical goals and specific actions to remedy the problems include:

1. Achieving a work force that is representative of the population in the community, which might require:
    a. Increasing the number of women and minority employees being considered for all position levels.
    b. Restructuring entry-level positions to allow qualified minority and women employees to become eligible.
    c. Establishing a procedure for ensuring that recruiting materials, vacancy announcements, and so on reach minority groups and women in the community.
    d. Appointing individuals to coordinate the program with minority and women's community organizations.
2. Providing lower-grade employees opportunities to prepare for higher positions and giving economically or educationally disadvantaged persons opportunities to gain more marketable skills. This might require:
    a. Restructuring positions to allow movement from dead-end jobs.
    b. Establishing percentage goals for enrolling employees in career-development programs.
    c. Identifying positions requiring bilingual ability, and encouraging those with poor English language skills to study English.
3. Establishing procedures to process discrimination complaints, ensuring prompt resolution, and providing corrective action procedures. This could be achieved through:
    a. Reviewing procedures to ensure that they do indeed bring improvement, and revising procedures when they do not.
    b. Ensuring that the appeals procedure is fair, and revising it when necessary.

International Association of Black Professional Fire Fighters (IABPFF): Another effect of the Equal Opportunity laws was formation of the International Association of Black Professional Fire Fighters. The IABPFF, which is a life member of the National Association for the Advancement of Colored People (NAACP), was organized in 1970 to: 1) create a liaison between black fire fighters across the U.S.; 2) compile information on unjust working conditions in the fire service and implement corrective action; 3) collect and evaluate data on all deleterious conditions where minorities work; 4) ensure that competent blacks are recruited and employed as fire fighters; 5) promote interracial progress throughout the fire service; and 6) motivate black fire fighters to seek promotions.

Selecting, Hiring, and Placement

A personnel division must determine a fire department's staffing needs and organize to fill any openings as they occur, keeping in mind the Equal Employment Opportunity requirements. These openings could be the result of planned expansion, retirement, disability, voluntary terminations, or dismissals.

When a department is subject to Civil Service regulations, the Civil Service roster is used to obtain qualified candidates. Otherwise, a department recruits through normal procedures, such as advertising, using a community network, maintaining a list of interested persons, and so on. Once applicants are identified, the selection usually is made by doing most, or all, of the following: 1) reviewing applications, 2) interviewing applicants, 3) testing to determine capabilities and physical fitness, 4) analyzing the interview results, 5) checking references, 6) repeating interviews where necessary, and 7) selecting the most qualified individuals.

In many states the Civil Service Commission maintains a roster for individuals wanting to join a career fire department. To become eligible for this roster, a candidate usually must pass a written examination, a practical examination (in some locales), and a physical checkup. Those who qualify usually are included on the roster in the order of their test results. Several names from the top of the list are submitted to a fire department for specific selection. Either a personnel officer, the company officer, or a small selection team must then choose from these candidates the one who is best qualified to fill the position.

Because human life and safety can be at stake, competency in the fire service is of major importance; therefore, the interviewer must try to establish how an applicant is likely to perform under emergency conditions. The procedures discussed near the end of Chapter 4 ("Use of Questions") can be helpful in determining personality characteristics, in predicting what an applicant will do when under pressure, and deciding how an applicant will fit into the team — to what extent an applicant will bring to the team the strengths it needs.

Considerations for Effective Selection Interviews:[2] Planning of interviews is of great importance. It provides an opportunity to review thoroughly what needs to be discovered. Then, during the interview when the interviewer's mind is on many different subjects, none of the important questions will be overlooked. While new questions can be developed during the interview, the basic structure of the interview can be decided beforehand. Planning of each interview can best be done by preparing a checklist to include:

1. Ideas for starting the interview informally so that the candidate will feel comfortable.
2. A few notes to help explain the requirements, difficulties, and opportunities of the position.
3. Notes to serve as reminders of specific information to be obtained in order to receive a full picture of the applicant. These might include: a) work background, b) feelings about new experiences, c) interest in learning and self-development, d) career aspirations, and e) attitudes about people, work, and responsibility.

In obtaining information, it is useful to help an applicant speak as freely as possible about background and experiences. This can be achieved with open-ended questions that elicit more information than simple questions that can be answered merely with a "yes" or a "no." Many interviewers have a tendency to accept factual information about experience as being equal in importance to the more subjective judgments about knowledge and abilities. Experience is much easier to measure than the potential of an applicant; it is, therefore, understandable that experience is given considerable weight. However, the extra effort it takes to explore beyond experience usually proves to be worthwhile, even though such exploration requires searching questions and continual, careful evaluation while interviewing.

During the interview, some personnel representatives develop a list of questions for later use when checking references. If the references prove satisfactory, they often call one, two, or three applicants for a second interview before making the final selection.

Interviewing for volunteer fire departments is similar to interviewing for career staff positions. The primary difference is that applicants for paid positions are screened to determine if they would be desirable in a particular position. Applicants for volunteer positions usually are screened to see how their services or skills might be used in activities other than the ones for which they are applying. Often, volunteers are interviewed when they apply, and not specifically when an opening exists. Following are some specific suggestions for interviewing volunteers:

1. The position, its requirements, and the amount of time it will take to do the job should be clearly and honestly described.
2. Training requirements should be explained in detail.
3. The psychological impact of the fire service on a volunteer's family should be outlined clearly.
4. Policies and procedures of the department should be discussed.
5. Volunteers should be allowed some time to think about the position and its requirements before acceptance.
6. It should be made clear what support the volunteer can expect from the paid staff, if one exists, and what financial assistance will be provided.
7. Under no circumstances is it desirable to use high-pressure tactics or to continue to persuade a volunteer who shows reluctance.
8. Volunteers should be informed that the first few months of affiliation are considered a probationary period.
9. Opportunities for obtaining prestigious or paid positions should be described realistically.

If accepted, new volunteers should be assigned as soon as possible. The fire department should confirm such assignments by letter. A letter is also an appropriate way to confirm training dates, uniform requirements, and other job specifications. A file copy of the confirmation letter gives the department a record of the details of specific assignments. If training is required before assignment, letters can be sent after the volunteers have successfully completed the course.

Acceptability of Pre-Employment Interview Questions: Questions that have been proved as having a discriminatory effect on the selection process are explicitly prohibited by court rulings under Equal Employment Opportunity legislation, and cannot be asked. The following considerations apply not only to interviews, but to any part of the selection procedure, including the tests that are used to differentiate qualified from unqualified candidates. The basic principle that should be applied is that all selection must be based on criteria that actually are job related—not only in the mind of the interviewer, but factually job related from experience or by job description. To ascertain whether or not an interview question is discriminatory, ask the following questions:

- Does the question have a disproportionate effect in screening out minorities and/or women?
- Is the information necessary to judge an individual's competence for performance of this particular job?
- Are there alternate, nondiscriminatory ways to secure necessary information?

Major questions that should be eliminated from employment interviews, or carefully reviewed to ensure that their use is job related and nondiscriminatory in effect, include:

1. **Age and Date of Birth**: A request for date of birth or age on an employment application form cannot be included.
2. **Maiden Name or Previous Name if Name was Legally Changed**: Inquiries concerning whether the applicant has worked or been educated under another name are allowable only when the data are needed to verify the applicant's qualifications.
3. **Birthplace**: It is discriminatory to inquire about the birthplaces of applicants and their parents.
4. **Race, National Origin, Religion**: Pre-employment inquiries concerning an applicant's race, color, national origin, or religion are looked upon with disfavor by Equal Opportunity Commission and the Wage Hour Administrator. None of the federal civil rights laws specifically outlaws such questions; however, in the absence of any logical explanation for the questions, they will be viewed as evidence of discrimination because the race, national origin, or religion of an applicant has nothing to do with the job performance.
5. **Gender, Marital, and Family Status**: Whether a candidate is married or single and the number and age(s) of children are examples of questions frequently used to discriminate against women. Such questions do not relate to capacity for job performance. Although an employer might believe that women with young children are more prone to absenteeism or turnover, actual studies show that there is little difference in the absentee rates of men and women; turnover is more related to type of job and pay level than to gender or family status. Investigation of an

applicant's previous work record is a valid method of evaluating employee stability. It is a violation of the law for employers to require pre-employment information on child-care arrangements. The supreme court has ruled that an employee cannot use different hiring policies for women and men.

6. **Education**: Educational requirements that are not job related and that have a disparate effect on projected groups are a major area of discrimination. The Supreme Court has explicitly affirmed the Equal Employment Opportunity Commission guidelines prohibiting requirements of a high school education as a condition of employment or promotion where this requirement disqualifies minorities at a substantially higher rate than others, and where there is no evidence that it is a significant predictor of job performance.

7. **Experience Requirements**: Such requirements should be reviewed and reevaluated to ensure necessity for specific jobs. Requirements should be eliminated where jobs can be learned quickly, or reduced if not necessary for job needs.

8. **Physical Requirements**: Questions related to height, weight, and other physical requirements can be asked only if necessary for performance of a particular job.

9. **Credit Rating**: A negative employment decision based on an applicant's poor credit rating also has been found unlawful where credit policies have disproportionate negative effect on minorities and the employer cannot show "business necessity" for such rejection. Inquiries about charge accounts or home or car ownership (unless the latter is required for the job) have been found to have an adverse effect on minorities and are unlawful unless required by "business necessity."

10. **Arrest and Conviction Records**: An individual's arrest record has been ruled by the courts to be an unlawful basis for refusal to employ. An arrest is not indication of guilt. Courts have found that where minorities are subject to disproportionately higher arrest rates than whites, refusal to hire on this basis has a disproportionate effect on minority employment opportunities. Also, a federal court has ruled that conviction of a felony or misdemeanor should not, by itself, constitute an absolute bar to employment, and that the employer should give fair consideration to the relationship between the nature of the act resulting in conviction and the applicant's qualifications for the job in question.

11. **Appearance**: Employment decisions (hiring, promotion, discharge) based on factors such as length or style of hair, apparel, and other aspects of appearance have been found to violate the law if they disproportionately affect employment on the basis of race, national origin, or gender. Some courts have ruled it illegal to refuse to hire or to discharge men with long hair where similar restrictions are not imposed on women. Hairstyle requirements also can be racially discriminatory.

12. **Availability for Saturday or Sunday Work**: Although it might be necessary for an employer to have this information, the law requires

that employers make reasonable accomodations for an "employee's or propective employee's religious observance or practice without undue hardship on the conduct of the employer's business."

13. **Friends or Relatives Working for the Department**: This question can reflect a preference for friends and relatives of present employees, and would be unlawful if it has the effect of reducing employment opportunities for women or minorities. It would have such an effect if the makeup of the present work force differs significantly from the proportion of women or minorities in the relevant population area. The question also reflects a rule that only one partner in a marriage can work for the employer. There is growing recognition that such rules have a disproportionate, discriminatory effect on employment of women, and that they serve no necessary business purpose.

After selecting an individual, the personnel officer must make the new employee aware of the department's organization, insurance and health benefits, duty hours, vacation, sick leave, holiday policies, educational benefits, retirement and social security plans, and any other rules and regulations necessary for policy adherence. When new fire fighters are assigned to duty stations, they usually are subject to a probationary period of several months so that their capabilities and attitudes can be evaluated before they are given permanent status.

NFPA Guidelines: NFPA 1201, *Recommendations for the Organization for Fire Services*,[3] provides recommended guidelines for selection of fire service personnel as well as for minimum qualifications for fire fighters. Abbreviated applicable sections from the standard follow:

5-2 Selection, Promotion.
5-2.1 Selection of Personnel.
5-2.1.1 Recruitment. The fire department should establish a recruitment program. It should be coordinated with procedures of municipal or other personnel or civil service agencies having jurisdiction. The recruitment program should consist of the following steps:

(a) Conducting an active search for the best qualified persons available for membership in the department and encouraging them to apply for appointment.

(b) Rejecting without examination candidates who show on their application form that they clearly fail to meet department standards for entrance.

(c) Interviewing each candidate and giving tests measuring aptitudes, physical agility, and achievement motivation characteristics.

(d) Subjecting candidates to a thorough physical and medical examination which they should pass in order to fully perform fire department work.

(e) Investigating the character of candidates by interviewing former employers, personal references, neighbors, and others familiar with their record, taking fingerprints for police record checkings.

(f) Requiring applicants to complete an intensive program of work and training in the department's operations with a satisfactory rating.

5-2.1.2 Age. A maximum age limit should be specified for acceptance to membership on the fire department suppression force. A minimum age limit should also be specified to [ensure that members] are mature physically and mentally.

NOTE: A maximum age limit may not be necessary if entry examinations are adequate.

5-2.1.3 Education. A high school education, or state-recognized equivalent, should be required as a minimum. It is desirable to give preference to candidates that have taken fire science, fire technology, and public administration college courses.

5-2.1.4 Character. The candidate's application should be required to give a full employment history and personal references. When candidates report for an interview or tests, photographs, fingerprints, and signatures should be taken for identification purposes. The applicant's credit rating should be checked to eliminate irresponsible persons. Police and motor vehicle records should be obtained [as well].

5-2.1.5 Physical Requirements. Job-related physical requirements should be stated in applications to eliminate candidates who are physically unqualified. A series of tests should be given after the medical examination to determine the applicant's strength, coordination, agility, dexterity, and endurance.

5-2.1.6 Medical Examination. The fire department should adopt job-related medical standards unless those of a personnel agency serving it are adequate. All applicants should meet the medical requirements as outlined in NFPA 1001, *Fire Fighter Professional Qualifications.*

5-2.1.7 Testing. Job-related written, oral, and performance tests for aptitudes and intelligence should be given when such tests are available to the fire department. Intelligence testing and measures of reading, thinking, and deciding should be validated for job relatedness and freedom from illegal discrimination.

5-2.1.8 Adaptability. For a period of at least 12 months before permanent appointment to the department, applicants should be assigned to probationary training and supervision. Completion of Fire fighter Levels I and II should be achieved before permanent appointment. Written reports from their supervisors during this period and from the department training officer should be used to evaluate the cooperation and ability of the individual to be a successful member of the department.

Fire fighting is primarily a team function, especially in the case of a very large fire or emergency. Furthermore, the everyday life of a fire fighter is a group life and members must have a high degree of ability to get along with other people. It is desirable that the candidate work under at least three supervisors during probation and receive a satisfactory written rating from each supervisor before permanent appointment.

5-2.1.9 Appointment. Applicants should be kept in probationary status until all parts of the selection process are completed, including the 12-month period of probationary training. The chief should dismiss any candidate at any point in the period for unsatisfactory performance after reasonable written warning and notice.

The fire chief's authority may be limited to recommend action where a personnel agency outside the fire department has jurisdiction over probationers or where another agency makes the actual appointments. Where a pre-employment training procedure is not used, it often turns out that those who can meet physical and written tests for candidates cannot meet the actual performance requirements of department work. Many candidates voluntarily drop out when they find that they cannot handle the work during the probationary period.

5-2.2 Promotion.

5-2.2.1 Promotion Program. The fire department should establish a documented job-related personnel evaluation program for internal and lateral entry promotion to the various ranks. It should be coordinated with procedures of municipal or other personnel or civil service agencies having jurisdiction and should consist of the following steps:

(a) Preparing lists of members for in-service training for promotion to company officers, chief officers and to positions requiring special qualification.

(b) Arranging assignments so that officer candidates may have a variety of duties (in several companies or districts) and experience in various staff work, such as fire prevention, training, maintenance, and communications.

(c) Requiring a formal procedure whereby supervisors report on candidate's aptitudes, participation, and ability to function as part of a company for the purpose of evaluating the candidate's qualifications for promotion.

(d) Requiring candidates to complete an in-service training program, based on a job analysis for each position, and the passing of an examination on such training.

(e) Arranging assignments so that interested members may pursue courses for academic credit or college degrees at accredited and approved colleges and schools.

(f) Appointing candidates to positions after procedures of the fire department as well as those of personnel jurisdictions have been met.

As far as promotions are concerned, fire departments are moving away from the traditional written examination as the sole criterion for promotion. Assessment centers, formally structured interviews, and practical performance tests are being used to evaluate the ability to perform. These tools give the examining authority information on a candidate's ability that is more relevant than a written examination.

Salary Administration[2]

Another major function of a personnel department is administering salaries and recommending appropriate pay scales to higher authorities if not already set by state civil service regulations. Even though fire service officers rarely become directly involved in salary administration matters, some of the general principles of salary administration are presented below in order to acquaint fire management students with them. From a practical perspective, this knowledge can help to explain salary structure to new fire fighters, and can be useful in discussing salary-related problems. The key elements of a good salary administration program include the following:

Job Analysis: Information about the position must be determined. This information concerns the purpose of the job, the job to be performed, working relationships, inherent authority, and so on.

Preparation of Job Descriptions: Job descriptions are used to record the facts and information obtained during the job analysis process. Job descriptions provide a written record of job duties and responsibilities. They usually are written in a uniform manner, utilizing a standard format. In addition, the descriptions frequently outline the education, experience, special knowledge, and desirable qualities necessary to perform the duties.

Job Evaluation: The relative worth of the job within an organization must be determined. There are basically four formal job evaluation methods in use, and many variations of these basic systems. They are described briefly as follows:

1. **Ranking** — a comparison and ranking of jobs in the order of most difficult to least difficult. Ranking is a nonquantitative method and, because it is subjective in nature, it is often difficult to explain and justify.

2. **Classification** — establishes predetermined definitions for each salary classification or grade. Jobs are compared against these predetermined definitions, and are then slotted into the classification that best describes the characteristics and difficulty of the job. This method, which also is a nonquantitative system, is used by the federal government and some state and local governments.

3. **Point System** — defines factors that are present in all jobs. Different degrees of each factor are also identified, and point values are assigned to each degree in order of relative importance. Jobs are evaluated and points compiled based on this method. The total point value then determines the relative worth of the job. This is a quantitative system that is used widely today.

4. **Factor Comparison** — similar to the point system, except that factors are selected and assigned values. Jobs are compared to one another, one factor at a time, and are ranked accordingly. This also is a quantitative system, which is widely used.

Job Pricing: Based on the job evaluation results, jobs are grouped and grades assigned. The next step is to price these grades. This normally is accomplished by conducting an outside salary survey utilizing key or benchmark jobs to make comparisons of salaries being paid by other agencies. As a result of this survey, base salary and pay ranges are established consistent with the organization's wage policies (above, below, or comparable to what is being paid elsewhere). Salary ranges (minimum to maximum) within each classification differ among different organizations. The most commonly used are based on a scale ranging from 30 to 50 percent of the minimum salary.

Determination of Pay Increases: In addition to individual pay increases, most organizations raise all ranges simultaneously from time to time in order to maintain a comparable relationship with salary ranges in the community, and to keep salaries compatible with rises in the cost of living.

1. **Individual.** Methods for an individual to move within a salary or wage grade can be either automatic, on a merit (pay for performance) basis, or a combination of both. The automatic system provides increases at a fixed rate based primarily on longevity or seniority. Under this system, an individual receives either a predetermined fixed amount if performance is satisfactory, or no increase at all if performance is less than satisfactory. The merit system, on the other hand, compensates employees on the basis of individual performance and output: An employee receives an increase that is directly related to performance. In general, automatic increases are small compared to possible increases under a merit system. However, an automatic system combined with a merit increase can provide a capable and competent person with more than a simple automatic system, causing a poor performer to receive much less.

2. **Frequency and Timing of Increases.** Generally, increases under a merit system can occur more frequently depending on the individual's performance rating and location in the salary range; however, each department must decide on some method for awarding increases.

Communication: The salary administration plan must be communicated to supervisors and fire department personnel so that they can carry out and support the program. In addition, for purposes of information and guidance administrative practices and procedures relating to the program should be in writing.

Control: Large departments not only need budgetary controls for salary increases, but also need a system to ensure that proper approvals are obtained for individual, promotional, and special salary increases.

Other Considerations: Interwoven with the preceding elements are a number of principles for sound salary administration.

1. Equal pay for equal work.
2. Appropriate pay differentials for work requiring different levels of knowledge, skill, and physical exertion.
3. Pay scales that have a reasonable relationship to the salaries and wages paid in the job market in which the organizational unit competes, taking into consideration all the tangible and psychological benefits a position offers.
4. Each position should have a pay range that allows for raises over a number of years. These pay scales should have an appropriate relationship to each other with respect to the principles in item (3) above.
5. Capabilities of the individual that are beyond the requirements of the position the person holds should not be considered when a pay scale for a position is established.

6. Employees with several years of service should receive somewhat higher pay than new employees in identical positions. These differentials, however, might become very small among employees with several years of service and those with many years of service.

7. Salaries should reflect in some way an individual's contribution to the mission of the organization.

8. As much as possible, pay scales should be known to employees.

9. Pay scales should be in line with the organization's ability to pay.

Some of these principles are in obvious conflict with others. For example, awarding fire fighters appropriate merit raises might be in conflict with the fire department's ability to pay. This is why it is so difficult to develop a salary system that all employees consider fair and acceptable.

Fringe Benefits and Employee Services

The members of most paid fire departments are considered civil service employees. As such, their benefits usually are determined by state or municipal legislation. For example, the pension plan might be under control of a legislative commission, while health insurance might be under the jurisdiction of the Fireman's Benevolent Association or a union. When fringe benefits are not subject to outside control, the department must provide administration of these benefits, including 1) workmen's compensation, which is a statutory requirement; 2) life insurance; 3) hospitalization and medical (surgical) insurance; 4) accidental death and dismemberment insurance; 5) major medical expense (nonoccupational) insurance; 6) disability insurance (weekly payments in case of illness or accident); and 7) retirement income (pension).

Other important fringe benefits that require administration include: 1) annual leave or vacations, 2) holidays, 3) sick leave, and 4) other leave with pay, including a death in the immediate family, time to vote, administrative leave, military training, and short-term educational leave.

There are some personnel functions that usually are considered among fringe benefits, and which can contribute toward satisfying tangible, social, and esteem needs by encouraging fire fighters and officers to participate in various activities. Some programs that satisfy tangible needs are: 1) credit unions, 2) educational-incentive programs, and 3) employee assistance programs. Programs that provide social needs satisfaction include: 1) donating to blood banks, 2) car pools, and 3) bowling or baseball teams. Esteem needs can be met by special commendations and awards for such activities as: 1) training and education-alachievements, 2) special services, 3) transfers and travel, and 4) action above and beyond the call of duty.

Training and Development: Training and development of fire fighters is not only necessary for operational effectiveness, but also to prevent injury and possible death. For these reasons, as well as for self-preservation, fire fighters are motivated to learn about the problems they will encounter and about good solutions. Even though many aspects of training are personnel functions, in most fire departments the basic job training is the responsibility of the line officer. Analyzing and advising management of training needs in others areas, such as in personnel work, or in supervision, on the other hand, usually is done by the personnel division or officer. In addition, representatives from personnel often assist line officers in improving their on-the-job training techniques. This is an important function because most fire departments do not hire several people at one time, and therefore must train new fire fighters one at a time. The entire subject of training and development is so important to the fire service that Chapter 14 is devoted entirely to the subject.

Safety and Physical Fitness: Fire fighting has always been recognized as a dangerous occupation. "According to 1986 data from the NFPA, more than one-half of the 113 fire fighter deaths were stress-related and caused by heart attacks. Approximately three percent are due to strokes . . . [and] nine of the 59 stress-related deaths are attributable to physical exertion . . . "[4]

Historically, the fire service took pride in being a dangerous occupation. However, during the early 1980s attitudes began to change. Fire department administrators recognized people as a resource that must be protected and conserved. Programs were developed that sought to improve fire fighter physical fitness and raise the level of fire department safety.

Several National Fire Protection Association standards deal with health and safety issues. NFPA 1500, *Standard on Fire Department Occupational Safety and Health Program,* was approved in 1987. "The intent of this standard is to provide the framework for a health and safety program for a fire department or any type of organization providing similar services."[5] This standard covers the following topics:

- Organization.
- Training and education.
- Vehicles and equipment.
- Protective clothing and protective equipment.
- Emergency operations.
- Facility safety.
- Medical matters.
- Member assistance programs.

A companion document, NFPA 1501, *Standard for Fire Department Safety Officer,*[6] contains the minimum requirements for the assignment, duties, and responsibilities for fire department safety officers. NFPA 1403, *Standard on Live Fire Training Evolutions in Structures,*[7] also provides guidance in developing safe training.

Suggestions for developing and managing safety programs are available in NFPA's *Fire Department Safety Officer's Reference Guide.*[8] Fire Department officials can call on local health and fitness experts for help in developing physical fitness programs. Municipal risk managers can also provide assistance.

Career Development: On December 14, 1972, the National Professional Qualifications Board for the Fire Service directed four technical committees to develop minimum standards for each of the following areas: fire fighter, fire instructor, fire investigator, and fire officer. These standards were planned to accomplish several major objectives, including the following:

- To identify and define levels for an effective organization so that positions exist which ensure that each company has staff with the skills to accomplish its mission.
- To provide for comprehensive training programs and testing of competence.
- To provide career steps for individuals.

The intent of the committees was to develop clear and concise performance standards that could be used to determine if a person possesses all the necessary skills to be a fire fighter. These performance standards can be used in any fire department in any city, town, or private organization throughout North America.

NFPA 1001, *Standard for Fire Fighter Professional Qualifications*, states that a Fire Fighter I must be capable of demonstrating certain skills and knowledge with regard to forcible entry, protective breathing apparatus, first aid, ropes, fire hose, nozzles and appliances, and fire streams. For example, in order to qualify for Fire Fighter I, NFPA 1001 requires the following level of achievement concerning fire streams:[9]

3-14.1 The fire fighter shall define a fire stream.
3-14.2 The fire fighter shall manipulate a nozzle so as to attack a Class A fire and a Class B fire.
3-14.3 The fire fighter shall define water hammer and at least one method for its prevention.
3-14.4 The fire fighter shall demonstrate how to open and close a nozzle.

In order to obtain a Fire Fighter II rating, a higher level of skills and knowledge is expected. NFPA 1001 specifies the following requirements regarding fire streams:[9]

4-14.1 The fire fighter shall define the following methods of water application:
(a) Direct.
(b) Indirect.
(c) Combination.

4-14.2 The fire fighter, given fire situations, shall select the proper nozzle and hose size for each.
4-14.3 The fire fighter shall identify characteristics of all types of fire streams.
4-14.4 The fire fighter shall identify precautions to be followed while advancing hose lines to a fire.

4-14.5 The fire fighter shall identify three conditions that result in pressure losses in a hose line.

4-14.6 The fire fighter shall identify four special stream nozzles and demonstrate at least two uses or applications for each.

4-14.7 The fire fighter shall identify and define foam making appliances, and shall demonstrate a foam stream from each.

4-14.8 The fire fighter shall identify three observable results that are obtained when the proper application of a fire stream is accomplished.

4-14.9 The fire fighter shall identify and define those items required to develop three types of fire streams, and shall demonstrate each.

Similarly, to achieve Fire Fighter III, the following skills and knowledge should be demonstrated:[9]

5-14.1 The fire fighter shall diagram the types of fog nozzles, identify the major parts, and trace water flow through each.

5-14.2 The fire fighter, given a selection of nozzles and tips, shall identify the type, design, operation, nozzle pressure, and flow of each.

5-14.3 The fire fighter shall identify the rate of water flow necessary to control fire in a room of specified volume.

Record Keeping

An important function of the personnel officer is maintaining complete and accurate records. Records are necessary for volunteer departments as well as for paid and for partially paid departments. Such records provide the following:

- A detailed history of an individual's association with the department.
- Data for determining personnel availability and qualifications for planning purposes.
- Information necessary for future contract negotiations.
- Records for tax and insurance purposes.

Personnel Records for Career Employees: If records are not kept by a personnel office in the local government, the fire department must maintain a complete file on each employee. Besides containing the data necessary to provide reports to government agencies, such a file enables management to select individuals objectively for promotion. The file should include:

1. The completed application form, interviewer's notes, reference checks, and results of all tests taken.
2. Payroll records, including salary or grade status; federal, state, and municipal income tax deduction authorizations as well as those for bond, credit union, insurance, union, and pension deductions; annual leave and sick leave taken; and insurance claims filed.
3. A work record that includes complete information pertaining to on-the-job-training programs and courses or schools attended; performance evaluations; commendations and special awards; grievances, complaints, and disciplinary actions; and positions held (including dates).

In addition to keeping records on individuals, a personnel officer in a unionized department should maintain a record of significant factors that could affect future negotiations with the union. These would include records of:

- Complaints about unilateral policy changes by management.
- Complaints about changes in job assignments.
- Complaints about promotions or transfers.
- Problems encountered in job assignments.
- Numbers and types of disciplinary actions by types of infraction.
- Contract settlements by other departments.

Personnel Records for Volunteers: A volunteer fire department is responsible for maintaining records related to the overall relationship of the volunteers to the organization. This responsibility includes keeping the following items for each volunteer:

1. A master file containing complete data related to the selection of each individual, such as the application, interview report, committee investigation report, and physical examination results.
2. A record of training received.
3. Insurance information.
4. A record of participation in various areas of activity, including leadership positions, and information regarding interest in and availability for other assignments.
5. Performance evaluations and recognition of achievement, such as service awards, expressions of appreciation, or honor awards.
6. A record of the reason for discontinuing service.

LABOR RELATIONS

Labor relations can be defined broadly as management's relationship with the nonmanagerial people of the organization. Good labor relations are actually good human relations because a supervisor who establishes and maintains rapport with the team is likely to have equally good labor relations.

The concept of labor relations applies to all organizations, whether a union contract is in effect or not. In a unionized organization, there is a formal contract between management and an agent (the union) that represents the employees. The contract specifies the rights and obligations of all three parties — management, the union, and the employees. In nonunionized organizations, an implied contract exists in the form of a verbal agreement, customary practices, statutes, and possibly employee handbooks and supervisor manuals.

The personnel office for career fire fighters is an active participant in labor relations by providing advice and guidance relevant to labor relationships. Supervisors can best use the services of the personnel office for the following labor relations functions:

1. Providing a personnel policy manual with written statements of personnel practices.
2. Determining whether personnel policies are fair and equitably administered throughout the department.
3. Determining whether personnel policies are kept current with existing court rulings and statute changes.
4. Investigating and recommending changes in policy that are unfair, inequitable, or no longer applicable.
5. Arranging for discussions and conclusions on any significant incidents and problems between supervisory personnel and fire fighters or their representatives that might affect the labor relations climate or the labor-management agreement, if one exists.

To achieve the purposes of both management and labor (i.e., job performance and job satisfaction), both sides must be committed to a course of cooperative action. The key factors in achieving cooperation are determined by the attitudes and approach of all parties involved. Management, however, has the primary responsibility for establishing and maintaining good relations with labor, and every officer has an important role in that endeavor.

Early in this century, joining a union was a dangerous thing to do because employers were quick to fire the people they believed engaged in union activities. The conflict caused by such firings resulted, at first, in many lawsuits, and later, enaction of laws, so that today an employee has extensive rights to join a union or to participate in union organization activities without fear of retaliation.

Labor Relations Laws

Before 1932, labor-relations problems were resolved in the courts. Judges, through the use of common law, decided the rights of both management and labor. Since the New Deal era, four pieces of federal legislation established the rules and regulations for the present collective bargaining system. These four laws are: 1) the Norris-LaGuardia Act of 1932, 2) the Wagner-Connery Act of 1935 (often referred to as the Wagner Act), 3) the Taft-Hartley Act of 1947, and 4) the Landrum-Griffin Act of 1959. These laws, together with the Railway Labor Act of 1926 and some antitrust legislation, are the basis for all labor negotiations in the United States.

The Norris-LaGuardia Act

The Norris-LaGuardia Act set the stage for additional labor relations laws by specifying that an employee cannot be forced into a contract by the employer in order to obtain and keep a job. Before this act, many employers made workers sign a pledge that they would not join a union as long as they were employed by the company. Workers who violated the pledge were fired. Unions called those who signed the pledge *yellow dogs*, and the contracts were so named.

Partly because the "yellow dog" contracts were legal, and partly for other reasons, courts were apt to side with management in a labor dispute and issue an injunction that prohibited striking or, if a strike was in effect, prohibited picketing. These injunctions were enforceable by the police.

The Norris-LaGuardia Act did two things: 1) it said that "yellow dog" contracts were not enforceable in any court in the United States, and 2) it made the conditions for getting an injunction to prevent strikes almost impossible.

It is important to note that, in 1932, the only way a union could gain recognition was by striking or by threatening to strike. In effect, the employer had to be forced to recognize the union. Even with the passage of the Norris-LaGuardia Act, employers could threaten and discharge workers engaged in union activity. What the act did was to give the unions the right to use their major weapons to gain recognition: striking, picketing, and boycotting, without interference from the courts.

When Franklin Roosevelt became President in 1933, the Great Depression was three years old. In an attempt to bolster the faltering economy, Roosevelt took many steps, including instituting the National Industrial Recovery Act (NIRA). Section 7a of the NIRA guaranteed unions the right to collective bargaining in order to keep wages up and thus maintain the purchasing power of the workers. This was the "shot in the arm" that unions needed. Workers flocked to join both the American Federation of Labor (AFL) and the new Congress of Industrial Organizations (CIO).

The Wagner-Connery Act

In 1935, the Supreme Court struck down the NIRA as unconstitutional. Senator Robert Wagner (NY) then introduced a bill, the Wagner-Connery Act, which was quickly passed by Congress. In 1936, a strike in the automobile industry brought the act before the Supreme Court where it was upheld. The Wagner-Connery Act included the following provisions:

- Allowed workers to decide, by a majority vote, who was to represent them at the bargaining table.
- Established the National Labor Relations Board (NLRB).
- Defined unfair labor practices, and gave the NLRB the power to hold hearings, investigate such practices, and to issue decisions and orders concerning them.
- Prohibited management from interfering or coercing employees when they tried to organize.
- Required management to bargain with a union, although management was under no obligation to agree to any of the union's terms.
- Outlawed "yellow dog" contracts entirely (the Norris-LaGuardia Act had only made them unenforceable).

The entire area of unfair labor practices, as covered by the Wagner-Connery Act, restrained management. The act, in effect, was an attempt to equalize the positions of both management and labor. However, the act imposed no penalties for any violations, nor did it provide the NLRB with any real power to enforce its decisions or orders. Not until the matter went to the courts did the act become effective. For example, when the NLRB decided that some employees had been fired in violation of the Wagner-Connery Act, the courts upheld the decision, and the employees were reinstated with back pay.

Throughout the Great Depression and World War II, the unions, under the protection of the Wagner-Connery Act and favorable court decisions, continued to grow; with their growth came increasing strength. Shortly after World War II, a series of industry-wide strikes threatened the smooth return of the economy to civilian production. During these strikes it became apparent that the power of unions had grown to such an extent that they were now substantially stronger—thanks to government protection—than their management adversaries. Congress, in an attempt to redress the balance, passed the Taft-Hartley Act of 1947 over the veto of President Truman.

The Taft-Hartley Act

Besides spelling out specific penalties, including fines and imprisonment for violations, the Taft-Hartley Act modified the Wagner-Connery Act in the following five major areas:

1. **Union Representation:** The act gave workers the right to refrain from joining a union and the "closed shop" was outlawed. The act specified that only one election a year can be held to determine whether a union, and which union, should represent the employees. The act gave employers the right to express "any views, argument, or opinion" about union representation, provided "such expression contains no threat of reprisal, or force, or promise of benefit."

2. **Unfair Labor Practices for Unions:** The act protects employees from coercion by unions. Employees are protected from paying exorbitant dues and initiation fees. If nonunion employees refuse to join, they are protected against possible union reprisals because unions no longer can force employers to fire anti-union people. The act requires unions to "bargain in good faith," as the employers had been previously forced to do by the Wagner-Connery Act.

3. **Bargaining Procedures:** The Taft-Hartley Act provides for a 60-day cooling-off period when a labor agreement ends. Section 8(d) of the act stipulates that written notice must be served if one party to the agreement is terminating the agreement. The written notice must be given to the other party 60 days before the contract ends. Thirty days later the Federal Mediation and Conciliation Service must be notified of the dispute.

4. **Regulation of the Union's Internal Affairs**: Union rules regarding membership requirements, dues, and initiation fees, elections, and so on, must be made available to the government and to the union membership.

5. **Strikes During a National Emergency**: In the event an imminent strike affects an entire industry or a major part of an industry and imperils the health and safety of the nation, the president has been granted certain powers to help settle the dispute.

The Landrum-Griffin Act

In 1955, the AFL and CIO merged. Two years after the merger, Senator John McClellan (AR) conducted committee hearings that revealed evidence of crime and corruption in some of the older local unions. At the height of the resulting furor, the Landrum-Griffin Act was passed by Congress. The Landrum-Griffin Act of 1959:

- Established a bill of rights for members of labor organizations so that unions would be run in a more democratic manner.

- Requires that labor unions file an annual report with the government listing the assets of the union and the names and assets of every officer and employee of the union. In addition, every employer is required to report on any financial relationship it has with a union or union representative.

- Established minimum requirement guidelines for the election, responsibilities, and duties of all union officers and officials.

- Amended portions of the Taft-Hartley Act concerning secondary boycotts, union security, and the rights of some workers to strike, and imposed additional restrictions on the rights of unions to picket for recognition.

Unions in the Public Sector

Federal legislation had allowed unions to grow in the private sector, and labor relations between management and unions matured. Fewer than 1 million government employees were members of unions in 1956. By 1970, membership in public employee unions had grown to 4.5 million persons.

Until 1970, under existing legislation, government employees were forbidden to strike. The unions' most effective weapon, therefore, was denied to them. The first rumblings of discontent and rebellion to this disenfranchisement began in the late 1960s. Several major cities, notably New York and Baltimore, suffered strikes by sanitation workers, teachers, police, and fire fighters. The federal government was no longer immune to strikes. At one time, air traffic controllers called in sick in such large numbers that commercial flight operations were severely hampered.

In 1970, post office employees went on strike and thereby set the tone for all government employees. Although the strike was illegal and the postmaster general was, by law, forbidden to negotiate with the strikers, he nevertheless did negotiate. The result was that the strikers were reinstated without penalty, received raises, and Congress recognized the union as representing the employees for the purpose of collective bargaining.

The civil rights demonstrations of the 1960s precipitated the growing militancy of government employees. In January 1962, President Kennedy issued an order which, for the first time, allowed federal employees the right to bargain collectively under restricted rules. The order stipulated the rights of management, grievance procedures, and the rules for union recognition. In 1969, President Nixon further expanded the rights of the government employee unions. He established a Federal Labor Relations Council that is similar to the NLRB for unions in the private sector.

At the state and municipal level, little union activity had occurred before the favorable climate of the 1960s. If they belonged to any organization at all, state and local employees were members of associations that did not try to represent their members in collective bargaining, but instead tried to work through the governing bodies and existing civil service regulations.

Unlike the 1970s, the 1980s have been difficult times for unions in the public sector. In 1981, in a strike by air traffic controllers, President Reagan took a hard line with the Public Air Traffic Controllers Organization. When the air traffic controllers failed to return to work as ordered, he fired all striking members and decertified the union. This action set the tone for employer/employee relations during the remainder of the Reagan administration. The growing militancy of public sector workers was met by a rising tide of right-to-work activity by employers.

International Association of Fire Fighters (IAFF)

As the other government employee unions grew so did the IAFF. In 1988, the IAFF represented more than 65 percent of the full-time career fire fighters in the United States (158,600 of 243,200 fire fighters).

Unlike most unions, the IAFF enrolls and represents supervisory personnel in the fire service. Although not every employee is a member of the union in every unionized department, some departments are completely unionized, including the chief. In many of the communities where the IAFF represents the fire fighter at the collective bargaining session, some members also hold membership in benevolent associations. Some benevolent associations provide health and insurance benefits, while others are more concerned with professional activities (e.g., continuing education) and social events.

Like unions in the private sector, the IAFF also has taken a more militant attitude. In 1968 it removed a 50-year-old rule prohibiting strikes. Subsequently, fire departments in several communities have gone on strike when they could not reach agreement with the municipality.

Collective Bargaining Procedures in the Public Sector

The collective bargaining procedures at the local level in the public sector are different from the methods used by private industry. In the private sector, management and labor leaders generally "hammer out" an agreement and, once ratified by the employees, the agreement becomes the contract. However, state and local employees generally go through a two-stage process: 1) the labor leaders and a government-appointed representative or committee negotiate the terms of the new contract, and 2) once agreement has been reached at this level and the employees have ratified the agreement, the contract must go before the governing body for final approval.

Several states have adopted legislation that sets up specific steps for working out difficult negotiations. Impasses are often referred to as a fact-finding process where both the employer and the unions can present their case. Agreements are sometimes settled this way. Some states allow binding arbitration where an outside arbitrator rules on the merits of positions taken by the union and the employer. However, because in many cases legislative approval is customary, a contract is often subject to further modifications and negotiation.

The Collective Bargaining Agreement

As a result of the labor relations laws, management and labor must bargain collectively and in good faith on the subjects of wages, hours, and working conditions. The result is an agreement containing a series of clauses, each relating to a particular area. The agreement outlines the conditions to which both parties agreed, and the duration of the agreement. One-year agreements are the most common, although recently the trend has been toward three-year agreements with, at times, two-year agreements becoming compromises.

Typical types of clauses found in all labor-management agreements can be grouped into five segments: 1) routine clauses, which contain the preamble and purpose, term(s) of the agreement, reopening condition(s), and amendment(s); 2) union security clauses, which contain the bargaining unit definition and union recognition; 3) management rights clause, which reserves for management the right to make decisions in any area not specifically covered by the agreement, and stipulates in detail those areas that are solely the rights of management; 4) grievance procedure clauses, which spell out the steps in the grievance and arbitration procedures; and 5) conditions of employment clauses, which include details concerning wages, work hours, strikes and lockouts, holidays, vacations, leaves, reporting, shift differentials, discharge, benefits, safety, apprenticeship training, and so on. Further details on union security clauses, management rights clauses, and grievance procedures follow.

Union Security Clauses: A union must develop and maintain a secure organization so that it can speak with assurance for its members. A union must have strength in order to be able to bargain effectively with management. To help develop and maintain a secure organization, unions insist on a clause that defines the bargaining unit and recognizes the union as the agent (third party) representing the employees in that union.

The bargaining unit is an important concept during organizing drives. The union prefers to define the bargaining unit in such a way that a majority is assured during an election vote. Management, on the other hand, usually prefers a different, wider, bargaining unit. In the event of a dispute, the final decision on the bargaining unit is made by the National Labor Relations Board (NLRB) when it certifies the election. A bargaining unit can be selected by function, by craft, by location, or by some other logical entity. For example, in some locals of the IAFF, officers are members of the bargaining unit; in other locals, officers are excluded.

A municipality can have agreements with separate unions representing police, fire, and municipal employees, or with one union that represents all municipal employees. When several unions represent employees of a department, the possibility of jurisdictional disputes (disputes over who represents whom) can occur. In such an event, the personnel officer has the responsibility of cautioning all supervisory personnel to remain neutral and to refrain from taking sides in the union dispute. This is most important because any comments or actions by a supervisor showing or implying favoritism toward one union can be considered by the regulatory agency as an unfair labor practice. In addition to the bargaining unit definition contained in the agreement, union security clauses might also contain one or several of the following provisions:

- **The Preferential Shop**—Management agrees to give the first chance for employment to union members (not usually applicable to the fire service).
- **Maintenance of Membership**—New employees do not have to join the union to gain employment; however, any employees who voluntarily join the union must maintain their membership for the duration of the contract.
- **Union Shop**—New employees must join the union to retain their jobs after the probationary period.
- **Agency Shop**—Employees do not have to join a union, but they must pay dues to the union.
- **The Checkoff**—Employers must deduct dues from the wages of employees and remit them to the union.

Management Rights Clauses: Initially, unions came into being because employees believed, often with good justification, that management misused its power in order to gain economic advantages at the expense of others. Employees formed or joined unions for mutual protection. After the formation of the unions, capricious and arbitrary decisions by management forced unions to spell out more and more detail in their contracts to protect the employees against unjustified detrimental actions. Management frequently objected that some areas, such as work assignment or overtime, were not subject to bargaining. Arbitration awards and court decisions, however, gradually have established that any subjects not specifically reserved for management must be negotiated. To protect its rights against encroachment, management has always endeavored to maintain and strengthen management rights clauses in contracts.

Management rights clauses reserve for management the right to make decisions in any area not specifically covered by the agreement. In addition, such clauses stipulate in detail those areas that are strictly the rights of management. They usually include the right to:

- Direct the work force.
- Hire, promote, transfer, and assign without interference.
- Suspend, demote, discharge for cause, or take other disciplinary action.
- Take action necessary to maintain a department's efficiency.
- Make reasonable rules and regulations.

When management is weak, arbitrary, or inept, a union often has cause to demand that one or the other of these rights be removed from the management rights clause and be made the subject of separate contract clauses that specifically delineate what managers can and cannot do. To avoid such additional restrictions on their freedom to manage, management people must be careful not to abuse any of these rights, and management representatives at the bargaining table must be skillful in protecting their rights clause.

Grievance Procedures: In negotiating an agreement, both management and labor realize that it is impossible to anticipate every conceivable problem. Both parties also realize that some problems will occur that are not directly covered by the agreement. Therefore, every contract provides for a grievance procedure that is intended to serve as a mechanism for bringing about a peaceful settlement and resolution of such problems. The grievance procedure is so important to contracts that any agreement with a federal agency that does not contain such a clause is in violation of President Nixon's order. Although actual grievance procedures might vary somewhat from contract to contract, most of them are comparable to the following example (all of the steps have time limits):

- The aggrieved fire fighter discusses the problem with an immediate supervisor.
- If the problem is not settled at that time, the fire fighter discusses the problem with a union representative who then submits the grievance in writing either to the same officer or to the officer at the next higher level.
- If the grievance is not settled, the union can appeal to the chief, the fire commissioner, or the governing body.
- If the grievance is not answered or resolved to the satisfaction of the employee or the union, it can be submitted to an arbitrator or a panel of

arbitrators. Arbitrators usually are agreed on by both parties or, depending on the stipulations of the contract, can be appointed by an impartial group, such as the American Arbitration Association or the Federal Mediation and Conciliation Service. Once an arbitrator has handed down a decision, it is final. Either party can, of course, challenge the decision in court. However, judges rarely overturn the rulings of arbitrators, and do so only when an arbitrator has clearly gone beyond the authority granted by a contract.

Sometimes the grievance procedure is deliberately used by either management or the union to obtain a ruling on an issue where the wording in the contract is not clear. For example, if there is a difference of opinion and no agreement can be reached, either party can act on its interpretation. The union or employee would file a grievance, or management would take some disciplinary action to bring the issue to an arbitrator for a decision.

This is very rare, however, because unions and management generally try to avoid referring disputes to an outsider. Both unions and management consider it a failure of their ability to maintain good working relationships with each other, and both are concerned that the outsider (unfamiliar with all the subtle relationships that exist) could inadvertently resolve the issue in a way that is unsatisfactory to both sides.

An officer can take several steps to ensure that grievances due to misunderstandings do not arise, and that those grievances that reach arbitration will be resolved in favor of management. These steps require that the officer:

- Ensures that all facts are available to both sides. It is always possible that either side misunderstood the situation or did not know all the facts.
- Maintains accurate and complete records of every occurrence related to the problem.
- Maintains as cordial a relationship with the aggrieved employee(s) as possible.

Union Negotiations

Management and union representatives meet to negotiate the terms of a new agreement either immediately after a union has been recognized as the collective bargaining agent, or before a contract approaches the expiration date. This process usually is initiated by the union with the submittal of a list of requested changes to the previous agreement. Because the union is a political body operating under a constitution, bylaws, and democratic procedures, these requests are either the result of meetings by the union members or by a large group of union officials who have been elected for this purpose.

During contract negotiations, management representatives listen to the proposed changes and then, after discussion, submit counterproposals. The counterproposals might just be responses to the items brought up by the union, or they might contain contract changes that management would like to make. Union representatives answer these counterproposals, and either side (or both sides) will gradually make concessions that narrow the issues separating them. A new contract gradually emerges from these discussions and compromises. Often there is considerable tension as the contract renewal date approaches, or as negotiations continue beyond the renewal date. Threats of a strike or other job actions, such as refusal to perform nonessential duties, are not uncommon. In the event that talks break down, management, union, or both might call on the services of a third party (a mediator) to break the deadlock. The mediator has no specific powers, but acts strictly as an impartial go-between in reconciling differences.

The attitude of both parties is extremely important during negotiations. In order to achieve an amicable agreement, each side must exercise restraint. On the management side, this places heavy and often difficult responsibilities on company officers, especially if they are, themselves, members of a union. As managers, they must see to it that the work of the unit continues to be performed without interruption. Simultaneously, as human beings, as union members, and as members of the team, they are under great pressure to help their subordinates achieve the negotiating goals to which they aspire. Considerable competence and good judgment are needed during these negotiating periods to retain the enthusiasm and devotion that required so much effort to build.

The major function of the department's personnel officer (if one exists) during negotiations is to prepare for the negotiations and to serve as a source of information and technical expertise for the other members of management's negotiating team. Some of the data personnel officers should have available during negotiations include:

- Information about settlements by other fire departments or local governments, and by industrial facilities in the area.
- A list of contract changes that would help to improve the effectiveness of operations. These should have been obtained from the officers in the department during the life of the union contract.
- Basic statistical information about numbers of fire fighters, hours worked, costs of benefits, benefits used, etc., that would help to estimate the probable cost of the union's requests.

Union—Management Relations: The relationship between union leaders and managers contains some curious contradictions. This is understandable because, on the surface, each represents a threat to the other, and the general public as well as union members perceive their roles that way.

During negotiations, union leaders usually visualize management representatives as their antagonists because management is the force that prevents them from obtaining the legitimate improvements in working conditions, salary, and benefits that they believe their members deserve. At the same time, managers often see the union leaders as irresponsible opportunists who would do thoughtless damage merely for the sake of getting their way. In many ways, this picture possesses some truth. Managers and union leaders can plot strategy in such a way that any confrontation will result in their respective sides "winning" in the negotiations. Also, both of them can often claim victory by comparing a particular feature of the settlement with initial demands, or offers, or with other settlements.

At any single moment, with respect to any single issue, the union leaders and the organization's managers are clearly antagonists. Although it seems as though, in every issue, the interests of one side are opposed to those of the other, on closer examination it becomes apparent that many of these differences are not as fundamental, or serious, as it first seems. Whenever management and the union discuss grievances, wages, fringe benefits, or working conditions, their positions are opposed. On each issue a serious loss for one side might endanger the security of the individual manager or union leader. If their respective sides see them as frequently losing, or as coming up with unfavorable compromises, sooner or later they will not be able to retain their respective positions. This is the situation as far as the tactical considerations are concerned.

However, strategic, long-term thinking reveals a different picture in which the three major issues are 1) wages and fringe benefits, 2) working conditions (including satisfaction of psychological needs), and 3) the job security of the union leaders and of the organization's managers, respectively.

Wages and Fringe Benefits: The union leaders' objectives in negotiating for wages and fringe benefits are to obtain the best possible package as defined by their membership. It must be remembered that the requests the union places on the table early in the negotiations have been arrived at by a political procedure, at one or many union meetings, where these requests have been established through a democratic process. During these discussions, all the people involved are clearly aware that, by asking for more, it is likely they will receive more than if they started by asking for less or for the amount they really want. During negotiations the union can concede some demands and still obtain at least the minimum that they are willing to accept. The constraints on the union to request more than most members believe can be obtained are, therefore, not very strong. Obviously, the union will not come in with requests that are foolish; nevertheless, it generally requests substantially more than the union leaders or the members expect.

Management's immediate interests are to hold cost increases to a minimum. In a profit-making enterprise, amounts that are not paid out as additional wages are available as profit to the owners. In a governmental organization, there are so many demands on the funds available to the governmental unit that managers are under pressure to avoid giving greater increases or benefits than necessary. All are aware that, to some extent, their performance is evaluated on the basis of their ability to achieve favorable settlements.

However, this is only the immediate picture. In the long run, no organization can remain healthy and effective if it fails to adhere to reasonable salary administration principles. One of the most important principles of salary administration concerns the requirement that an organization pay wages and fringe benefits that are equal, or possibly even superior, to those for similar positions in the community. Every manager is aware that, if the organization can pay higher wages and provide a richer benefit package, the opportunities for retaining people with exceptional competence and high abilities are much greater than if wages are low, or lower than the average. For this reason, competent managers do not oppose a union's legitimate and reasonable demands when such demands are based on good salary and fringe-package administration principles; nor will competent managers try to obtain the very lowest settlements they are able to force on the union when they are in a position to do so. They will, instead, start to bargain at a figure that is lower than what they believe the membership should receive; at the same time, however, they will work diligently to obtain agreement either from stockholders or from higher-level government officials for amounts that will establish fair salaries and fringe benefits.

Working Conditions: The term *working conditions* includes more than just the physical facilities and amenities; it also concerns the extent to which supervisory personnel can help satisfy psychological needs. Also, to some extent, what is true of salary and fringe benefits is often true of working conditions. Organizations having substandard working conditions have greater difficulty retaining qualified and competent people.

Managers know that good working conditions, including reasonable work rules, provide a more desirable work climate and lead to higher productivity. Similarly, union leaders prefer to work with organizations where little conflict exists and where employees have few complaints. Such organizations demand little attention, thus permitting union leaders the freedom to pursue activities they consider more important than settling grievances or processing complaints. Because it is in the best interests of the unions that their members have good working conditions and adhere to reasonable rules, competent union leaders willingly help management establish such environments.

Job Security of Union Leaders and Managers: Because unions are political bodies, union leaders advance in their careers or remain in office only if they are competent leaders, or if they do what the membership wants them to do as long as the membership is not too badly split in its opinions. On the other hand, managers advance, in part, on the basis of their competence in working with union officials. If union leaders and managers have difficulty establishing a good relationship, and if grievances mount, their career goals can become more difficult to achieve.

Consequently, there is mutual interest in the competence of the people on the opposite side. Capable managers do not try to use their powers to undermine the strength of capable union opponents. Enlightened managers are aware that, ultimately, competent union leadership is in everybody's best interest because only capable union leaders are able to control those members who make unreasonable demands or who attempt to undermine a fair settlement that they consider inadequate. Similarly, competent union leaders are aware that when they do have the power, it is not wise to use it so as to endanger the security or career advancement opportunities of competent managers. This is true even though competent managers are difficult to take advantage of, and even though less-competent management might allow a union to obtain more favorable short-term settlements. Over the long term, a lack of management competence, combined with the repercussion of excessive settlements, can lead to a period of considerable difficulties. Under these circumstances, either fewer increases or no increases at all can be obtained, or even worse, the organization might lose the strength to survive.

The Role of the Steward: Management's actions are restricted by a union agreement and, as previously discussed, by the Wagner-Connery Act of 1935. However, the union agreement and the Taft-Hartley Act of 1947 similarly restrict the activities of a union. Supervisors can still run their organizations by insisting on adherence to safety rules, attendance regulations, maintenance standards for equipment, apparatus, and facilities, and regulations that apply to fire fighting. The major effect of the union agreement for the first line officer is that day-to-day operations now involve another individual—the union's shop steward.

Establishing good relations is the joint responsibility of the line officer and the shop steward. New contract clauses, in particular, are subject to varied interpretation. When a question arises, competent officers consult with their respective superiors who often seek advice from the personnel officer to clarify the intent of a particular clause. Only after having obtained such clarification of the management position should an officer take a firm stand with a shop steward.

The steward occupies the same position, relative to the union, that the supervisor enjoys with the organization. However, the steward is elected by the employees, is never paid, and the job is totally voluntary. Therefore, in dealings with the steward, the supervisor must keep in mind that the steward, whose job is awarded by constituents, might conceivably lose the position at the next election if constituents become displeased. The supervisor must also remember that, although the steward could be well-informed on union matters, stewards rarely have any formal training in settling disputes.

Nonunion Labor Relations

In a nonunion environment, serious dissatisfaction on the part of the employees can lead to performance problems and can bring employees to seek outside representation. Major sources of dissatisfaction include the following.

Threat to Job or Security of Position: This can stem from several reasons, including inattention to complaints or grievances, unsympathetic management, harsh or erratic disciplinary steps, or other high-handed actions on the part of officers. Such actions can be viewed as favoritism or unfair treatment.

Wages, Salaries, Benefits, and Promotions: If these are not competitive with comparable community positions or with other communities, if pay raises are unfair, or if promotion procedures are unknown or unfair, dissatisfaction is likely.

Employees Do Not Know Where They Stand with Management: This generally is the result of inadequate, improper, or irregular appraisals of work performance, or the failure to communicate to employees the established criteria used in making evaluations.

Lack of Involvement Concerning Policy and Decision Making: Employees feel they are not involved in decisions affecting their jobs, or they do not know what policies are in effect. Employees like to know not only what is happening, but why it is happening.

Poor Working Conditions: If the physical environment is poor, it creates an unfavorable effect on employees.

Discrimination: Discrimination, in any way and on any basis, is not to be tolerated.

Because many employers, both in industry and in government, have failed to create a climate where these six major sources of dissatisfaction are minimal, employees have sought the protection of unions and the safety that labor-management contracts are intended to provide.

Administration of Grievances in Departments Without a Union

In any organization, there are times when an individual or group of individuals has occasion to be dissatisfied. What sometimes starts as a minor complaint can lead to a more serious grievance if a supervisor does not give it fair consideration. If a department is unionized, the contract spells out the procedure a fire fighter can follow to obtain satisfaction. If there is no union, there must be an established procedure that specifies the way in which fire fighters can air their complaints. This is necessary because the way grievances are handled is important to the atmosphere of a department. Effective handling of a complaint at the earliest possible time prevents dissatisfaction from building up. This does not mean that officers should accede to all requests from fire fighters or lower-level officers. It is important, however, to give everyone a serious and fair hearing.

If a request must be denied, thorough explanations are necessary to ensure that, at the least, the petitioner clearly understands why a personally favorable resolution of the request is not possible. Employees are often dissatisfied when they believe that a particular decision is unfair, even if such an opinion is based on incomplete knowledge of the facts. Often, therefore, a thorough explanation is all that is needed to resolve the dissatisfaction.

Sometimes the problem is primarily an emotional one where the employee does not really expect any action on the part of the officer. In such cases, a friendly, empathetic listener usually is all that is necessary. As a fire fighter discusses the problem, it might become clear to him/her that the problem is not as important as it first seemed to be, that nothing can be done about the problem, or that something has already been done to avoid a similar problem in the future.

Sometimes the problem an employee presents cannot be resolved through discussion and explanation. In such instances, considerable dissatisfaction can build up and spread if a fire fighter cannot go to higher authority to file an appeal against a first officer's decision. Therefore, a grievance procedure that is clearly communicated to all fire fighters and officers represents an important and necessary safety valve. The procedure must be a fair one that does not subject the fire fighters to possible reprisals for using it.

In departments where the officers are alert about identifying practices and policies that could lead to complaints, few complaints are likely to become serious. This points to the need for managers at all levels to maintain good communications with their subordinates so that all actions that affect people will at least be explained if a decision cannot be made through some form of participative process. Complaints can stem from many sources, as shown in the following brief listing:

- Inadequate or unsafe parking facilities.
- Favoritism in the assignment of jobs.
- A suggestion that is given little consideration.
- A privilege that is not granted.
- Physical conditions in the station.
- Inadequate or old uniforms.
- Lack of facilities for personal belongings.
- A rule that is disliked.
- Disciplinary actions.

Labor Relations in Volunteer Fire Departments

In a volunteer fire department, there is no clear management-employee relationship because every member of the department can be, potentially, a manager next year. There is, therefore, no clear line between manager and fire fighter because management is selected by the members at an election. Many volunteer organizations have two lines of command: 1) the administrative line and 2) the tactical, or fire fighting, organization.

The administrative organization usually is headed by elected officers and operates like any democratically run organization. Members can bring up any policy or procedural change suggestions at a regular meeting. Any changes that are made must be in accordance with the constitution and the bylaws of the fire department or volunteer organization.

At a fire or fire drill, the situation is different because there is a clear line of command. The elected chief is in charge, and officers are in command of their respective units. If members are dissatisfied with the way the chief sets strategy or determines tactics or with the way an individual officer performs, the matter can be brought up at a regular administrative meeting. On the other hand, officers can discipline member fire fighters in a manner similar to that of paid fire fighting companies.

Administration of Disciplinary Action in Union or Nonunion Departments

By its very nature, the fire service is a paramilitary organization. Thus, strict adherence to rules and regulations by its members is necessary—particularly when fighting fires. As in similar organizations, because there are times when an individual or group of individuals fail to adhere to reasonable rules, some form of disciplinary action becomes necessary. Disciplinary action is a serious matter and a significant source of dissatisfaction, not only for the individual involved, but also for others who sympathize with that person. Therefore, it is of utmost importance that disciplinary actions be taken only on infracted rules that have been communicated thoroughly and understood by all. Furthermore, every officer is responsible for identifying and helping to change rules that are no longer appropriate. However, while seemingly inappropriate rules are in effect, officers must enforce them fairly and impartially.

In many fire departments the rules are established by the chief, or by volunteer committees. The penalties for infractions often are established in the same way. In some states and municipalities, the penalties for infractions are stipulated by legislative action. Typical penalties for various offenses are shown in Table 13.1.

Whether or not the disciplinary procedure is mandated by higher authority, employees usually can appeal any action through the grievance procedure and, if treated unfairly, appeal to the courts. Thus, the procedure must be thorough, and must effectively protect an employee against unfair and arbitrary disciplinary action so that any action sustained through the procedure will be upheld in the courts.

TABLE 13.1 Typical penalties for various offenses.

| | Penalty: | | |
Infraction	First	Second	Third
Consumption of alcoholic beverages or using nonprescription drugs while on duty	Warning and suspension of 1–5 days; mandatory enrollment in counseling and random testing	Suspension (4–10 days)	Dismissal
Reporting for duty while under the influence of alcohol or drugs	Warning and suspension of 1–5 days	Suspension (4–10 days); mandatory enrollment in counseling and random testing	Dismissal
Violation of a safety regulation	Warning	Warning and suspension (1–5 days)	Dismissal
Fighting while on duty	Warning and suspension (1–30 days)	Dismissal	
Stealing from fellow workers	Warning or dismissal	Dismissal	
Stealing from the department	Warning or dismissal	Dismissal	

Where grievances are subject to the Civil Service Procedure, an appeal from a disciplinary action is usually heard by a three-member board that has been established by law or is appointed by the head of the fire department. One member of the board is often elected by the employees or approved by the employee making the appeal. Even in the case of volunteer fire departments, a board can be convened to hear and settle the dispute.

Whatever the appeals procedure, it might result in an officer's action being overturned. Because this possibility always exists, it is important for officers to be careful when resorting to formal disciplinary action. Nevertheless, to preserve the validity of rules and policies, disciplinary action must be taken from time to time. On such occasions, the following precautions should be observed by the officer involved:

- The fire fighter or other person involved should be clearly informed that a rule violation is involved and that disciplinary action might result. At this point, it generally is wise for an officer not to be specific about the consequences in order to avoid commitment to a specific course of action.

- If the employee persists in violating the rule, or if the violation has already occurred, it usually is best for the officer to move deliberately and slowly by first consulting either with a personnel officer or with a superior officer before imposing any penalty greater than a verbal warning.

- To avoid possible future embarrassment, an officer should always point immediately to the appeals procedure and suggest that the offender utilize this procedure if he/she feels the disciplinary action is not warranted.

ACTIVITIES

1. Describe the organization of the personnel function in the fire department where you work.

2. What are some ways to achieve a work force that is representative of the population of a community?

3. What advances has your fire department made in fulfilling the requirements of affirmative action programs?

4. Explain the usual procedure for hiring people for paid fire departments that are subject to Civil Service regulations and that are *not* subject to Civil Service regulations.

5. Four formal job evaluation methods are used by most supervisors of salary administration programs when determining the worth of particular jobs within an organization. In outline form, describe the method you think is the most objective. Discuss your choice with your class. Use your outline in defense of your choice.

6. Before 1932, judges decided the rights of both management and labor in labor relations disputes. After 1932, four federal laws established the rules and regulations for the present collective bargaining system. Explain how each of these laws contributed to establishing these rules and regulations.

7. How do collective bargaining procedures at the local level in the public sector differ from the methods used by private industry?

8. Collective bargaining agreements contain a series of clauses, each relating to a particular area.
   (a) Name four typical clauses found in labor-management agreements.
   (b) Write brief descriptions of the purposes of at least two of these clauses.

9. Although grievance procedures vary somewhat from contract to contract, most of them follow steps comparable to the example presented in this chapter. Review the example, and then describe a more satisfactory

procedure for settling management/labor problems by either: 1) rewriting the procedure in the example, or 2) adding other steps to the example.

REFERENCES

[1]Title VII, Civil Rights Act of 1964 (amended by Congress in 1972), U.S. Government Printing Office, Washington, D.C.

[2]*Personnel Administration: Basic Administrative Skills — Reading Material*, The American National Red Cross, Washington, D.C., 1976; revised edition, 1977.

[3]NFPA 1201, *Recommendations for the Organization for Fire Services*, National Fire Protection Association, Quincy, MA, 1984, pp. 17-18.

[4]Kimmerly, Janet, "As Firehouse Sees It," *Firehouse*, May, 1988, p. 5.

[5]NFPA 1500, *Standard on Fire Department Occupational Safety and Health Program*, National Fire Protection Association, Quincy, MA, 1987, p. 1.

[6]NFPA 1501, *Standard for Fire Department Safety Officer*, National Fire Protection Association, Quincy, MA, 1987.

[7]NFPA 1403, *Standard on Live Fire Training Evolutions in Structures*, National Fire Protection Association, Quincy, MA, 1986.

[8]*Fire Department Safety Officer's Reference Guide*, National Fire Protection Association, Quincy, MA, 1985, 173 pp.

[9]NFPA 1001, *Standard for Fire Fighter Professional Qualifications*, National Fire Protection Association, Quincy, MA, 1987, pp. 19–20, 22, 24.

CHAPTER

14

Training as a Management Function

Many fire department chiefs consider training to be one of the most important functions in fire department operations because it is so central to operational competence. One reason for this is that rather than basing the selection of fire fighters on experience alone, other factors are also considered, such as physical condition, mechanical ability, personality, educational background, and ability to learn. Many people enter the fire service every year, most with no previous experience as fire fighters. Training, therefore, is essential for effective performance, and it is only with a comprehensive training program that a fire department is able to establish and maintain a competent and well-trained force.

The importance of training in a fire department's operations and the responsibility of the fire service instructor in such training is emphasized in the following excerpt from *Fire Service Instructor's Guidebook*:[1]

> The fire service's main objective is protecting life and property, so all people employed in it must be fully qualified to successfully and efficiently perform the wide range of skills necessary to accomplish this goal. This competency is, in large measure, the responsibility of the fire service instructor.
>
> Great pressure, from both public and private sectors, requires that the level of efficiency and the level of performance of all fire service personnel be constantly and consistently upgraded. The instructor is accountable for the level of up-to-date efficiency, education, and skills.
>
> The instructor is one of the important cohesive forces in any fire department. Whether a group functions like a well-oiled machine or like the scattered pieces of a puzzle is due in large part to the training, guidance, and encouragement of the instructor.

The instructor's role is demanding and challenging. The instructor must not only consider training personnel who show various levels of proficiency, but also must train personnel of all ranks within the department. In addition to ensuring that the recruit understands the duties and responsibilities of the position, the instructor must train the recruit for specific job skills. Experienced fire fighters and officers also must be kept familiar with all of the latest prevention and suppression techniques. They must be aware of updated standards, new laws, and new procedures. They must be able to recognize their current performance levels and skills, and correct any deficiencies or weaknesses. The instructor must prepare them for promotions, make them proficient in all fire-related skills, and generate a spirit of pride and commitment to the fire service.

This chapter outlines some of the principles of learning and training relevant to the fire service. People learn best when they are highly motivated; this fundamental principle is the foundation for the discussion of principles and techniques. The instructor—the fire officer in this case—is the manager of a learning process, which involves the following procedures:

- Analysis of learner's needs.
- Setting of learning goals.
- Identifying and overcoming obstacles to learning.
- Providing an environment where learning can take place.

This means that the instructor must place equal emphasis on *process* and on *content* of learning, and thus strive for a motivational climate in which learners seek greater knowledge and improved skills. Following a discussion of the principles of learning and various techniques is an explanation of how these principles can be applied to on-the-job training and classroom instruction.

PRINCIPLES OF LEARNING AND TRAINING DESIGN

Most people spend a portion of their lives in classroom situations where learning involves the presentation of information. The traditional concept of teaching is an instructor who lectures to a class and students who strive to absorb meaning from the lecturer's words. There is some give-and-take when class size and instructor temperament permit questions during the lecture; unfortunately, few adult learners ask questions in most classroom situations.

The Learning Process

The traditional perception of the instructor is changing to one in which the instructor pays as much attention to the *process* of learning as to the *content* of the material presented. Process refers to the particular steps necessary to ensure that learners gain the greatest benefits from the learning experiences. The instructor who strives to be a manager of the learning process seeks to shift the responsibility for learning to the student. Such an instructor does not concentrate solely on the topic and how it can best be presented in logical fashion but, instead, seeks answers to the following questions:

- What do the students already know?
- What is most important for them to learn next?
- How can they best be helped to learn it?

Answers to these questions are especially important in the fire service. The importance of paying attention to the process as well as the content of a topic cannot be overemphasized. A lecture that is well organized and clearly delivered can be self-defeating for learners who do not seek complete understanding. It would seem that a clear, logical presentation would enable students to learn a topic by leading them step-by-step from the fundamentals to a complete picture of the topic. Although this is correct to a limited extent, an educator who strives to increase quality must also evaluate trade-offs between a clear, logical presentation of material and optimal, long-term student comprehension.

Although it might seem contradictory for a logical subject explanation to be in conflict with learner comprehension, this *is* often the case. A well-organized learning experience often provides learners with little awareness of the practical limits of their new knowledge: Because learners follow a presentation, they assume that they fully understand the message. Few questions come to their minds and, even though they have mastered some difficult thoughts, they leave the training environment with only a shallow, practical comprehension of the subject—a comprehension that is inadequate for application to complex, real-life situations.

The circle (A) in Figure 14.1 graphically depicts this kind of learning experience—where learners have little contact with the unknown that surrounds the small island of knowledge gained. The learners believe they have developed what seems to be an adequate understanding of a subject, and, therefore, they are not likely to probe for more information. At some later time, however, when they attempt to apply what they have learned to the solution of a problem, they discover their lack of understanding. By this time the educator is no longer readily available to supply guidance, and the learner must either devote more effort to learning the necessary material or forego a clear comprehension of the subject.

The star shape (B) in Figure 14.1 is a representation of information given in a rugged, uneven format. Material presented this way gives learners only enough information to provide a basis for further exploration. In this type of

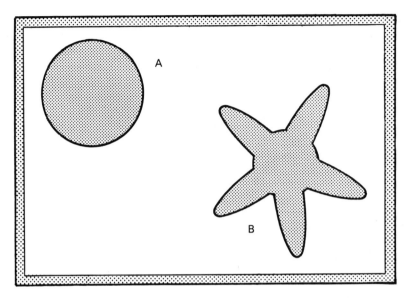

FIGURE 14.1 Depiction of (A) a learning experience in which learners are not likely to probe beyond the small circle of new knowledge for more information, and (B) a learning experience in which learners are given enough information to motivate them to explore a topic further.

learning situation, learners probe for understanding in terms most meaningful to each individual. If such a learning experience is designed carefully, it involves some form of problem-solving and provides individualized answers to questions that arise in the process—as the answers are needed, and asked for, by the learner. Outreach programs offered by the National Fire Academy frequently use this problem-solving approach to learning. It allows students to practice skills learned in the classroom to tackle real-world problems and scenarios.

An instructor also needs to be concerned with the level of difficulty a topic or learning goal presents to the learner. Figure 14.2 compares the learner's level of aspirations with the task level in order to define the zone of ego involvement at which a learner can devote maximum attention to the task of learning. The factors involved include: 1) level of aspiration, 2) complexity of task level, and 3) zone of ego involvement. These factors suggest that high motivation is possible only if the task level is set so that it is perceived to be within the experience and competence of the individual (even if some failures are expected). Aspirations, of course, will influence the way a task is seen and the attitudes with which it is approached.

If a task is perceived as much too difficult and has never been attempted, it is outside the zone of ego involvement shown in Figure 14.2. For example, a Russian language literacy test would fall into this category for most Americans. At the other extreme, any task that is immediately recognized as much too easy also fails to bring ego involvement and, therefore, presents little challenge and

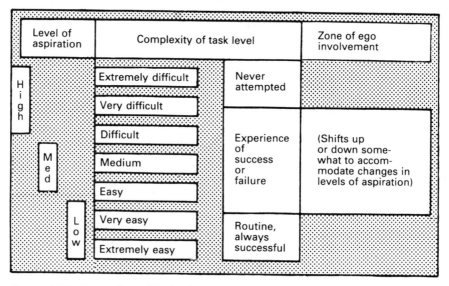

FIGURE 14.2 *Comparison of the level of aspiration, the complexity of task level, and the amount of ego involvement.* (Based on work by Wallace Wohlking[2])

will quickly be considered a waste of time. Most satisfying are those experiences that are achieved within a narrow margin: failure is a constant threat, and challenge is great. Here, of course, the payoff in satisfaction of accomplishment is high and motivation to tackle the task is greatest. Reports on research with children have shown that those who have a history of success usually will set realistic goals, while those who fail regularly tend to set unrealistic goals — either too high or too low.[2] Those who set goals that are too high seem to do so because they usually are rewarded for trying, while those who set goals that are too low do so as a defense against possible failure. The conclusions for training design are fairly obvious:

- For all complex tasks, the designer of a training experience must set goals.
- Goals must be attainable so that successful experiences are developed.
- Specific effort must be made to teach toleration of making mistakes.

The four diagrams in Figure 14.3 emphasize the importance of motivation and show the limitations of teaching presentations from still another perspective. If, as shown in part A of Figure 14.3, the large rectangle (no. 1) can be considered to completely contain the currently available knowledge about a specific subject, then it can reasonably be assumed that an instructor will know, at best, only a portion, as indicated by rectangle no. 2.

The instructor, faced with limited class time, prepares an outline that presents that portion of knowledge the instructor considers most important. Often, the instructor encounters various interruptions and delays, and thus talks about less than had been planned. The prepared material compared to

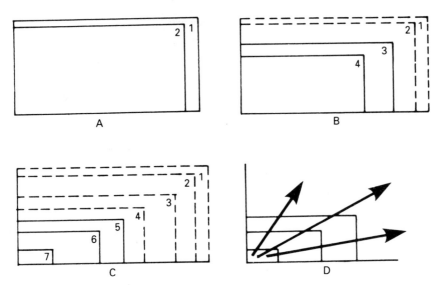

FIGURE 14.3 *Pictorial representation of the importance of motivation in learning experiences.*

what is actually discussed is represented by the two smaller rectangles (nos. 3 and 4) shown in part B of Figure 14.3.

The communication process results in different people assigning different meanings to words and phrases (see Chapter 10) because of lapses of student attention, screens of personal biases, misunderstandings, misinterpretations, and false impressions of concept clarity. All in all, what reaches the student is far less than what the student was exposed to. What is retained a few weeks, months, or even years later is still another matter. The three small rectangles (nos. 5, 6, and 7) in part C of Figure 14.3 represent what the student hears (no. 5), what penetrates the student's consciousness (no. 6), and what the student remembers at some later date (no. 7).

The intention of this somewhat exaggerated analogy is not to portray the futility of conscientious effort; rather, it is included to help illustrate the point that *how* a subject is presented is often far more important than *how much* of the subject is presented. The curiosity of learners can be aroused by presenting only that portion of the material which they can readily absorb. If presented in an interesting, stimulating format, learners usually will seek out more information (see part D of Figure 14.3). Thus, more information will be absorbed, more will be retained, and the ability to apply the newly acquired knowledge will be enhanced substantially. However, to do this is more easily said than done. To change the traditional emphasis, instructors must make use of all the teaching techniques that are geared to stimulating inquiry on the part of learners and thus motivate learners to accept the responsibility for their own learning.

To achieve an environment in which learners can find maximum motivation requires consideration of all elements of the Linking Elements concept, which was discussed in the previous chapters—including, in particular, linking elements concerned with goal-setting (see Chapter 5). In addition, the instructor must have an understanding of what learners already know, and the extent of their knowledge or skill deficiencies.

Before an instructor can determine the order in which topics should be presented and the specific subtopics that should be taught, an analysis of learning needs must be made. Such an analysis is necessary to help determine the type of information to be presented.

Analyzing Individual Learning Needs

It often can be assumed that new trainees know very little, if anything, about a subject. Classroom sessions or on-the-job training can be planned by looking solely at the topics the learner must master, and at the characteristics of the learner so that information can be presented in a stimulating way.

The situation is more complicated when planning on-going or continuing development. Not only must the instructor be concerned with logical sequence of topic segments and with presenting them enticingly, but the plan must concentrate on those subtopics (knowledge or skills) where additional learning is desirable. Thus, in a formal sense, an analysis of learning needs attempts to answer two basic questions:

1. What do learners need to know or be able to do?
2. What do learners already know or are already able to do?

Based on the answers to these questions, a specific learning program can be prepared and scheduled. Learning needs can best be analyzed by developing a knowledge/skill profile that lists all the things the learner should know or be able to do. Table 14.1 is a sample of a knowledge/skill profile for a fire fighter. There are many ways such a profile can be developed, including the following three alternative ways:

1. Base the profile on a detailed job description even though it usually does not match the job description exactly. For example, two lines on a lower-level officer's job description might read:
   - *Supervise the activities of the company's fire fighters during overhaul operations.*
   - *Supervise the activities of the company's fire fighters during salvage operations.*

These two tasks cover many things a lower-level officer must know or be able to do: communicate clearly, know the technical aspects of each operation, and apply the knowledge and skills involved in supervision. On the other hand, another job description task for an officer might concern a single topic:

TABLE 14.1 Sample knowledge/skill profile for fire fighters.

Knowledge	Skills
Organization of fire department	Hose evolutions
Scope of fire department operation	Ladder evolutions
Standard operation procedures	Breathing apparatus use
Fire department rules and regulations	Forcible entry
Safety policies	Ventilation operations
Fire behavior—chemistry of fire, types of fire, etc.	Hydrant operation and connection
	Salvage operations
Basic physiology of body systems	Rope use
Fire streams and use of nozzles and couplings	Basic apparatus maintenance operations
	Cleaning, maintaining, and inspecting equipment such as breathing apparatus, ropes, salvage equipment, and ladders
Use and types of equipment, such as breathing apparatus	
Life-threatening injuries	Care of hoses and nozzles
Ventilation methods	EMT skills
Salvage process	Recognizing, identifying, and working with hazardous materials
Inspection procedures and standards	
Reporting	Use of chemical protective equipment
Safety	
Basic chemistry	
Hazardous materials	

- *Must be thoroughly familiar with hydraulic principles related to fire streams.*

2. Another way to construct a profile is by listing all goals that apply to a particular situation. These goals can be converted to knowledge and skills in the same way as a profile that comes from a job description. Some goals require more than one skill while some overlap closely with a single skill or specific knowledge.

3. The third way to develop a profile is to do it cooperatively with a fire fighter or lower-level officer directly, by listing knowledge and skill requirements. A jointly developed profile will probably lead to learning goals that are challenging, goals that a fire fighter or lower-level officer would put forth significant effort to achieve.

Analyzing Team Learning Needs

An analysis of learning needs cannot concentrate exclusively on the knowledge and skills that individuals must acquire. There are team needs that go beyond the individual needs of the team members. Even when every person on a team has all of the knowledge for performing specific tasks, if the team has not learned how to coordinate them, many problems can occur. These problems can be mitigated through joint team practice which gradually develops the necessary coordination. First, team skill needs must, of course, be identified. For example, each fire fighter in a specific company must have clear knowledge of the standard attack evolution:

- Officer and fire fighter 1 advance one preconnected 1¾-in. line to fire for immediate fire attack.
- Operator charges 1¾-in. line from engine tank.
- Fire fighter 2 pulls supply hose from body and connects to hydrant, and then prepares to advance 2½-in. line.
- Fire fighter 3 assists fire fighter 2.
- Operator switches from tank to hydrant supply as soon as connection is made.
- Operator connects 2½-in. hose to pump discharge gate and charges it.

Although these steps might be followed without joint drills to develop team skills, fire fighters 2 and 3 will not perform their tasks as fast unless they practice together. It is conceivable that a snag could develop in the timely switching from tank to hydrant, thus making the team's skill deficiencies a major problem.

Setting Learning Goals

A positive change in behavior is the ultimate purpose and end result of new learning. This is especially true with respect to new or enhanced skills. In the fire service it is important that everyone continue to improve the way each job is done.

Goals define the new behavior that is to result from new learning. When properly set, each goal represents a contract to oneself (or to others) to achieve such new behavior. For this reason, when educators discuss the goals learners have agreed to achieve, they often speak of a learning contract.

As discussed in previous chapters, joint goal-setting defines both what is expected of a fire fighter or lower-level officer and what support a manager is expected to provide. Similarly, a learning contract defines the goals and the responsibilities of learner and instructor and thereby places these responsibilities clearly where they belong.

After the knowledge and skills needs of a person or team have been identified, goals can be set and developmental activities can be planned to stimulate the greatest desire for achieving the goals. When planning a learning program, the concept described below can be a useful guide.

The Goal Achievement Sequence: A complete learning experience is composed of the three phases shown in Figure 14.4.

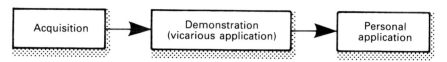

FIGURE 14.4 *The three phases of a complete learning experience.*

1. **Acquisition:** New knowledge is obtained through the written word, from live presentations, and in group or one-on-one discussions.

2. **Demonstration:** The new material is made more meaningful or more explicit by demonstrating the practical application of new data, principles, or concepts. This can take the form of dramatic presentations, films, slides, audio or video tapes, or actual demonstrations with models.

3. **Personal Application:** Learners come face-to-face with their individual ability to apply the material to various situations. If the learning experiences are designed properly, they will be quite similar to those the learners deal with in their jobs.

Instructors who work with simulations and other participative learning experiences consider the third phase to be the most important one. This personal application phase gives both the learner and the instructor an opportunity to evaluate the success of the learning experience. In so doing, two basic feedback loops emerge (see Figure 14.5):

- A loop for the instructor to observe the progress of the group in meaningful terms.
- A loop for the learner to diagnose areas where particular knowledge deficiencies exist.

The two feedback loops become the basis for a continuing process that can be used to achieve any learning objective that is not blocked by attitudinal or emotional obstacles.

The process of achieving an objective involves a spiral-type repetition of the three phases of learning (acquisition, demonstration, and personal application) and the feedback loops; less and less new knowledge has to be acquired in each turn (see Figure 14.5). This becomes especially apparent to instructors when they experiment with various types of simulated experiences. Serious-minded learners inevitably ask more precise and penetrating questions during and after the personal application than they are able to ask beforehand.

It should be kept in mind that for new knowledge to be meaningful, it must be incorporated on a learner's own terms. Although this might seem obvious, the point cannot be overemphasized because words and images have individualized, personal meanings to each person. Therefore, application of new knowledge in a classroom or training session must be in situations that are similar to those a learner normally experiences in the work environment. Also, learning must proceed at a learner's own pace, must be adapted to personal ability, and should be related to previous experience. Therefore, learning programs should make use of techniques that permit adaptation to individual needs in order to help instructors and learners achieve learning goals as easily as possible. In addition to the application of the goal achievement spiral (Figure 14.5), there are several additional learning principles that must be considered by an instructor.

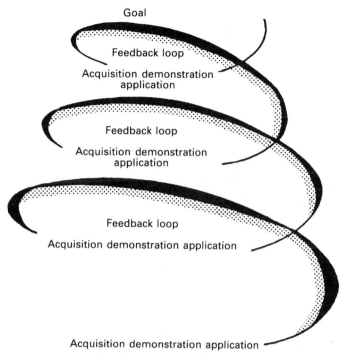

FIGURE 14.5 Model of the continuing process for achieving learning objectives.

Identifying and Overcoming Blockages to Learning

The spiral shown in Figure 14.5 can be useful in helping learners overcome knowledge/skill deficiencies only if learning is not subject to some type of blockage. Generally, in the fire service there is little negative attitude toward learning because fire fighters instinctively realize that learning is essential to effective performance. However, the learning process can be obstructed if someone has physical or emotional obstacles or negative attitudes toward specific topics or instructions. These obstacles are referred to as blockages. Some learning blockages are unique to individual learners. For example, learners are sometimes psychologically opposed to training. At other times a subject can be so complex that comprehension is difficult for some people. Figure 14.6 depicts most of the common blockages, including the following, as well as some of the basic strategies for overcoming them.

Unwillingness to Admit Lack of Knowledge/Skill: People are sometimes reluctant to admit that they have a specific knowledge or skill deficiency and are ashamed to admit that, after having been exposed to a subject, they still do not understand an idea, principle, or procedure—especially if others seem to understand it. As a result they try to avoid contact with the topic.

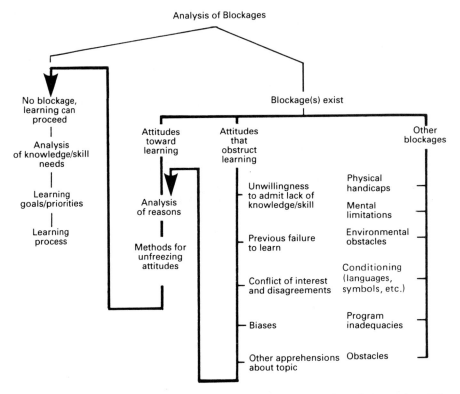

FIGURE 14.6 *Flow chart showing usual steps in acquiring new knowledge and/or skills and some of the blockages that can interfere with the learning process. (*Source: Erwin Rausch, Didactic Systems, Inc.)*

Previous Failure to Learn: Failure to learn in the past can result in a learner feeling that the subject is too difficult; thus, learners often fail to devote the effort necessary to master a particular subject. Also, if learners believe that something is simply the result of common sense, they will sometimes tune out in the erroneous belief that the message does not contain anything of value to them. Similarly, if the subject is perceived to be too theoretical or irrelevant, learners might not pay adequate attention. Any of these beliefs can lead to failure to learn a topic.

Conflict of Interest and Disagreements: Learning can be blocked by various attitudes. For example, a fire fighter who believes that a good fire fighter is a "smoke eater" believes that a person who can last the longest in the dense smoke of a fire is, in some way, the best type of fire fighter. Such a fire fighter might view instruction in the use of protective breathing apparatus as being negative or unnecessary because the instruction would be in conflict with the fire fighter's beliefs about what a good fire fighter should do.

Biases: A person might have biases against the instructor(s) based on race, religion, area of origin, personal appearance, or other characteristics. A fire fighter who holds such a bias with respect to an instructor is not likely to learn much from that instructor.

Other Apprehensions About a Topic: Other apprehensions can come from concerns generated when other learners describe a topic as difficult or when the topic requires contact with materials that are unpleasant to the person, e.g., odors, slimy materials, wounds, and so on. All of these apprehensions can lead to insufficient learning.

Methods for Unfreezing Attitudes: In attempting to overcome learning blockages, an instructor must first determine the actual reason(s) behind the learning difficulty. If the reasons are based on the perception or attitude of the learner, the instructor can use counseling to "unfreeze" the belief. Specific devices that can be used as an extension of the counseling process for unfreezing attitudes include:

1. **Peer Pressure:** When learners become clearly aware that their attitudes are different from those of their peers, or if they find that acting on their own views and attitudes will actually hurt team effort, then it is likely that they will question and modify their views. An instructor can therefore make individuals aware that their attitudes are either inappropriately different from those of their peers, or that their attitudes might hurt team achievement.

2. **Words of Respected People:** When learners become aware of a conflict with respected and successful people in the field, attitudes also are likely to be questioned. Presenting irrefutable evidence of the attitude of successful professionals in the field (through guest appearances in classes, or through testimonials) can help an instructor cultivate better student attitudes toward a subject.

3. **A Direct Order:** Giving a direct order (or setting a policy or procedure) is sometimes the only way to oppose strongly held attitudes. Many behavioral scientists claim that training cannot be effective against strong attitudes unless there is first an organizational requirement that learners must follow. Training can then help people satisfy the requirement more easily, and that, in turn, frequently leads to revised attitudes toward the subject.

Other Blockages

The extreme right side of Figure 14.6 lists blockages to learning that result from limitations that are not based on attitudes or emotions. They include the following:

Physical Handicaps: The instructor should be sensitive to any physical handicaps, and be aware that some learners might be embarrassed about them. For example, a fire fighter might be aware that an old knee injury makes it increasingly difficult to climb a ladder, and might have successfully hidden this minor handicap during the physical examination and the probationary period. This fire fighter might resist training sessions on using ladders. If an instructor is not aware of a fire fighter's handicap, considerable effort can be wasted in misdirected attempts to teach a skill. A more common example concerns hearing and sight impairments. People with these impairments often are reluctant to obtain and wear hearing aids or glasses. The obvious blockages to learning that result cannot be resolved unless an instructor is aware of them.

Mental Limitations: Such limitations can include slow learning, perceptual problems and minor emotional problems such as fear of heights, unreasonable resentment of authority, or superstitious beliefs. Once these limitations are recognized, they usually can be overcome. Like many physical disorders, learners might be reluctant to face their mental limitations objectively. Only when an instructor is aware of such problems can the learning program be adjusted to take them into account. Often, a slower pace and some extra help (coaching) are all that is needed for a learner to achieve the same learning goals as other members of the group.

Environmental Obstacles: These include noise, movement, and other distractions that interrupt the thought process of instructors and learners alike.

Inadequate Conditioning: Some actions must be practiced repeatedly so that they can be performed automatically when signaled. For example, fire fighters have a specified routine to get ready to answer an alarm. If this routine is practiced enough in response to the alarm, the fire fighters will react automatically when a real alarm sounds. In this way, certain tasks will be performed almost instinctively in the shortest possible time. Successful conditioning requires that all fire fighters understand and use the same jargon, symbols, and signals.

Program Inadequacies: These include illogical presentation of topics and other instructor-related deficiencies, such as talking above the learning level of students, talking condescendingly to students, and ineffectively using the chalkboard and other visuals. All of these can detract from a learning experience. These instructor-related deficiencies primarily apply to lectures and demonstrations. Similarly, participative types of learning experiences that provide personal application might be poorly designed so that they are not perceived as relevant or, for other reasons, stimulating to the learning of a specific topic.

Additional Obstacles: Other blockages to learning involve time conflicts or illness which can prevent full comprehension of the material, especially if absence occurs when critical topics are covered.

The effect(s) of any of these obstacles and attitudes can be destructive to the learning process. It is therefore important for instructors to be alert to problems or inadequacies in all of these blockage areas and to take prompt corrective steps as soon as the problems or inadequacies are noticed.

Specific Learning Principles

Motivation

Although mentioned previously, it is worth repeating that learners who are motivated will master a subject faster and more thoroughly than learners who are less motivated.

Motivation is achieved only if learners can find sufficient benefits in a learning experience. The pleasure of gaining new, useful information or desired skills is one of the strongest psychological satisfactions for learners and can be provided through interesting, varied presentations that hold a learner's attention. When a learner is motivated, the learning situation can be as emotionally rewarding as entertainment if it is truly appropriate to the learner's interests and capabilities. The satisfaction of psychological needs (which is essential to motivation) can also be provided by rewards, such as greater professionalism, better self-protection, winning in a competition, or achieving something a learner wants. Additionally, in order to achieve a climate where learners can find appropriate instruction, *linking elements* pertaining to *control* and *competence* (see Chapter 4) must be satisfied. These particular linking elements involve:

1. **Setting learning goals.** Attention must be given to satisfying the eight problem areas discussed in Chapter 5 (see Figure 5.3).
2. **Ensuring coordination.** Good coordination between learning activities and learning needs must be obtained. The demotivating impact of confusion or lack of clear direction should be avoided. The sequence of topics must be built logically and carefully to ensure that all new concepts are understood before they are used to explain other matters that will serve as a basis for drawing conclusions.
3. **Establishing rules.** Doubt, confusion, and distractions are reduced when rules are clearly communicated and consistently enforced. Simple rules, such as insisting that learning assignments be completed on time, or starting and stopping learning sessions at the appointed times (when emergencies do not interrupt), can significantly influence confidence in a training program.

Pace

The learning pace must be adapted to the learner's ability to absorb new concepts if the learning process is to proceed without interruption. All learners have different capabilities for learning. Some understand quickly, others possess good memories, and still others have good attention spans. For these reasons a lecture that is fairly fast-paced can lose some learners, and a slow-paced lecture usually holds only the attention of the least capable learners.

Absorption

Learning will be absorbed better and retained longer if it is directly work-related and can be applied on the job. Most subjects covered in fire service training are work-related, although some subjects rarely are applied, such as some complex rescue operations. If the task is one that might be very important during fire fighting, then regular practice in a simulated environment might be necessary to ensure adequate skills when they are needed.

Understanding

Things that are learned and understood readily tend to be retained better than things that are learned by rote. Learners should be tested to determine that a subject is thoroughly understood and not just memorized.

Practice

Practice distributed over several periods of time is more valuable to the learning process than the same amount of practice concentrated into a single period. If an important skill has to be practiced extensively in order to achieve full mastery, practice sessions do not have to be continued until this goal is reached: Pauses of several days between relatively short sessions can help bring better retention.

Order

The order of presenting materials is of major importance. Although this learning principle might seem obvious in many programs, complex topics are sometimes presented before establishing an adequate foundation for them.

Recognition

It is easier to recognize something than it is to recall it. This principle is of great importance in selecting ways to test the knowledge of learners. Testing should emphasize recall, not recognition. For example, requiring fire fighters to draw their own prefire plans and insert appropriate symbols and tables correctly tests the learning process more accurately than presenting a ready-made prefire plan and only requiring that a given list of symbols be placed correctly on the plan. The fire fighters must recall much more information to draw their own plans than they would need to simply recognize proper symbol placement on a plan drawn by someone else.

New Knowledge

Learning something new can interfere with remembering something that has been learned earlier. This principle is often overlooked by instructors who, when helping learners acquire new skills or knowledge, fail to reinforce previously acquired subject matter or skills. Consideration of this principle is especially important when the new subject overlaps or is similar to a previous one. For example, learning a new set of code numbers can hinder retention of the previous group of numbers.

Feedback

If learners are unsure that they are acquiring knowledge correctly, or if they are wondering if what they are learning is correct, they will be hesitant about devoting their full efforts to learning. Therefore, testing and participative activities in which learners receive feedback on the correctness of what they are learning are important segments of satisfactory learning experiences.

Although these learning principles are not the only ones to be considered when planning an instructional program, they are of major concern. The instructor who successfully incorporates these principles into a teaching plan can be a manager of a motivational learning experience rather than merely dispensing information.

Techniques for Acquisition of New Knowledge and Skills

Once learning needs have been identified and goals set, an instructor can plan the instructional strategy. An instructional strategy consists of two major segments: 1) topic sequence (content) and 2) processes to be used for each segment. As discussed earlier, these are closely interrelated. Segments of the subject must be presented in a logical thought progression. Simple concepts or skills should be presented first, followed in logical sequence by more complex concepts and skills. Also, in order to further improve the motivational aspects of a learning situation, each topic segment must include the three phases shown in Figure 14.4: *acquisition, demonstration,* and *personal application*. The remainder of this chapter examines the techniques that can be used for all three of these phases, followed by an in-depth presentation of their application in the two major teaching environments—classroom instruction and on-the-job training.

Instructional Programs

When preparing an instructional program, a planning chart is useful because it can help to ensure that: 1) topic segments are arranged in logical sequence; 2) appropriate techniques will be used for each topic segment; 3) acquisition, demonstration, and personal application phases will have been considered for each topic segment; and 4) there is sufficient variety in techniques to present a stimulating environment for the students. Table 14.2 is an example of such a chart.

TABLE 14.2 Sample planning chart for segment of a course in communications.

Topic segment	Acquisition	Demonstration	Personal application	Correction of deficiencies
Receiving and recording fire calls	Lecture (communications officer)	Simulated call in dispatcher room and discussion	Receiving and recording four simulated calls	Comprehensive drill and supervised work assignment as dispatcher
Establishing location and nature of emergency	Discussion	Demonstration role play by instructor and experienced dispatcher	Role playing by students (as dispatcher)	Supervised work assignment as dispatcher
Dispatching equipment and apparatus	Assigned reading	Discussion and equipment demonstrations	Individual using equipment for specific tasks	Written and verbal tests

The more varied instructional techniques an instructor can use effectively, the more interesting and stimulating the learning experience will be for learners. Instructors and officers should, therefore, constantly strive to become acquainted with a wide range of instructional techniques, and should experiment with using these techniques as tools for helping students learn.

Everyday environment and past experience account for the major portion of how the average person becomes exposed to unknown subjects. For most people, formal education usually consists of 1) lectures and explanations, 2) reading, 3) other media (tapes, films, video tapes), and 4) conferences.

Lectures and Explanations

Lectures to groups and one-on-one explanations are the most widely used instructional techniques for transmitting information. Often, they are the least expensive and the most readily available instructional techniques. They are flexible, they can be changed on the spot by an instructor who perceives a previously hidden learning need, and they can be used to teach one person or many. Lectures can be given by one lecturer or many lecturers.

However, like all instructional techniques lectures have disadvantages as well as advantages. Lectures are essentially one-way communication with little or no opportunity for practice, reinforcement, or knowledge of results.

Many disadvantages of one-sided explanations can be reduced by the instructor's ability to handle questions adequately. Instructors who encourage the asking of questions and then answer them effectively can often clarify subjects that were confusing to many learners.

Reading

For acquiring new knowledge, independent study by reading or programmed instruction materials are alternatives to lectures and explanations.

Reading provides an opportunity to stop when necessary, to make notes, to clarify a point by referring back to earlier material, and to consult various sources for more detailed information. With reading, obtaining answers to questions sometimes can be more difficult than during lectures where a question can be explored with the instructor(s).

Programed Instruction: Programed instruction is a special form of guided reading that usually is used as the basis for an independent learning situation. In programed instruction, frequent questions are included for the learner to answer before proceeding. The learner is told whether a response is correct by comparing it with the answer in the program. There are several advantages to using programed learning:

1. Knowledge is acquired at the individual's pace.
2. The learner follows a logical progression of thought.
3. The learner must respond to questions after each presentation of material, which encourages learner acceptance and retention of the material.
4. A wide variety of materials and audiovisuals can supplement the programed instruction.
5. Programed instruction is self-administered whenever the learner is ready to learn.

Programed materials, however, often are considered to be tedious. Currently, programed courses of instruction are in limited use.

Media

The use of media is an excellent way to enhance knowledge about a subject. The use of chalkboards, transparencies, storyboards, display posters and materials, slides, filmstrips, and videotapes help a presenter to 1) control and maintain group attention and 2) organize the message or lesson. Media help the audience better retain what is said and understand the message more clearly.

Conferences

Using conferences or group discussions can provide immediate reinforcement to newly acquired knowledge with small groups. For this reason, group discussions often follow a lecture. Unlike a lecture, the discussion is two-way communication, which gives the learner an opportunity to compare personal reactions to the subject matter with the reactions of other learners, and with the views of the instructor(s). This technique can be combined with brief lectures to provide a mixture of acquisition, demonstration, and limited personal application.

A conference, then, is a planned learning experience where the instructor is not a lecturer, but a facilitator. The instructor encourages group thinking and, when necessary, provides background information that enables all learners to take part in the discussion. The instructor should summarize, at the end of each discussion topic, what the participants should have learned from the experience.

Conferences tend to get learners or trainees to give more thought to the subject matter, and help to show each conferee how others think about a subject or problem. Presentation of the subject matter is adapted to the needs of the group and, by exposing group opinions, helps to change those attitudes that are detrimental to learning. The use of satellite technology has spurred the use of teleconferences where people, at a number of sites in widely scattered locations, participate in a common learning effort.

One major disadvantage of the conference technique is that it requires a highly skilled instructor—one who can carefully plan for a variety of unknown eventualities that could occur during the conference. Another disadvantage is that it is fully effective only when all participants have adequate knowledge of the subject. Therefore, it might require prior learning to ensure that all learners have reached that level of knowledge.

Techniques for Demonstrating New Knowledge and Skills

Demonstrations show learners how the information, concepts, or materials that were discussed during the preceding acquisition phase can be applied. Illustrating a piece of equipment and showing how to don breathing apparatus are demonstrations, as is a role-playing situation where an instructor takes the part of a building owner while a student explains a violation.

Demonstrations can use most of the techniques available to an instructor, including lectures, slides or filmstrips, and audio or videotapes. Demonstrations can also utilize some participative techniques (discussed later), including case-study exploration, simulated use of equipment (or of a concept), and a role-playing demonstration.

Although they are usually considered to be some of the most important parts of the learning process, demonstrations are often overlooked. The result of such oversight is a gap in the student's learning experience—a gap that can take considerably more effort to fill at a later date than would have been necessary immediately after the acquisition phase.

Techniques for Personal Application

The instructional techniques used in a classroom (as distinct from field practice) during the personal application phase are based, in one way or another, on case studies. Although there are many kinds of case studies, all of them are basically descriptions of real or imaginary situations that vary from single paragraphs or brief verbal statements to greatly detailed books.

Case Studies or Case Method

The applications of the case method to learning situations vary as widely as their types. Sometimes they serve as foundations for simulations and role playing, but most often they are used more directly in various ways:

Simple Descriptions: Learners are expected to review a case, decide what issues it raises, and then draw conclusions about them. For instance, fire fighters could be given a prefire plan of a particular building with instructions to review and comment on it. Or questions written by the instructors could be presented for learners to answer.

Staged Cases: Learners are provided with only part of the information necessary to thoroughly analyze a case. They must first decide what additional information is needed so that they can work on the case. After they have asked for and received the additional information, they can work on the case. For instance, in a staged fire situation, the instructor might delete such information as distances from the hydrants, wind direction, and other conditions, even though they are important to the case. The students must then figure out the missing elements to derive an effective conclusion.

Cases can be used with one learner, with small groups, or with large classes. Cases help stimulate creative thinking because learners are required to determine what is essential about the situation and then decide what actions, if any, should be considered. Cases are easy to use because much of the material available to instructors—records of previous fires, prefire plans, histories of inspections, articles from fire magazines, and newspaper stories—can form the basis for case studies. Also, cases can be used spontaneously when it becomes clear that learners need to explore specific issues, especially after a lecture when the questions indicated inadequate understanding of the topic, or in situations where it is obvious that the learning process needs a change of pace to maintain learner interest.

Simulations

If learners are asked to imagine that they are one of the people described in a specific scenario, they can begin to participate in a simulation and solve specific problems. Simulations are an ideal vehicle for learning in the fire service. They can dramatically enhance interest in training sessions and contribute greatly to awareness of hazards in the district. In addition, simulations can help to make valuable use of existing prefire plans and, coincidentally, serve as a basis for continual improvement in the prefire plans and in inspections.

A company officer or instructor who builds most instruction around exploring strategies and tactics at local properties can expand them into simulations. These simulations can concentrate on rescue, fire streams, forcible entry, ventilation, or on ladder evolutions as well as on specific fire fighting tactics and strategies based on fire location, weather conditions, or time of day. The inevitable outcome of such simulations is greater interest in learning, greater knowledge of local conditions, enhanced interest in inspections, and improvement of prefire plans.

Simulations can be supported with various media or can be worked out on paper. Some can be programed for use with computers, some can be expanded into field work, and still others can become actual fire drills at real locations (in cases where the owner's or official's permission has been obtained to do so).

Simulations, like case studies, can be elaborate descriptions of a situation, with detailed data, pictures, charts, graphs, or floorplans, or they can be simple verbal descriptions created spontaneously by the instructor. During simulations, learners in a class can either assume that they are all the same person or they can take on different roles in the situation.

Role-Playing

If the "What should be done in this situation?" simulation is sharpened to encompass "Exactly what words and actions should be used?," then a simulation is likely to involve role-playing. Role-playing usually involves simulations in which learners act out specific roles that were assigned to them. Role-playing is applicable primarily to instructional situations where the learning objectives involve communicating between individuals or groups.

Even though the most common form of role-playing is a live demonstration staged with one person per role and all others as observers, this is rarely the most effective form. Much more effective for skill development is the type of role-playing that involves all the members of the group simultaneously. Following are some of the ways role-playing sessions can be made more interesting.

Use of Recorders: Role-playing can be recorded on an audio- or video-tape so that it can be critiqued later. In this way members of the group do not feel that they are criticizing actual people, and they are more willing to discuss correct actions or errors they observe. Various topics for such role-playing tapes include consoling a victim's grieving relative, calming an irate owner, explaining a violation, critiquing a performance discussion between an officer and a fire fighter, and responding to a citizen's question.

Role-Playing in Small Groups: When role-playing is done with several observers or under the critical eye of a supervisor, it often is intimidating for the performers. On the other hand, in the intimacy of a small group of friends or peers it does not carry the same implications. As a result, it is a much more relaxed activity in which each participant behaves naturally and realistically.

Number of Participants per Role: Another important feature of successful role-playing can be the number of participants who play a given role. In most cases, only one person assumes a given role. Another effective way to analyze specific phrasing or approaches is to have two people who consult with each other play each role.

In addition to the major variants of role-playing, there are other variations that help make it an effective teaching device. For example, a situation can be interrupted after a few moments and participants told about a change in the situation, e.g., a particular emergency or information received by telephone. Still other variations can result from a specific hidden point that must be uncovered by the person playing the learner's role.

Applying Learning Principles and Techniques to Coaching

Classroom training and drills provide most of the knowledge and skills needed by fire fighters or officers for their jobs. However, due to the many ways people perceive their jobs and the differences in extent of learning they obtain from classes and drills, there is considerable need for individual coaching by superiors. Such coaching is usually in one of the following forms:

1. Suggesting self-study goals to eliminate deficiencies and helping with any difficulties the learner encounters.
2. On-the-job training in the particular knowledge and skills that require individualized attention in order to help eliminate deficiencies, or where only one person needs training.

Self-Study

Self-study recommendations (such as guided reading programs) and individualized help (such as advice from superiors) in achieving training goals are excellent methods for the continuing development of professionals. Such methods should be specifically geared to the needs, aspirations, and the knowledge and skill level of the individual.

On-the-Job Training

Many topics, especially skills, are so important that they cannot be left to the more leisurely self-study approach; thus, they require the more intense activity of on-the-job training. As a general guide for the training of civilian employees, the U.S. Army uses a comprehensive chart that describes the four steps in the process of on-the-job training (see Table 14.3).[3] Three of the four steps shown in Table 14.3 parallel the stages of the complete learning experience illustrated in Figure 14.4.

TABLE 14.3 The four steps of on-the-job training. (*Source: United States Army*[3])

	Step	Purpose	How accomplished
Acquisition	1. Prepare the learner	A. Relieve tension B. Establish training base C. Arouse interest D. Give confidence	A. Put learner at ease B. Find out what learner already knows about task C. Tell relation of task to mission D. Tie task to learner's experience E. Ensure that learner is in a comfortable position to see you perform the task clearly
Demonstration	2. Present the task	A. To make sure learner understands what to do and why B. To ensure retention C. To avoid giving more than learner can grasp	A. Tell, show, illustrate, question carefully and patiently, and use task analysis B. Stress key points C. Instruct clearly and completely, one step at a time D. Keep your words to a minimum; stress action words
Personal Application	3. Try out the learner's performance	A. To be sure learner has right method B. To prevent wrong habit forming C. To be sure learner knows what to do and why D. To test learner's knowledge E. To avoid putting learner on the job prematurely	A. Have learner perform the task and do not require an explanation of what is being done the first time through. If learner makes a major error, assume the blame yourself and repeat as much of Step 2 as necessary. B. Once learner has performed the task correctly, have learner repeat it and explain the steps and key points as the task is done. C. Ask questions to ensure that key points are understood D. Continue until you know that learner knows the material.
	4. Followup	A. To give learner confidence B. To be sure learner takes no chances, and is not left alone C. To be sure learner remains alert D. To show your confidence in learner	A. Make learner responsible; praise as fitting B. Encourage questions; tell learner where help is available C. Check frequently at first D. Gradually reduce amount of checking

Applying Learning Principles and Techniques to Classroom Instruction

Unlike on-the-job training (which is highly structured and follows a very specific pattern), classroom instruction is extremely varied. However, if the principles of learning and training are to be honored, some pattern should be followed. Therefore, the following general guidelines are suggested:

1. Lectures should be of limited duration. Many educators feel that uninterrupted lectures that last more than 20 minutes are likely to result in seriously reduced attention span.

2. The sequence of acquisition, demonstration, and personal application (see Figure 14.4) and correction of deficiencies, should be followed carefully. One way to use this sequence follows:

   a) Give a lecture to explain concepts, supported with visuals if possible, that offers learners as much opportunity as possible to ask questions.
   b) Either in the lecture or at its conclusion, show how the new learning can be applied on the job.
   c) Assign an appropriate activity that is done individually, in small groups, or both.
   d) Review the activity through reports and individual or group discussions.
   e) Give learners an opportunity to ask questions.

3. As much as possible, the atmosphere should be informal and relaxed so that learners can ask questions freely and explore points in terms familiar to them. Encouraging questions from quiet learners is very important because if a group contains several highly motivated learners, it might seem to the instructor that the entire group is exploring a subject in detail when, in reality, only a few are doing so while others, often seriously confused by the subject, are reluctant to speak. To help create an informal atmosphere, lectures must almost continually allow for questions, and instructors must answer questions without being condescending or belittling the learners. At the same time, instructors must be careful not to allow questions to draw the lecture away from the logical sequence of thought necessary for an orderly presentation. Furthermore, the instructor must be honest and open with learners. An instructor who cannot answer a question should admit it, and either offer to obtain an answer or assign one of the learners to research it.

4. There must be opportunities for slower learners (or those whose attention had strayed) to catch up with the class, and for fast learners (or those who are more familiar with the subject) to be challenged by the learning process. Individual and small group activities can provide such opportunities because the slower learners or those inclined to attention lapses feel more free to ask questions in individual or small group environments. At the same time, those with a better understanding of the

topic can verify their command of it by helping to explain it to others. Such explanations serve to further strengthen understanding and help to achieve full mastery.

5. There must be effective but polite discipline. This helps learners pay greater attention to the subject. Instructors who have difficulty maintaining order can find help in many readily available books on conference leadership or classroom discipline.

To follow these guidelines requires a willingness to experiment with different ways of managing learning experiences as well as thoroughness in keeping the learning process in mind.

It is most important for instructors to be comfortable allowing learners to take an active role in the classroom. Much can be gained from allowing fire fighters to take turns in leading the discussion of the various cases. Assignments for leading the discussion should be made at a previous session so that fire fighters can prepare themselves. Rotating the leadership of discussion with team or class activities can be especially valuable if prefire plans or records of properties in the district are used as foundations for the training sessions.

Training in the Fire Service

At present, there is no single national, mandatory formula for training fire fighters to which local fire departments are compelled to conform. However, the most formal set of basic requirements — a series of model fire training standards — was developed through the auspices of the Joint Council of National Fire Service Organizations.

The Joint Council of National Fire Service Organizations consists of leaders of the principal national organizations representing the Fire Service of the United States. In the early 1970s the Council established national standards of professional competence. The council decided that national collective action was desirable to determine levels of competency within the fire service. Professional qualification standards have been developed covering the following functional areas:

- Fire Fighter (NFPA 1001, *Standard for Fire Fighter Professional Qualifications*).
- Fire Apparatus Driver/Operator (NFPA 1002, *Standard for Fire Apparatus Driver/Operator Professional Qualifications*).
- Airport Fire Fighters (NFPA 1003, *Standard for Professional Qualifications for Airport Fire Fighters*).
- Fire Fighter Medical Technicians (NFPA 1004, *Standard on Fire Fighter Medical Technicians Professional Qualifications*).

- Fire Officer (NFPA 1021, *Standard for Fire Officer Professional Qualifications*).
- Fire Inspector (NFPA 1031, *Standard for Professional Qualifications for Fire Inspector*).
- Fire Investigator (NFPA 1033, *Standard for Professional Qualifications for Fire Investigator*).
- Public Fire Educator (NFPA 1035, *Standard for Professional Qualifications for Public Fire Educator*).
- Fire Service Instructor (NFPA 1041, *Standard for Fire Service Instructor Professional Qualifications*).

These standards provide in-depth coverage of the professional competencies in the fire service. Levels of competency have been developed in each of the classifications, which allow fire personnel to progress in an orderly manner.

How fire departments organize to fulfill most of these requirements is as varied as the information that can be found on training programs. This is understandable because the construction of fire department training programs—their priorities, content, and methods—all ultimately are left to individual localities, chiefs, and training instructors. For this reason, it is difficult to discuss a typical training program. Discussion of the training process, therefore, can only deal with those aspects of training that seem to be common elements.

One common aspect of training is a formal method of introducing probationary fire fighters to the job. New fire fighters are provided with a course of basic training that attempts to provide the foundation for more thorough on-the-job training. Some of the material contained in such a basic training course is often used in the refresher sessions of in-service programs.

Basic training periods vary from one week to 12 weeks. Various organizations in the public and private sectors supply fire departments with a wealth of materials for use in local training programs:

- National Fire Protection Association (NFPA).
- International Fire Service Training Association (IFSTA).
- Federal Emergency Management Agency (FEMA).
- National Fire Academy (NFA).
- United States Fire Administration (USFA).
- International Society of Fire Service Instructors (ISFSI).

Various insurance companies and trade associations also provide specialized training materials in their areas of expertise.

A training officer, usually a high-ranking officer approved by the Fire Chief, coordinates all classroom activities. The training officer in medium or large municipal fire departments is responsible for selecting textbooks, writing department manuals, presenting materials in the classroom, and ensuring that training records are kept on probationary and in-service fire fighters throughout their terms of employment.

The training officer's role is as important to on-the-job training as it is to classroom instruction and record keeping. For example, after a trainee has completed a basic course, the training officer will assign the trainee to a company for on-the-job training. The company officer then assumes the responsibility for arranging trainee schedules so that evolutions of every type are covered as soon as possible.

In-service training for fire fighters is an on-going process. Fire fighters cannot always maintain their skills in all essential fire fighting evolutions because many of these operations are used only at large or special types of fires. It is, therefore, essential that each member of a department be required to put in enough training work not only to retain skills in performing standard evolutions, but also to keep abreast of current technical developments in his/her respective field(s). Good fire departments devote part of every day to drill and training work.

Through regular drill procedures at a training school, methods of performing all operations are standardized so that personnel can be transferred to various companies without compromising efficiency. In well-run departments, companies periodically are assigned to drill at their fire training academy.

Company training activities usually are recorded by the company officer and presented to the training officer for inspection. Table 14.4 is an example of a form that can be used to record training activities within a fire department. These reports, usually prepared by the various company officers throughout a department, supply the training officer with a consolidated monthly training activity report that is reviewed periodically by the chief. An annual training report can be compiled easily from these monthly reports. Another form should be maintained to track the training activities of each individual (see Table 14.5).

Small departments that lack budgets for full-time training staffs usually train new fire fighters by sending them to statewide or regional fire fighter's training programs. These programs operate in most states and include state or regional fire schools; courses are conducted annually with sessions held either for a few days or for a full week of intensive training. The state courses include officer and leadership conferences, instructor training classes for fire department instructors, industrial fire brigade training courses, and training conferences for fire prevention officers. Some states have traveling training instructors who work year-round with local fire departments that are too small to have full-time training officers.

ACTIVITIES

1. How has the concept of the instructor's role changed from that of a person who merely dispenses information? Include in your explanation definitions of the *process* and *content* of learning.

TABLE 14.4 Sample report form to be completed for each training activity.

Date _____

Officer in Charge of Drill _____

Drill Subject _____

Audio-Visuals Used _____

Number of Training Hours _____

Members Attending

1. _____   13. _____

2. _____   14. _____

3. _____   15. _____

4. _____   16. _____

5. _____   17. _____

6. _____   18. _____

7. _____   19. _____

8. _____   20. _____

9. _____   21. _____

10. _____   22. _____

11. _____   23. _____

12. _____   24. _____

_____ Officer in Charge

_____ Training Officer

_____ Fire Chief

TABLE 14.5 Sample of an individual training activity record.

Name _____ Date joined company _____

Subject	Location	Date	Hours

2. Explain the importance of motivation in training design.

3. A complete learning experience comprises three major phases. Describe them.

4. List at least five common blockages to learning and some of the basic strategies for overcoming them.

5. There are many learning principles that must be considered when preparing a training course prescribed in this chapter.

   (a) Choose five of the principles that you consider most important and describe the importance of each as they apply to learning situations.

   (b) Briefly outline guidelines for applying the learning principles and training techniques to actual classroom situations.

6. (a) Explain the use of a planning chart in the preparation of an instructional strategy for a fire fighter training course.

   (b) Using Table 14.2 as a general guide, and based on what you have learned previously, prepare a planning chart for a segment of a course entitled "Prefire Planning." Compare your chart with those prepared by your classmates, and discuss any suggestions for improvements. Revise your chart to include appropriate suggestions.

7. As a learning technique, a conference is a planned learning experience in which the instructor's role is that of facilitator rather than lecturer. What are some of the advantages of the conference technique? What are some of the disadvantages?

8. What is the difference between simulation and role-playing as instructional techniques, and how can each be used most effectively?

9. Write a brief, informal essay that explains the importance of training in a fire department's operations and the responsibility of the fire service instructor in such training.

REFERENCES

[1]Granito, A. R., *Fire Service Instructor's Guidebook*, National Fire Protection Association, Quincy, MA, 1976, p. 1.

[2]Based on work by Wallace Wohlking, New York State School of Industrial and Labor Relations, Cornell University, Ithaca, NY.

[3]United States Army, "The Four Steps of On-The-Job Training," U.S. Government Printing Office, Washington, D.C.

A

Steps and Techniques for Decision Making in Management

The following steps and techniques are intended to provide assistance in making complex decisions. Decision-making skills will be sharpened each time these steps are used.

The steps listed below do not identify the best solution to a problem or opportunity. They can, however, help sharpen one's ability to think about which alternatives clearly are not likely to achieve an effective solution, and which appear to be among the best alternatives available.

This process can be applied to most decisions without use of mathematics or probability calculations. The steps are described from the point of view of the officer or manager; however, one need not be an officer or manager to use the process. In step 10, which calls for the evaluation of alternatives, no consideration is given to the decision maker's personal attitude toward risk taking. This attitude, however, will clearly affect which alternative(s) is (are) selected; those managers who are more conservative are more likely to select alternatives with less risk.

1. Which basic chain is involved with the decision: a problem-solving, an opportunity-exploiting, or a project-management chain (see Chapter 1)?

2. Is something important at stake and/or is the decision a complex one? (If not, there is no need to use a formal decision-making process.) Remember that sometimes decisions that might seem unimportant or not very complex might still have very complex alternatives.

3. What should be the result of the decision? What do you expect to happen if the decision is made well? Often these questions are omitted in decisions, and the final decision satisfies only one of several desirable outcomes. People, often make poor decisions because they consider this question unnecessary; they believe that they have an intuitive sense of all

aspects of the desired outcome. In fact, careful consideration of this question will often lead to at least one good solution.

4. Decide whether to make the decision alone or whether to involve others (see Figures 3.3 and 3.4). If you decide to make the decision alone (because it is a simple decision or because it must be made immediately) your best judgment at that moment will have to be adequate to make the decision. If you decide to make a decision alone because it is confidential or because it cannot be shared for other reasons, you might want to use the formal decision-making process to be sure you have chosen the best alternative.

5. Decide which other people should be involved, e.g., peers, subordinates, people from other fire departments, or people not in the fire service. If other people should be involved, the manager must decide who they are and how or when they will participate in the decision-making process (see figures in Chapters 3 and 5 and the "Participation" section in Chapter 5).

6. Identify preliminary alternatives (possible solutions deserving consideration).

7. Collect additional data to refine the known alternatives. One of the alternatives should always be the postponement of the decision. Additional data will generally lead to other alternatives and possibly to the need to obtain still more data.

8. Determine when adequate data have been obtained and whether the number of alternatives is adequate.

9. Evaluate the alternatives to isolate those that appear to be most desirable. This evaluation should include three questions: 1) How will this alternative affect control? 2) How will this alternative affect competence? 3) How will this alternative affect climate? (see the "Three Cs of Management" section in Chapter 4).

10. Make a decision by selecting one of the alternatives that the evaluation has shown to be most desirable.

11. Monitor results closely after the decision is implemented to determine whether adjustments have to be made to ensure that the alternative selected continues to satisfy the desired outcome requirements.

Two additional techniques in decision making are explained briefly below: decision trees and decision matrices.

Decision Trees

Decision trees can help to define and evaluate alternatives because they help identify the questions that should be asked at every step in a decision chain (see Chapter 1): What alternatives are available at this point? What consequences should be expected? A decision tree starts by asking what alternatives exist at the moment. For example, a simple decision tree could be created for a short trip from one town to the next. Thus, assuming that three routes are available, that the trip must be made during the rush hour, and that it is important to get to the next town within a specific time, the possible alternatives might be a limited-access highway and two major truck routes, each of which contains some traffic lights. These alternatives are depicted in Figure A.1.

Once these alternatives have been drawn on the tree, the consequences for each end point of this first set of "branches" need to be considered (see Figure A.2). In order to select the best course, some experts believe that probability should be estimated for each branch of the tree. Other experts believe that probabilities are not practical, and that decisions should be based on the decision maker's informed judgment about the value of the various alternatives, without mathematical analysis.

It is important to note that simple decision trees are usually quite obvious and therefore not needed. Nevertheless, drawing decision trees for more difficult decisions (even if the alternatives seem evident) can often bring awareness of additional alternatives that were not immediately apparent.

One other advantage to using decision trees is clear communication of alternatives when several people are involved in making a decision. Decision trees have one major disadvantage: They are cumbersome. Therefore, decision trees should be used with discretion, and only with those decisions where they can provide significant advantage to justify the effort.

Decision Matrices

Decision matrices can be useful for those who want more help with evaluating various alternatives. Any decision that has at least two dimensions can be organized as a matrix, which allows some insights into the relative advantages and disadvantages of the alternatives. Tables A.1 and A.2 illustrate two simple matrices (because they contain only three basic alternatives) that lead to some interesting insights. Table A.1 partially evaluates the decision tree alternatives. Table A.2 compares the desirability of several pieces of fire department apparatus, and could be much more complex if all of the advantages and disadvantages of actual pieces of apparatus were shown.

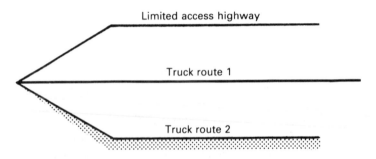

FIGURE A.1 Diagram of alternatives in a simple decision tree.

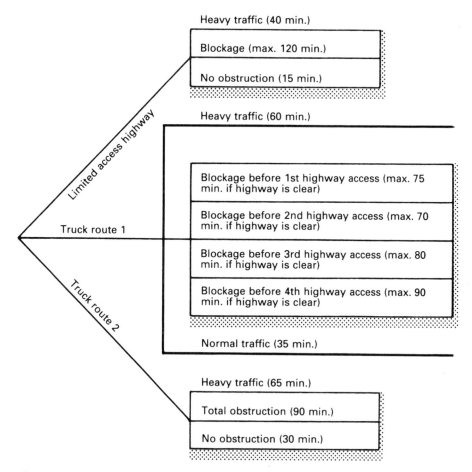

FIGURE A.2 *Diagram illustrating the consequences for each end point of the simple decision tree shown in Figure A.1.*

Although a matrix such as the one shown in Table A.2 does not provide a definitive answer about which piece of equipment is the most desirable, it does ensure that the relevant data have been considered and that a detailed evaluation has been made. Strict adherence to the decision-making process and the use of these techniques does not necessarily guarantee that only good decisions will be made; however, such adherence does guarantee that poor decisions will be made less frequently.

When a manager faces a difficult decision, it should be noted that the preceding techniques provide considerable support due to the following reasons:

1. The steps in the decision-making process ensure an orderly and organized approach to the decision sequence.

TABLE A.1 Matrix for a simple decision tree.

	Shortest possible time (minutes)	Longest probable time (minutes)	Reliability (assurance that estimate is accurate)
Limited access highway	15	120	Low
Truck route 1	35	90	Medium
Truck route 2	30	95	High

TABLE A.2 Matrix for evaluation of engines being considered for purchase.

	Cost	Maximum pump capacity	Operating costs per hour	Special advantages	Special disadvantages	Fire fighters' preferences
Engine (manufacturer A)	X dollars	R gpm	O dollars	Best piping arrangement, good crew cover	Highest expected maintenance	High
Engine (manufacturer B)	Y dollars	S gpm	P dollars	Best controls and air-pack mounts	Difficult to connect to more preconnects	Medium
Engine (manufacturer C)	Z dollars	T gpm	Q dollars	Best hose bed size and turning radius	Smallest water tank	Medium

2. Decision trees provide a framework for reviewing the possible causes of action and help stimulate creative thinking about more desirable alternatives than those that are immediately apparent.

3. Decision matrices are useful in evaluating which alternative represents the best choice.

Each of these techniques serves three purposes: 1) in difficult decisions they provide a path and tools to help arrive at the best possible source of action; 2) when thoroughly understood, they form an automatic thought process that serves as a guide to making good judgments for all decisions; and 3) they provide a shorthand record of the thinking that led to the decision without needing lengthy documentation.

Index